TEACHER'S ANNOTATED EDITION

Vocabulary Workshop

New Edition

Level F

Jerome Shostak

Series Consultants

Sylvia A. Rendón, Ph.D.
Coord., Secondary Reading
Cypress-Fairbanks I.S.D.
Houston, Texas

Mel H. Farberman
Director of English
 Language Arts, K–12
Bay Shore U.F.S.D.
Bay Shore, New York

John Heath, Ph.D.
Department of Classics
Santa Clara University
Santa Clara, California

Sadlier-Oxford
A Division of William H. Sadlier, Inc.

CONTENTS

INTRODUCTION

VOCABULARY WORKSHOP has for more than five decades been the leading program for systematic vocabulary development for grades 6–12. It has been proven a highly successful tool in helping students expand their vocabularies, improve their vocabulary skills, and prepare for the vocabulary strands of standardized tests.

This New Edition of VOCABULARY WORKSHOP preserves and improves upon those key elements of the program that have made it so effective *and* introduces important new features that make the series more comprehensive in scope and current in approach to vocabulary instruction, especially with respect to standardized testing.

Key Elements

- At each Level, a **word list** of 300 main entries, plus hundreds of synonyms, antonyms, and other related words

- Proven and effective **five-step approach to instruction**, leading students to mastery of word meanings and usage

- Excellent **preparation for the SAT** and other standardized tests with strong correlations between word lists and words that frequently appear on the SAT, as well as practice in types and formats of exercises found on the SAT

- Frequent **review and assessment** both in Student Text and in supplementary programs

New Features

To address recent changes in such standardized tests as the SAT and the ACT, the New Edition of VOCABULARY WORKSHOP introduces two features designed to provide students with further opportunities to prepare for new challenges presented on these standardized tests and, at the same time, to apply and extend their vocabulary, reading, and writing skills. These new features appear in each of the Reviews.

- **Vocabulary for Comprehension**, a two-page feature, consists of a reading passage and a page of exercises that give students practice in the kinds of comprehension and vocabulary questions that appear on such standardized tests as the "new" SAT and the ACT.

- Following the Vocabulary for Comprehension exercises is a new feature called **Grammar in Context**. Referring to a grammar or usage topic illustrated in the preceding reading passage, Grammar in Context provides instruction and practice in a grammar or usage skill tested on the Writing section of the "new" SAT and on other standardized tests.

Other Features

Among the features that were introduced in the previous edition of the VOCABULARY WORKSHOP program and that have been carried over to the New Edition are the following:

- In the Units, an expanded **Definitions** section that includes synonyms, antonyms, and complete illustrative sentences for each part of speech for every taught word

- Also in the Units, **Vocabulary in Context**, a reading passage that provides examples of how Unit words are used in more fully developed contexts than simple sentences

- Instruction in and examples of key vocabulary **strategies**—using context and using word structure—for decoding word meanings

- In the Reviews, the **Building with Classical Roots** section, an exercise that acquaints students with Latin and Greek roots and provides a strategy for finding the meaning of words derived from these roots

- In the Cumulative Reviews, the **Enriching Your Vocabulary** section, designed to broaden and enhance students' understanding of the relationships, history, and origins of the words that make up the English language

- For all Levels, A–H, **interactive online activities** that provide students with engaging word puzzles and games using the vocabulary presented in the Units

- For all Levels, A–H, a **Test Generator CD-ROM** that adds a secure and customizable assessment option to the program, eliminating the risk of "secondhand" tests that may distort assessment results

In the following pages of this Teacher's Edition, you will learn more about the VOCABULARY WORKSHOP program, including these new features and components, as well as how to get the most out of the program for your classroom.

OVERVIEW

"Pure Vocabulary" Approach: Systematic Vocabulary Instruction

The VOCABULARY WORKSHOP program focuses on words themselves, their meanings (both literal and figurative), their ranges of application (or usage), and their relationships to other words.

The approach is systematic in the sense that it begins with and builds upon a word list compiled to provide students with vocabulary they will encounter in their reading both in and out of the classroom. It is designed to provide students with the vocabulary skills they will need in order to achieve higher-level reading proficiency and to succeed at standardized tests.

The VOCABULARY WORKSHOP systematic approach differs from a literature-based approach in that each Unit begins with a thorough consideration of the words themselves rather than with a reading selection featuring words to be studied. (This is not to say that VOCABULARY WORKSHOP cannot be profitably used as a complement to a literature-based approach. See pages T30–T31 for suggestions on how this might be done.)

Rather than in the circumstantial context of literature, VOCABULARY WORKSHOP introduces and exemplifies vocabulary usage in varied and controlled contexts. These range from short phrases to full sentences to the Vocabulary in Context reading passages.

For effective study, the "pure vocabulary" approach also offers these advantages:

- It provides unlimited flexibility in the choice and placement of grade-appropriate material.

- It avoids the problem of trying to deal with a literary passage both as literature and as a vehicle for vocabulary instruction.

- It focuses more directly and completely on the words themselves, their meanings, their usage, and their relationships to other words.

- By economizing space, it allows a greater range of practice, reinforcement, and enhancement.

- It allows maximum coverage of a maximum number of key words.

One of the cornerstones of the VOCABULARY WORKSHOP approach is intensive practice through varied and abundant "hands-on" exercises. This method ensures that students are provided with:

- maximum exposure to different meanings of the key words studied;

- maximum coverage of the range of each key word through its appearance in many different contexts;

- fullest understanding of the key words' relationships to other words.

The aim of the pattern of intensive practice is to include the words in the students' active, daily-use vocabulary. This implies the ability to use a given word not only in its literal, or narrow, sense but also in a figurative way. Furthermore, it means that students will be able to use the word with confidence both as speakers and as writers.

Grade-Level Placements

The chart below shows the suggested grade placement for each Level of VOCABULARY WORKSHOP, depending on the overall ability of the student population involved.

In determining "proper" placement of a particular Level of VOCABULARY WORKSHOP in a given situation, the following considerations should be taken into account:

- Grade placements are based on actual teacher experience and recommendations throughout the long course of VOCABULARY WORKSHOP's history.

- Differences in grade are reflected not only in the "difficulty" of the words presented but also in the "maturity" of the sentences and other contexts in which those words are used.

- Grade levels indicated in the chart should not be taken in too literal or rigorous a sense. A certain amount of experimentation, as well as the use of the diagnostic materials provided in the program, will establish the "correct" placement of a particular Level in a given situation.

- The use of Level H with "above-average" students is designed to enhance preparation for the SAT and other college-entrance examinations.

Grade Placements			
"Average" Students		"Above-Average" Students	
Level	Grade	Level	Grade
A	6	A	5
B	7	B	6
C	8	C	7
D	9	D	8
E	10	E	9
F	11	F	10
G	12	G	11
		H	12

Word Lists

Each Student Text in the VOCABULARY WORKSHOP program for Levels A–H contains 300 words organized in 15 Units.

Criteria for Selection

The selection of words for the VOCABULARY WORKSHOP program is based on four major criteria:

- currency in and usefulness for present-day American oral or written communication;
- frequency on recognized vocabulary lists;
- applicability to standardized tests, especially the SAT;
- current grade-placement research.

General Sources

The lists of key words were developed from many sources:

- traditional, classic, and contemporary literature, including novels, short stories, essays, newspaper and magazine articles, plays, films, videos, and TV programs;
- spelling and vocabulary lists recognized as valid bases for teaching language skills at the middle and secondary levels;
- current subject-area textbooks, glossaries, and ancillary materials (especially for general, nontechnical terms).

Dictionary and Reference Sources

The following were the primary dictionary resources used for word (and definition) selection:

- *Webster's Third International Dictionary of the English Language* (unabridged)
- *Merriam-Webster's Collegiate Dictionary* (Ninth and Tenth editions)

Other supplementary dictionaries consulted included:

- *The American Heritage Dictionary of the English Language* (all four editions)
- *The Random House Dictionary of the English Language* (unabridged; both editions)
- *The Compact Edition of the Oxford English Dictionary*

Standard Word-Frequency Sources

Standard word-frequency studies were employed to evaluate and revise the words on the tentative lists. These included:

- *Primary*
  Dale-O'Rourke: *The Living Word Vocabulary*
  Carroll-Davies-Richman: *Word Frequency Book*

- *Supplementary*
  Harris-Jacobsen: *Basic Reading Vocabularies*
  Thorndike-Lorge: *The Teacher's Word Book of 30,000 Words*
  Zeno-Ivens-Millard-Duvvuri: *The Educator's Word Frequency Guide*

"Sliding-Scale" Placement

Each word list works on a sliding scale based on these principles:

- No word that Dale-O'Rourke indicates as known in a given grade is presented in that grade. Instead, where possible, it is presented 2 or 3 grades earlier.

- Each grade level contains a preponderance of words not known (according to Dale-O'Rourke) 2 or 3 grades later, with an admixture (in decreasing numbers) of words not known 4 or more grades later.

- The higher the grade, the larger the percentage of more difficult words contained on the word list. This was done to accommodate as many "SAT-type" words as possible in the key word lists for Grades 10–12.

PROGRAM COMPONENTS

This New Edition of VOCABULARY WORKSHOP, Levels A–H, consists of the following components:

Components of the VOCABULARY WORKSHOP Program*

- **Student Texts,** 8 Levels (A–H)

- **Teacher's Annotated Editions,** 8 Levels (A–H)

- **Test Booklets**
  - Form A, 8 Levels (A–H)
  - Form B, 8 Levels (A–H)
  - Combined Answer Keys, 8 Levels (A–H)

- **Test Generator CD-ROM,** 8 Levels (A–H)

- SAT-Type **TEST PREP Blackline Masters** (answers included), 8 Levels (A–H)

- **Interactive Audio Pronunciation Program,** 6 Levels (A–F only)

- **Interactive Online Activities,** 8 Levels (A–H)

The components have been designed for use in an integrated year-long vocabulary program, as suggested in the chart on pages T23–T25.

*Note that, in its entirety, the VOCABULARY WORKSHOP program now includes Student Texts, Teacher's Editions, and Supplementary Testing Programs for Grades 2–5 (Levels Purple, Green, Orange, and Blue).

The Student Texts

All eight Student Texts (Levels A–H) present 300 key words and are organized in the same way: 15 Units of 20 words each; 5 Reviews (following Units 3, 6, 9, 12, and 15); and 4 Cumulative Reviews. Preceding the first Unit is a section titled The Vocabulary of Vocabulary and a Diagnostic Test. Concluding each Student Text is a Final Mastery Test.

Vocabulary of Vocabulary (Student Text pages 7–17)

The purpose of this section is to familiarize students with some of the terms, concepts, and strategies that will be introduced and applied in the program. The practice exercises that accompany the discussions are meant to clarify and consolidate the concepts involved.

Some of these terms (for example, *synonyms* and *antonyms*) will already be familiar to most students. However, teachers should not hesitate to review these terms if doing so seems advisable, even at the upper levels of the program. Other, more complex concepts (such as analogies and context), however, may require more instruction and practice, both as preparation for related exercises and as review or reteaching for any students who have difficulty in successfully completing those exercises.

This is particularly true of analogies, which many students find especially challenging. One page of Vocabulary of Vocabulary is devoted to this important critical-thinking exercise so often found on standardized tests.

Diagnostic Test (Student Text pages 18–20)

A Diagnostic Test has been provided at the beginning of each Level as a means of assessing the students' overall vocabulary and test-taking skills. The Test covers a selection of key words introduced in the Level in question and is presented in the form of 50 synonym and antonym items.

Although the Diagnostic Test may be presented as a timed speed test, with the specific aim of determining how many items students can answer in 10 or 15 minutes, it is better used as an informal assessment and/or motivational device. Speed will come when confidence and vocabulary fluency have developed.

The Units

At the heart of the Student Texts—and of the VOCABULARY WORKSHOP program—are the 15 Units in which the 300 key words are introduced.

The work of each Unit is divided into a unique 5-part structure designed to give maximum coverage to each of the key words within the space available.

Structure of the Unit
(20 words)
1. Definitions
2. Completing the Sentence
3. Synonyms and Antonyms
4. Choosing the Right Word
5. Vocabulary in Context

The following descriptions of the individual exercises in a typical Unit of Levels A–H are designed to aid the teacher in using the text to maximum effect in the classroom.

1. DEFINITIONS

The first section of each Unit provides definitions, parts of speech, pronunciation, synonyms, antonyms, and illustrative sentences.

DEFINITIONS

The definitions provided are not of the dictionary type. They are, for the most part, relatively brief and simple. The intent is to give students a reasonably good "core" idea of what each word means, without extensive detail or secondary connotations.

Generally, only a single meaning of maximum usefulness is given the student. However, several meanings may be indicated if they are distinct, if they appear to be more or less equally useful, or if they will enable students to prepare for the vocabulary-in-context strand of the Critical Reading section of the new SAT.

PART OF SPEECH

The part of speech of each word is indicated at the beginning of the definition, using a simple set of abbreviations. When a word functions as several parts of speech, the appropriate abbreviation appears before the corresponding definition. (An explanation of the abbreviations used can be found on page 6 of each Student Text.)

PRONUNCIATION

With each word listing, the pronunciation is indicated by means of a simple set of diacritical marks presented at the beginning of every Student Text (page 6).

The practice has been to indicate only one pronunciation, even where alternate pronunciations are sanctioned by the dictionary. There are only a few exceptions to this—for example, when a word changes its pronunciation in accordance with its use as different parts of speech (ob´ ject and ob ject´).

Note that once they have completed the first section of each Unit, students may utilize the **Interactive Audio Pronunciation Program** (Levels A–F only) for that Unit. This program provides about four hours of spoken material per Student Text, including pronunciations, parts of speech, definitions, and illustrative sentences. For further details about the use of the Audio Program in this and other ways, see page T21.

SYNONYMS AND ANTONYMS

A list of synonyms and/or antonyms is given for each key word for which there is one or more of either. Some of these synonyms and antonyms will reappear in the Synonyms and Antonyms section (see page T13). By studying the given synonyms and antonyms, students will better understand the denotational family of words of which each key word is part; and by comparing specific usages of key words and their synonyms, students can better appreciate appropriate contexts for, and nuances in meaning and connotation represented by, these words.

Note that the lists of synonyms and antonyms are not meant to be exhaustive. Grade-level parameters have been taken into account; and obscure, archaic, and slang synonyms and antonyms have generally been avoided.

ILLUSTRATIVE SENTENCE

Concluding each key entry is an illustrative sentence including a blank space in which students must write the taught word. These sentences, although necessarily brief, provide a context that clarifies the meaning of each word and points up its idiomatic usage. By writing the word in such contextual settings, students begin to see how it can be used effectively in their own writing. Furthermore, the act of writing is in itself a form of reinforcement; and by writing the word, the student must focus attention on its spelling as well.

2. COMPLETING THE SENTENCE

The next activity, Completing the Sentence, is a simple completion exercise in which students are asked to choose and write the word that logically and meaningfully fits into a blank in a given sentence.

When using this activity in the classroom, the teacher should bear in mind the following considerations:

● The sentences in this activity call for the literal or direct (as opposed to the metaphorical or extended) meaning of the words involved. This is an easier usage for students to grasp and provides a good foundation for the more sophisticated con-texts that appear in Choosing the Right Word.

● The sentences are designed so that one and only one of the words fits in the given blank. Selection of the proper word has been facilitated by the incorporation of context clues in each sentence.

● The words are to be used as the part of speech given in Definitions. The only exceptions are: Nouns given in the singular in Definitions may be plural in the sen-tences; verbs given in the base form in Definitions may be used in any tense or form (including participial) required by the sentence.

3. SYNONYMS AND ANTONYMS

In this section students are given phrases that include synonyms or antonyms as presented in the Definitions section and must choose the appropriate key word for each phrase. Each of the 20 key Unit words is covered once in either the Synonyms or the Antonyms part of the section. Besides reinforcing meanings, this exercise pro-vides students with further examples of usage and context.

4. Choosing the Right Word

The fourth activity in each Unit is called Choosing the Right Word. In it students are asked to choose the member of a pair of words that more satisfactorily completes the sentence. At first appearance this exercise may seem an easier activity than Completing the Sentence. In fact, however:

- sentences in this activity are more mature linguistically and in subject matter;
- in many cases the words covered are used in a more figurative, extended, or abstract meaning;
- the part of speech or form of the key word has been changed (for example, from an adjective to an adverb) whenever convenient.

Accordingly, this activity is in reality more difficult than Completing the Sentence and requires real effort and a thorough understanding of the range of a word to complete successfully.

5. Vocabulary in Context

The fifth, and last, section of each Unit is an activity titled Vocabulary in Context. The activity is presented in the form of a reading passage, approximating a standardized-test format, into which a number of the key Unit words have been woven. Its purpose is threefold:

- to give further examples of usage for the selected words;
- to offer an opportunity to derive meaning from context;
- to provide practice in the sort of vocabulary exercises found on standardized tests.

With this activity, it may prove helpful to refer students, if necessary, to the section of Vocabulary of Vocabulary (see Student Text pages 7–17) that serves as an introduction to the strategies involved in studying vocabulary in context.

Follow-Up Activities

Once the work of the Unit is completed, you may find it useful to give a writing exercise in which students may apply and illustrate what they have learned about the words introduced in the Unit.

Writing Essays or Stories

Students might be invited to create their own brief essays or short stories and encouraged to use as many of the Unit's key words as is practical. (Students should, however, be discouraged from trying to "force" key words into their essays or stories indiscriminately, just for the sake of number alone. It is essential that students get in the habit of using these words correctly.) If they are to write essays, students might refer to the Vocabulary in Context passages as models.

WRITING SENTENCES

Depending on the ability level of individual students or of classes, you may prefer instead to administer a short writing exercise (5–10 items) such as the one shown below. This exercise is not so challenging as writing a story or essay but will give students an opportunity to "try out" some of the words they have learned and will provide the teacher with a means of assessing how well students have mastered the meaning and usage of these words.

Sample Writing Exercise (Level D)

Framing Sentences   *On the lines provided, write an **original** sentence that illustrates the meaning and use of each of the following words. Do **not** merely copy one of the sentences given in the Student Text.*

1. dilemma

_____

_____

_____

2. relinquish

_____

_____

_____

3. breach

_____

_____

_____

4. circumspect

_____

_____

_____

5. opinionated

_____

_____

_____

The Reviews

A Review follows every three Units. Every effort has been made to include all of the 60 key words at least once in the Review for the three corresponding Units.

Structure of the Review
1. Vocabulary for Comprehension
2. Grammer in Context
3. Two-Word Completions
4. Choosing the Right Meaning
5. Antonyms
6. Word Families
7. Word Associations
8. Building with Classical Roots

SAT SECTIONS

The first four parts of each Review have been specially designed to meet the needs of students seriously preparing for the verbal part of the SAT and similar standardized tests.

VOCABULARY FOR COMPREHENSION (PART 1)

This new feature is modeled on, and designed to help students prepare for, the Reading sections of standardized tests. Students first read a passage of expository or informational text and then answer vocabulary-in-context and comprehension questions relating to that text. An introduction to this feature may be found on pages 13–15 of the Student Text. It is recommended that students read this introduction and discuss it with their teacher before they undertake the Vocabulary for Comprehension exercises in the Reviews.

GRAMMAR IN CONTEXT (PART 2)

Also a new feature, Grammar in Context aims to provide review and practice in those grammar and usage skills most commonly tested on standardized tests. The grammar skill or skills covered in any given Review are linked to the Vocabulary for Comprehension passage that precedes it. A list of the skills covered in this Level, together with an introduction to the Grammar in Context feature, appears on page 16 of the Student Text.

Two-Word Completions (Part 3)

This part of the Review has been designed to familiarize students with the type of word-omission (cloze) exercise that appears on typical standardized tests, including the SAT. Again the aim here is to refine students' critical-thinking skills. Context clues are embedded within the passages to guide students to the correct choice.

Note: Explanations for the correct answers to the Two-Word Completions exercises can be found in the supplemental answer key on pages T38–T48.

Choosing the Right Meaning (Part 4)

Focusing on usage-discrimination skills, this part of the Review challenges students to choose, from among two or more taught meanings of a word, the only one that the specific context will reasonably allow. This activity gives students useful practice in determining a word's meaning by careful attention to the context in which it appears, a skill assessed in the critical reading section of the SAT.

Note: Explanations for the correct answers to the Choosing the Right Meaning exercises can be found in the supplemental answer key on pages T38–T48.

OTHER SECTIONS OF THE REVIEW

Antonyms (Part 5)

As it requires of students that they recall the meaning of a key word in order to determine its opposite, this activity helps students "situate" a word within the cluster of words of related meanings.

Word Families (Part 6)

This part extends the work of the Units by showing students that by learning one English word they often are acquiring a whole family of related words. It also provides practice in classifying words by part of speech.

Word Associations (Part 7)

The purpose of this activity is to reinforce and extend understanding of the meanings of key words with brief definitions or examples, situations, or allusions that in some way suggest key words.

Building with Classical Roots (Part 8)

Building on the foundation laid down in the Vocabulary of Vocabulary section titled Vocabulary Strategy: Word Structure (Student Text pages 11–12), this part of the Review introduces students to English words derived from common Latin and Greek stems and gives practice in the strategy of finding meaning by analyzing the parts of a word.

The Cumulative Reviews

Once students have completed the Reviews (and any follow-up activities), they may turn to the Cumulative Reviews.

Of the four parts of the Cumulative Reviews, two mirror activities presented in the Reviews: Choosing the Right Meaning and Two-Word Completions. These are presented in the same format and serve the same purpose as their counterparts in the Reviews, primarily to give students practice in types of questions they will encounter on the SAT and other standardized tests.

Each of the Cumulative Reviews begins with a set of analogy exercises. Analogies are valuable and revealing, not merely as a kind of mental gymnastics, but also as a means of pinning down the exact meanings of words and of remedying misconceptions or uncertainties about how those words are used. They also provide an excellent means of testing and refining the critical-thinking skills used on the college level. Furthermore, words that receive the attention necessary to complete an analogy successfully are much more likely to become part of the student's active daily-use vocabulary.

An introduction to the structure of analogies and strategies with which to solve them is provided in "Working with Analogies" on page 17 of the Student Text. It is recommended that students read this introduction and discuss it with their teacher before they undertake the analogies exercises in the Cumulative Reviews.

The fourth part of the Cumulative Review, Enriching Your Vocabulary, is designed to broaden and enhance student knowledge of the interesting origins, history, and relationships of the words that make up the English language.

The Final Mastery Test

The Final Mastery Test in the Student Text of Levels A–H is designed as a practice test of 100 items that gives students and teachers reasonably good insight into how much progress has been made during the year and what kind of additional work is in order.

The purpose of the Final Mastery Test is fourfold.

- It can serve as a dry run in preparation for the more formal (and "secure") tests available as optional components of this program.

- It can serve as an informal evaluation of achievement to date.

- It can serve as a reinforcement activity.

- It can serve as a before-and-after comparison when used in conjunction with the Diagnostic Test.

For whichever purpose the test is used, it is both a testing and a teaching device, the culminating step in a process involving many class periods and, therefore, should be given careful attention.

Supplemental Assessment Components (Optional)

Test Generator CD-ROM (Levels A–H)

The VOCABULARY WORKSHOP Test Generator CD-ROM provides an array of secure student tests that support the Student Texts for Levels A–H. With the Test Generator, teachers may create countless unique vocabulary tests with a variety of question formats, all within seconds. With a database of more than 3,000 questions per Level, teachers never have to administer the same test twice.

The Test Generator CD-ROM provides:

- new and secure Unit Tests, Mastery Tests, Cumulative Tests, Diagnostic Tests, Mid-Year Tests, and Final Mastery Tests

- a wide assortment of question types to choose from: pronunciation, part of speech, spelling, definitions, synonyms and antonyms, sentence completions, sentence framing

- the ability to customize tests to include any number of questions and to assess any Unit in the Student Text

- a method of flagging questions so that they will not appear on other tests

- the option to save a test for future use

- an on-screen Help program

- a printed Teacher's Manual

- technical support

The Test Generator provides a convenient and secure source of assessment and/or extra practice. With the Test Generator CD-ROM, teachers may tailor tests to suit the specific needs of either individual students or an entire class.

The flexibility of the Test Generator makes it easy to use either as needed or more systematically, as an integral part of the VOCABULARY WORKSHOP series. See pages T22–29 for recommendations on how it may be used in conjunction with the Student Text and other components of the program.

Test Booklets (Levels A–H)

Two Test Booklets (Form A and Form B) are available for each of Levels A–H. These Test Booklets have been designed to be used in alternating years, thereby reducing the risk of answers being passed on. Each Test Booklet contains a full set of testing materials and is designed to cover the work of one entire Level of the Student Text. Though the formats of the Test Booklets are the same, the items tested in any given section are completely different. The contents of the Test Booklets have been organized to reflect that of the Student Text and include the following:

- preparatory test-taking tips for students

- a Warm-Up Test (corresponding to the Diagnostic Test in the Student Text)

- 15 Unit Tests, each consisting of 25 items focusing on pronunciation, part of speech, spelling, definitions, synonyms, antonyms, and sentence completions

- 5 Cumulative Tests of 50 items each (plus 2 optional items)

The Warm-Up Test may serve either as an introduction to the Test Booklet as a whole or as an effective follow-up to the Diagnostic Test in the Student Text.

Each Unit Test has been designed for use as soon as the students have completed work on the Unit to which it corresponds or at any point thereafter.

Each Cumulative Test, including the Final Cumulative Test, covers all the work of the Student Text to the point at which it occurs and is designed to be used after the corresponding Review in the Student Text.

Note that these tests may also serve as effective "lead-ins" to the SAT-oriented Cumulative Reviews in the Student Texts and to the SAT-oriented PREP Worksheets in the corresponding TEST PREP Blackline Masters.

For recommendations on how to employ the Test Booklets as part of the complete VOCABULARY WORKSHOP program, see pages T22–T29.

TEST PREP Blackline Masters (Levels A–H)

For further assessment options, a booklet of reproducible TEST PREP Blackline Masters is available for each Level A–H. The TEST PREP component is designed to provide both practice in working with SAT-type test questions and formats *and* review tests covering the entire content of the corresponding Student Text.

- Prep Tests approximate as closely as possible, given the vocabulary that is to be covered, the analogy and word-omission sections of the SAT and provide practice in the vocabulary-in-context strand with brief reading passages as well.

- Answer sheets provide an SAT-type test format to develop student ease and familiarity with standardized testing materials.

- Mastery Tests are meant to be used when students have completed the corresponding group of three Units in the Student Text. Each test covers basic meanings, synonyms, antonyms, sentence completions, and analogies.

- Answer keys, including selected answer rationales, are provided for all tests.

For recommendations on the implementation of the TEST PREP Blackline Masters as part of the complete VOCABULARY WORKSHOP program, see pages T22–T25.

Interactive Audio Pronunciation Program (Levels A–F)

Available in CD format as well as cassette, the Interactive Audio Pronunciation Program provides a convenient and effective means of teaching and learning the recommended pronunciations of all key words introduced in the Student Texts for Levels A–F. It is designed to be used either by the teacher in a classroom setting or by the student in a language laboratory or at home.

- The audio program is ideal for English Language Learners of all cultures and backgrounds and for use in ESL classrooms.

- Students hear the recommended pronunciation of each word at least 6 times, both alone and in context.

- Students are provided with two opportunities to pronounce each word themselves.

- Pronunciations are followed by brief definitions.

- Usage examples in complete-sentence form extend student knowledge of how to use a word correctly in their speech and writing.

- Teacher's notes for the program are provided in Spanish as well as English.

For recommendations on when to use the program, see pages T22–T27.

Interactive Online Vocabulary Activities (Levels A – H)

For each Level, students are provided interactive word games using the vocabulary presented in the Units. These activities, which include crossword puzzles, word searches, "hangman," matching games, and others, are designed to reinforce and enrich student understanding of word meanings and usage. The activities are available free through the Sadlier-Oxford website (www.sadlier-oxford.com).

IMPLEMENTING THE PROGRAM

The format of the VOCABULARY WORKSHOP program allows for great flexibility. The teacher can easily adjust the activity assignments to conform to the special needs of an entire class, of groups within the class, or of individual students.

Schedule for the Year (28 Weeks)

The chart on pages T23–T25 shows how the various components of the VOCABULARY WORKSHOP program for Levels A–H can be scheduled effectively over an academic year lasting 28 weeks.

The following notes should prove helpful when adapting the chart to individual needs:

- Though the chart shows a disposition of material over 28 weeks, the time period can be extended to as many as 34 weeks simply by increasing to two weeks the time allotment for the items under weeks 6, 11, 16, 21, 26, and 28.

- It is not to be supposed that every item listed under Follow-Up Activities is meant to be covered during the week specified. The listings here are designed to offer the teacher options from which to choose in order to tailor the VOCABULARY WORKSHOP program to the specific needs of a particular class. This is also true of the sections or subsections into which some of the Follow-Up components are divided.

KEY

IAPP = Interactive Audio Pronunciation
     Program, Levels A–F only

TB A/B = Test Booklet
     Form A/Form B

BLM = TEST PREP Blackline
     Masters

TG = Test Generator
     CD-ROM

Using the Program Over the Year (28 Weeks)

Note: "Framing Sentences" and "Story/Essay Writing" are to be supplied by the teacher.

Week	Student Text	Follow-Up Activities
1	Vocabulary of Vocabulary	
2	Diagnostic Test	Warm-Up Test (TB A/B) Warm-Up Prep Test (BLM)
3	Unit 1 IAPP	Framing Sentences Story/Essay Writing Unit Test 1 (TB A/B) Unit Test 1 (TG)
4	Unit 2 IAPP	Framing Sentences Story/Essay Writing Unit Test 2 (TB A/B) Unit Test 2 (TG)
5	Unit 3 IAPP	Framing Sentences Story/Essay Writing Unit Test 3 (TB A/B) Unit Test 3 (TG)
6	Review 1-3	Mastery Test 1–3 (BLM) Mastery Test (TG)
7	—	Cumulative Test 1–3 (TB A/B) Prep Worksheet 1–3 (BLM)
8	Unit 4 IAPP	Framing Sentences Story/Essay Writing Unit Test 4 (TB A/B) Unit Test 4 (TG)
9	Unit 5 IAPP	Framing Sentences Story/Essay Writing Unit Test 5 (TB A/B) Unit Test 5 (TG)

(Continued on pg. T24)

(Continued from pg. T23)

Week	Student Text	Follow-Up Activities
10	Unit 6 IAPP	Framing Sentences Story/Essay Writing Unit Test 6 (TB A/B) Unit Test 6 (TG)
11	Review 4–6	Mastery Test 4–6 (BLM) Mastery Test (TG)
12	Cumulative Review 1–6	Cumulative Test 1–6 (TB A/B) Prep Worksheet 4–6 (BLM)
13	Unit 7 IAPP	Framing Sentences Story/Essay Writing Unit Test 7 (TB A/B) Unit Test 7 (TG)
14	Unit 8 IAPP	Framing Sentences Story/Essay Writing Unit Test 8 (TB A/B) Unit Test 8 (TG)
15	Unit 9 IAPP	Framing Sentences Story/Essay Writing Unit Test 9 (TB A/B) Unit Test 9 (TG)
16	Review 7–9	Mastery Test 7–9 (BLM) Mastery Test (TG) Mid-Year Test (TG)
17	Cumulative Review 1–9	Cumulative Test 1–9 (TB A/B) Prep Worksheet 7–9 (BLM) Cumulative Test (TG)
18	Unit 10 IAPP	Framing Sentences Story/Essay Writing Unit Test 10 (TB A/B) Unit Test 10 (TG)
19	Unit 11 IAPP	Framing Sentences Story/Essay Writing Unit Test 11 (TB A/B) Unit Test 11 (TG)

Week	Student Text	Follow-Up Activities
20	Unit 12 IAPP	Framing Sentences Story/Essay Writing Unit Test 12 (TB A/B) Unit Test 12 (TG)
21	Review 10–12	Mastery Test 10–12 (BLM) Mastery Test (TG)
22	Cumulative Review 1–12	Cumulative Test 1–12 (TB A/B) Prep Worksheet 10–12 (BLM) Cumulative Test (TG)
23	Unit 13 IAPP	Framing Sentences Story/Essay Writing Unit Test 13 (TB A/B) Unit Test 13 (TG)
24	Unit Test 14 IAPP	Framing Sentences Story/Essay Writing Unit Test 14 (TB A/B) Unit Test 14 (TG)
25	Unit 15 IAPP	Framing Sentences Story/Essay Writing Unit Test 15 (TB A/B) Unit Test 15 (TG)
26	Review 13–15	Mastery Test 13–15 (BLM) Mastery Test (TG)
27	Cumulative Review 1–15	Cumulative Test 1–15 (TB A/B) Prep Worksheet 13–15 (BLM) Cumulative Test (TG)
28	Final Mastery Test	Cumulative Mastery Test (BLM) Cumulative Prep Test (BLM) Final Test (TG)

Using the Units

On the top of these 2 pages the teacher will find 2 models for using the Units effectively on a weekly basis. Though there is no single formula or plan that will be sure to yield optimum results all the time, the models presented here and on the next 2 pages are designed to get the teacher thinking about how best to adapt the program to the needs of individual classes.

> **KEY:** IAPP = Interactive Audio Pronunciation Program
>
> TB = Test Booklet Form A or Form B
>
> TG = Test Generator CD-ROM
>
> ** Item to be supplied by teacher/student

Assignment
Classwork
Homework

MODEL B: 5 Sessions/Periods (20 Minutes)		
Assignment	**Day 1**	**Day 2**
Classwork	**1.** Collect Framing Sentences** **2.** Review Unit Test **3.** Present Definitions	Review Completing the Sentences
Homework	**1.** Completing the Sentence **2.** IAPP	Synonyms and Antonyms

Using the Reviews

On the bottom of these 2 pages the teacher will find 2 models for using the Reviews effectively on a weekly basis.

Assignment
Classwork
Homework

MODEL B: 5 Sessions/Periods (20 Minutes)		
Assignment	**Day 1**	**Day 2**
Classwork	Present Vocaulary for Comprehension	**1.** Review homework **2.** Grammer in Context
Homework	**1.** Word Associations **2.** Antonyms	Choosing the Right Meaning

Weekly Lesson Plans

MODEL A: 3 Sessions/Periods (35–40 Minutes)

Day 1	Day 2	Day 3
1. Collect Framing Sentences** **2.** Present Definitions	**1.** Review Completing the Sentence, Synonyms and Antonyms **2.** Present Choosing the Right Word and Vocabulary in Context	**1.** Unit Test (TB or TG) **2.** Review last week's Framing Sentences**
1. Completing the Sentence, Synonyms and Antonyms **2.** IAPP	Test Study	Framing Sentences**

Day 3	Day 4	Day 5
Review Synonyms and Antonyms	**1.** Review Choosing the Right Word **2.** Present Vocabulary in Context	**1.** Unit Test (TB or TG) **2.** Review last week's Framing Sentences**
Choosing the Right Word	Test Study	Framing Sentences**

MODEL A: 3 Sessions/Periods (35–40 Minutes)

Day 1	Day 2	Day 3
Present Vocabulary for Comprehension, Antonyms Word Families	**1.** Review homework **2.** Present Grammer in Context Two-Word Completions Word Associations	**1.** Mastery Test (TB or TG) **2.** Review homework
Choosing the Right Meaning	**1.** Test Study **2.** Building with Classical Roots	Remedial work as required

Day 3	Day 4	Day 5
1. Review homework **2.** Present Two-Word Completions	Mastery Test (TB or TG)	**1.** Review Mastery Test **2.** Review homework
1. Test Study **2.** Word Families	Building with Classical Roots	Remedial work as required

Using the Cumulative Reviews

On the top of these 2 pages the teacher will find 2 models for using the Cumulative Reviews effectively on a weekly basis.

Assignment
Classwork
Homework

MODEL B: 5 Sessions/Periods (20 Minutes)		
Assignment	**Day 1**	**Day 2**
Classwork	Present Cumulative Review	Cumulative Test Parts 1–4 (TB)
Homework	Test Study	Test Study

Implementing the Weekly Schedules

The following may prove helpful when adapting the foregoing schedules to specific situations.

- The models shown are, as their designation suggests, purely models—that is, starting points. Accordingly, the teacher is expected to adapt them to the particular situation at hand.

- The models make only minimal use of the Follow-Up Activities suggested earlier and no use whatsoever of the Alternative Approaches to Using the Program suggested on the following pages. The teacher should in all cases feel free to introduce such alternative approaches as are convenient.

- Place assignments and timings are to some extent hypothetical. Teachers should switch items around and adjust timings as needed. Similarly, items may be modified or deleted and new items inserted as the teacher sees fit.

- Multiple listings in a Day's entry for either Classwork or Homework are to be seen as options from which the teacher should select appropriate material. It is unlikely that the teacher could cover all the suggested material in the indicated time allotment.

- With some adjustment, the allotments for each Day can accommodate a 2- or 4-day arrangement. There is usually too much material to cover in 1 day, and a 1-day approach is, therefore, not suggested.

MODEL A: 3 Sessions/Periods (35–40 Minutes)		
Day 1	**Day 2**	**Day 3**
Present Cumulative Review	Cumulative Test (TB or TG)	**1.** Review Cumulative Test **2.** Review Prep Worksheet
Test Study	Prep Worksheet	Remedial work as required

Day 3	**Day 4**	**Day 5**
Cumulative Test Parts 5–6 (TB)	Review Cumulative Test	Review Prep Worksheet
—	Prep Worksheet	Remedial work as required

Alternative Approaches to Using the Program

Writing Approach

Research has shown that vocabulary acquisition is maximized when learning is authentically contextualized—when learners have a "real-life" purpose for acquiring and using a new word. Activities such as the following can provide these authentic contexts.

- Students can create journals or logs in which they use the key words to express experiences, thoughts, or feelings that are personally meaningful. They are free to keep these entries for their eyes only or to share them with others.

- Students can use the key words in personal letters to friends and relatives or in letters to the editor of the school or local newspaper. Students should write about subjects of real interest and concern to them.

- Students can use the key words to write descriptions of people they know or characters they are interested in. These character sketches or personality profiles may be written for a class yearbook, for a book report, or as a reference for a friend.

Literature-Based Approach

The VOCABULARY WORKSHOP program can be combined with some of the items listed below to form a *literature-based* approach to vocabulary study. Each of the items listed has been surveyed for use of some of the key words presented in the specified level of VOCABULARY WORKSHOP. Seeing the words they are studying in classic world literature will reinforce student appreciation of the value of possessing a good active-use vocabulary.

Classic Literature To Use With The Program

Levels D and E

Louisa May Alcott *Little Women*

Maya Angelou *I Know Why the Caged Bird Sings*

Ray Bradbury *Fahrenheit 451*

Charlotte Brontë *Jane Eyre*

Emily Brontë *Wuthering Heights*

Pearl S. Buck *The Good Earth*

Lewis Carroll *Alice's Adventures in Wonderland*

Willa Cather *My Antonia*

Sandra Cisneros *The House on Mango Street*

Daniel Defoe *Robinson Crusoe*

Charles Dickens *A Tale of Two Cities*

Arthur Conan Doyle *The Hound of the Baskervilles*

George Eliot *Silas Marner*

William Golding *Lord of the Flies*

Frank Herbert *Dune*

Harper Lee *To Kill a Mockingbird*

Carson McCullers *Member of the Wedding*

Nicholasa Mohr *El Bronx Remembered*

Walter Dean Myers *Fallen Angels*

George Orwell *Animal Farm*

Alan Paton *Cry, the Beloved Country*

John Steinbeck *The Pearl*

Level F

Sherwood Anderson *Winesburg, Ohio*

James Baldwin *Go Tell It on the Mountain*

Stephen Crane *The Red Badge of Courage*

Kate Chopin *The Awakening*

Ralph Ellison *Invisible Man*

Louise Erdrich *Love Medicine*

Jack Finney *Time and Again*

F. Scott Fitzgerald *The Great Gatsby*

Joseph Heller *Catch-22*

Ernest Hemingway *A Farewell to Arms*

Zora Neale Hurston *Their Eyes Were Watching God*

Nathaniel Hawthorne *The Scarlet Letter*

Henry James *Washington Square*

Maxine Hong Kingston *Woman Warrior*

N. Scott Momaday *The Way to Rainy Mountain*

Toni Morrison *Beloved*

John Steinbeck *The Grapes of Wrath*

Amy Tan *The Joy Luck Club*

Mark Twain *The Adventures of Huckleberry Finn*

Kurt Vonnegut, Jr. *Slaughterhouse Five*

Alice Walker *The Color Purple*

Edith Wharton *The House of Mirth* and *The Age of Innocence*

Richard Wright *Black Boy*

Levels G and H

Margaret Atwood *The Handmaid's Tale*

Chinua Achebe *Things Fall Apart*

Jane Austen *Pride and Prejudice*

Joseph Conrad *Lord Jim* and *Heart of Darkness*

Charles Dickens *David Copperfield*

Isak Dinesen *Out of Africa*

George Eliot *The Mill on the Floss*

Thomas Hardy *The Return of the Native*

Aldous Huxley *Brave New World*

James Joyce *A Portrait of the Artist as a Young Man*

Gabriel Garcia Marquez *One Hundred Years of Solitude*

Mark Mathabane *Kaffir Boy*

V.S. Naipaul *A House for Mr. Biswas*

Mary Shelley *Frankenstein*

Muriel Spark *The Prime of Miss Jean Brodie*

Jonathan Swift *Gulliver's Travels*

Virginia Woolf *A Room of One's Own* and *To the Lighthouse*

To coordinate reading and vocabulary study, the following may prove helpful:

• Instruct students to devote a special notebook to vocabulary. As they come across key words in their reading, they should head a page of the notebook with the word; copy the title of the work; and then indicate (a) the definition of the word used in that sentence, (b) its part of speech, and (c) whether it is used in a literal or figurative sense.

• Students may then be instructed to check *Bartlett's Familiar Quotations* for other famous examples of the use of the key word in question. These may be copied into the notebook and shared with others in the class.

Content-Area Approach

VOCABULARY WORKSHOP can be used to enhance student understanding and use of vocabulary in subjects such as social studies and history, science and health, and other curriculum areas.

In the following list of nonfiction print and video titles you will find works that relate in content to Vocabulary in Context exercises appearing in specific Units and Reviews of the VOCABULARY WORKSHOP Student Texts for Levels D–H. Students may wish to read or view some of these works and report on the topics and issues that they treat. In their reports, whether oral or written, students should be encouraged to use words they have come to know through their Student Texts.

Author & Title	Level & Unit
Lisa Aldred, *Thurgood Marshall*	Level G, U6; H, U6
Catherine Allgor, *Parlor Politics*	Level G, Unit 7
Isaac Asimov, "The Eureka Phenomenon" from *Left Hand of the Election*	Level E, Review 13–15
Russell Baker, *Growing Up*	Level E, U15; H, U4
Rachel Carson, *Silent Spring*	Level G, Unit 2
Agnes DeMille, "The Kosloff School" from *Dance to the Piper*	Level E, Unit 10
Benjamin Franklin, *The Autobiography*	Level E, Unit 3
James Herriot, *All Creatures Great and Small*	Level D, Unit 12
J.S. Holliday, *The World Rushed In*	Level E, Review 7–9
Washington Irving, *Dietrich Knickerbocker's A History of New York*	Level H, Review 10–12
Charles Kuralt, "Noah Webster's Dictionary" from *Dateline America*	Level H, Unit 2
Brian Lanker, "Daisy Bates," in *I Dream a World: Portraits of Black Women Who Changed America*	Level H, Unit 6
Patricia Lauber, *Volcano: The Eruption and Healing of Mt. St. Helens*	Level D, Unit 15
Bill Littlefield, *Champions*	F, Rev 4–6; H, U5, 12
John McPhee, "The Loch Ness Monster" from *Pieces of the Frame*	Level F, Unit 8
Tsuneo Nakamura, *Gentle Giant*	Level D, Unit 13
Ann Petry, *Harriet Tubman: Conductor on the Underground Railroad*	Level E, Unit 6
Franklin D. Roosevelt, *War Message to Congress, December 8, 1941*	Level F, Unit 11
Amy Tan, *The Joy Luck Club*	Level D, Unit 3
Ellen Harkins Wheat, *Jacob Lawrence, American Painter*	Level H, Unit 8

Title & Distributor Videos	Level & Unit
American Cinema (Discovery Channel Video)	Level F, Unit 1
American Photography (PBS Home Video)	Level F, Unit 7
American Visions (PBS Home Video)	E, U9; F, U3; G, U5; H, Rev. 1–3
Baseball: A Film by Ken Burns (PBS Home Video)	Level F, U5; Level H, U5
Cold War (PBS Home Video)	Level D, Unit 5
Flyers (PBS Home Video)	Level F, Review 1–3
Frank Lloyd Wright (PBS Home Video)	Level F, Unit 3
Gold Fever (PBS Home Video)	Level E, Review 7–9
The Great Depression (History Channel Video)	Level E, Unit 15
The Great Ships: Sailing Collection (History Channel Video)	Level E, Unit 7
John Ringling: Master of the Big Top (PBS Home Video)	Level E, Unit 1
Ken Burns' America: Statue of Liberty (PBS Home Video)	Level D, Unit 7
Liberty! The American Revolution (PBS Home Video)	D, U1, E, U3; F, U13; G, U4; H, U9
Not for Ourselves Alone (PBS Home Video)	Level H, Unit 7
Reflections on Elephants (National Geographic Video)	Level F, Review 7–9
Surviving the Dust Bowl (PBS Home Video)	Level H, Unit 14
Trains Unlimited (History Channel Video)	Level F, Unit 14
The Ultimate Guide: Birds of Prey (Discovery Channel Video)	Level E, Unit 12

Other content-related activities to which students might apply vocabulary study are:

- Working in pairs or small groups, they can choose sentences from Completing the Sentence or Choosing the Right Word and discuss a larger context in which these sentences could have appeared, such as a history or mathematics textbook, a daily newspaper, a book review, a personal letter, or a scientific article.

- Students can work together to link individual vocabulary words to a particular content area. Then working in pairs, they can find "real-world" examples of the words used in context in that content area.

- Students can work cooperatively to create sentence and paragraph contexts that illustrate the meaning of the content-area words that they have identified.

Useful Classroom Techniques

Classroom experience and research have shown that some students learn more readily when they can exercise a great deal of personal choice and can interact with others. VOCABULARY WORKSHOP can be adapted in the following ways to accommodate such students.

Cooperative Activities

Working cooperatively does not just mean working in proximity to other students or dividing an assignment or project into discrete tasks. Rather it means that students take individual and collective responsibility for the learning of all members of the group and for the successful completion of the group goal. Students who cooperate to develop their vocabulary should maintain an ongoing dialogue to monitor the comprehension of all group members.

Oral and Kinesthetic

- One student can write the key words in a given unit on the chalkboard while the rest of the class is divided into pairs or small groups. A member of each group will read a numbered item from the Unit aloud. The rest of the group will confer and then supply the required vocabulary word. The student reader will evaluate each answer and give reasons why it is correct or incorrect based on the word's definition and any context clues.

- Students in groups can discuss the shades of meaning or connotations among selected synonyms and antonyms for a given Unit and among the alternative answers in Choosing the Right Meaning.

- Students can work together to create puns, riddles, Tom Swifties, and limericks to illustrate the multiple meanings of appropriate vocabulary words. They may want to collect and publish their creations in illustrated books or an audio-anthology.

- Members of a group can work together to improvise stories, skits, or pantomimes that illustrate the meaning of a key word in a given Unit, while other group members guess the word being illustrated.

Written

- Students can work cooperatively to brainstorm their own vocabulary word lists based on their current reading and writing in all areas of the curriculum and on their personal reading and writing experiences.

- The class can collaborate to create their own Unit, covering vocabulary words they have chosen. Different groups can be assigned to develop each of the unit activities.

- Students may want to create their own minidictionaries, based on the word lists in VOCABULARY WORKSHOP or on categories of words that are especially meaningful or useful to them, such as sports, fashion, music, and career terms.

- Students can make use of semantic mapping and other graphic devices, such as flowcharts, to generate new vocabulary or to demonstrate understanding of word relationships. Semantic mapping, or webbing, can be used to illustrate word families, synonyms, and antonyms. Flowcharts can illustrate etymological and grammatical relationships.

Alternative Types of Assessment

The following types of assessment may be used in addition to or in lieu of the objective-scoring materials provided in the VOCABULARY WORKSHOP, Levels A–H. The emphasis here is on monitoring understanding rather than on ranking students.

Self-Evaluation

Students can use their journals to reflect on their own process of learning and use of new words. They may consider, for example, which words from VOCABULARY WORKSHOP they understood quickly and used frequently and why. They may want to use these insights to design their own vocabulary-acquisition strategies.

Teacher-Student Conferencing

Meetings take place at every stage of the vocabulary-acquisition process. Meeting over time allows teachers to assess students' developing understanding of words as used in specific contexts.

Observation

Using a checklist of 2 or 3 important criteria, the teacher can observe and evaluate students while they are interacting in groups or engaging in other oral activities. Teachers can also probe for deeper levels of comprehension by asking students to clarify or give reasons for their choice of word or context.

Peer Evaluation

Students meet in pairs or small groups to develop standards or criteria to evaluate their vocabulary acquisition. They then apply their standards to their peers' oral or written expression, giving positive feedback and concrete suggestions for improvement.

Portfolio Assessment

By having students collect and save self-selected samples of their writing over a period of time, teachers have an ongoing record of students' vocabulary development and of their facility in using words in context.

Multimodal Assessment

Students with strong nonverbal competencies can be given the opportunity to demonstrate in nonverbal media their understanding of new vocabulary. For example, they can draw, paint, model, dance, compose music, or construct objects to communicate their comprehension of a word and its definition.

TEACHER RESOURCES

The following lists have been compiled to assist the teacher in the effective presentation of the VOCABULARY WORKSHOP program, Levels A–H.

I. DICTIONARIES

Recommended

Merriam-Webster *Collegiate Dictionary* [Eleventh Edition] (Springfield, MA: Merriam-Webster, 2003)

Webster's Third New International Dictionary (Springfield, MA: G. & C. Merriam, 1993)

American Heritage Dictionary (Boston: Houghton Mifflin, 2000)

Oxford English Dictionary [Compact Edition] (Oxford: Oxford University Press, 1971)

Skeat, W.W. *A Concise Etymological Dictionary of the English Language* (NY: G.P. Putnam, 1980)

Supplemental

12,000 Words [A Supplement to Webster's *Third International Dictionary*] (Springfield, MA: Merriam-Webster, 1993)

The Random House Dictionary of the English Language [Unabridged Edition] (NY: Random House, 1987)

II. THESAURI

Recommended

Roget's II The New Thesaurus (Boston: Houghton Mifflin, 1995)

Random House Roget's Thesaurus (NY: Random House, 2001)

Rodale, J. [Revised by Urdang, L. and La Roche, N.] *The Synonym Finder* (Emmaus, PA: Rodale Press, 1979)

Supplemental

Chapman, R.L. (Ed.). *Roget A to Z* (NY: Harper Perennial, 1994)

Laird, C. *Webster's New World Thesaurus* (NY: Warner Books, 1990)

Roget's International Thesaurus [Fifth Edition] (NY: HarperCollins, 1992)

Abate, F. *The Oxford Dictionary and Thesaurus: The Ultimate Language Reference for American Readers* (NY: Oxford University Press, 1996)

III. OTHER REFERENCE WORKS

Recommended

Carroll, J., Davies, P., and Richman, B. *Word Frequency Book* (Boston: Houghton Mifflin, 1971)

Dale, E. and O'Rourke, J. *The Living Word Vocabulary* (Chicago: Scott & Fetzer, 1981)

Supplemental

Harris, A. and Jackson, M. *Basic Reading Vocabularies* (NY: Macmillan, 1982)

Thorndike, E. and Lorge, I. *The Teacher's Book of 30,000 Words* (NY: Teachers College Press, Columbia University, 1968)

IV. HISTORY

General

Baugh, A.C. and Cable, T. *A History of the English Language* [Third Edition] (Englewood Cliffs, NJ: Prentice-Hall, 1992)

Carver, C. *A History of English in Its Own Words* (NY: HarperCollins, 1991)

Jespersen, O. *Growth and Structure of the English Language* (Chicago: University of Chicago Press, 1982)

McCrum, R., Cran, W., and MacNeil, R. *The Story of English* (NY: Penguin, 1993)

Myers, L.M. *The Roots of Modern English* (Boston: Little, Brown, 1961)

Pyles, T. *The Origins and Development of the English Language* [Fourth Edition] (NY: Harcourt, Brace, Jovanovich, 1993)

Robinson, O. *Old English and Its Closest Relatives* (Stanford, CA: Stanford University Press, 1993)

American English

Dillard, J.L. *All-American English* (NY: Random House, 1975)

Dillard, J.L. *American Talk* (NY: Random House, 1976)

Flexner, S.B. *I Hear America Talking* (NY: Simon & Schuster, 1976)

Mencken, H.L. *The American Language* (NY: Alfred A. Knopf, 1979)

V. OTHER USEFUL RESOURCES

A Dictionary of American Idioms (Woodbury, NY: Barron's Educational Series, Inc., 1995)

Bryson, B. *A Dictionary of Troublesome Words* (NY: Viking Penguin, 1988)

Carroll, D. *Dictionary of Foreign Terms in the English Language* (NY: Hawthorn Books, 1973)

Dixson, R. *Essential Idioms in English* (Englewood Cliffs, NJ: Pearson ESL, 1993)

Evans, I.H. (Ed.) *Brewer's Dictionary of Phrase & Fable* (NY: Harper & Row, 2000)

Harrison, G. *Vocabulary Dynamics* (NY: Warner Books, 1992)

Hendrickson, R. *The Dictionary of Eponyms* (NY: Stein and Day, 1985)

Morris, W. and M. *Morris Dictionary of Word & Phrase Origins* (NY: Harper & Row, 1988)

Orgel, J.R. *Building an Enriched Vocabulary* (NY: William H. Sadlier, Inc., 1999)

Paxson, W. *New American Dictionary of Confusing Words* (NY: NAL-Dutton, 1990)

Room, A. *Dictionary of Contrasting Pairs* (NY: Routledge Educational Series Inc., 1988)

Room, A. *The Penguin Dictionary of Confusibles* (NY: Penguin Books, 1989)

Shipley, J. *Dictionary of Word Origins* (Glenville, IL: Greenwood Press, 1988)

Smith, R. *Dictionary of English Word-Roots* (Totowa, NJ: Littlefield, Adams & Co., 1980)

Spears, R. *Slang and Euphemisms* (NY: NAL-Dutton, 1991)

Webster's Word Histories (Springfield, MA: Merriam-Webster, 1989)

ANSWERS TO EXERCISES IN REVIEWS AND CUMULATIVE REVIEWS

Two-Word Completions (page 45)

1. (b) approbation (Contrast clue: "severest censure"; Inference clue: What kind of reaction do death-defying feats of gallantry deserve from the general public?) . . . merit (Restatement clue: "deserve")

2. (a) prerogatives (Inference clue: What would you call a teacher's right to use school equipment, etc?) . . . hiatus (Restatement clue: "break")

3. (c) nominal (Contrast clue: "actually") . . . ex officio (Restatement clue: "by virtue of that position")

4. (b) lassitude (Contrast clue: "vigorous and aggressive," "however"; Inference clue: In what sort of state would people who were feeble be likely to be?) . . . decadent (Restatement clue: "feeble")

5. (d) coalition (Restatement clue: "partnership") . . . transcend (Contrast clue: "become entangled in")

6. (c) exhorted (Inference clue: What would Senators who strongly favored a certain proposal suggest that other Senators do?) . . . inveigh (Inference clue: What would Senators who equally strongly opposed the bill suggest that other Senators do?)

Choosing the Right Meaning (page 46)

1. (d) (Inference clue: "disappearance") (a), (b), (c): irrelevant meaning of word (ir)

2. (a) (Inference clue: What might happen to a TV series after only six episodes?) (b), (c): wrong sense of word (ws); (d): ir.

3. (b) (Contrast clues: "British," "native") (c): ws; (a), (d): ir.

4. (c) (Contrast clue: "survive intact") (b): ws; (a), (d): ir.

5. (c) (Contrast clue: "congenital") (d): ws; (a), (b): ir.

Two-Word Completions (page 75)

1. (b) propensity (Inference clue: What does rubber possess in regard to its original shape?) . . . resilient (Inference clue: What would you call something that can resume its original shape?)

2. (c) reverberating (Inference clue: What sort of sound can be heard when you walk along an empty corridor?) . . . sepulchral (Inference clue: "It's . . . night")

3. (d) surreptitiously (Inference clue: How would a sneak thief move about?) . . . filch (Inference clue: What would a sneak thief attempt to do?)

4. (c) immutable (Inference clue: If something changes and develops over time, what wouldn't it be?) . . . irrevocable (Inference clue: same question)

5. (a) affable (Restatement clue: "courteous"; Contrast clue: "surly") . . . brusque (Restatement clue: "surly"; Contrast clue: "courteous")

6. (b) sedulous (Restatement clue: "worked . . . dog") . . . extricate (Contrast clue: "would . . . water")

Choosing the Right Meaning (page 76)

1. (a) (Restatement clue: "chain gang") (c), (d): ws (too abstract); (b): ws (inappropriate to context)

2. (c) (Contrast clue: "long-term visitors") (a), (b): ws (too specific); (d): ws (inappropriate to context)

3. (a) (Inference clue: What type of punishment was usual on a 19th-century naval vessel?) (c): ws (too general); (b), (d): ir.

4. (b) (Inference clue: What happens when one mirror is put in front of another?) (a), (c): ws; (d): ir.

5. (d) (Inference clue: Why would officials halt traffic when there was a fog?) (a), (c): ws; (b): ir.

Analogies (page 81)

1. (c) If you A something, you make it B than it was.
2. (d) A means the opposite of B.
3. (a) You would use an A to B.
4. (b) A means the same as B.
5. (c) A means the same as B.
6. (c) A indicates that a person is feeling very B.
7. (b) Something that is A lacks B.
8. (a) A means the same as B.
9. (b) Someone who is A is very likely to B.
10. (c) Something that is A lacks B.

Choosing the Right Meaning (pages 81–82)

1. (c) (Inference clue: "degenerated") (b), (d): ws; (a): ir.

2. (d) (Contrast clue: "less malleable") (a), (c): ws; (b): ir.

3. (a) (Inference clue: Why might it be inadvisable to test missiles near populated areas?) (c): ws; (b), (d): ir.

4. (b) (Inference clue: "eclectic") (c): ws; (a), (d): ir.

5. (b) (Inference clue: How might a group of explorers look at one another when they had finally discovered what they were looking for?) (a), (c), (d): ir.

Two-Word Completions (page 82)

1. (b) lurid (Context clue: "flames") . . . permeated (Inference clue: What would the stench of burning rubber do to the air around a fire?)

2. (a) reverberated (Inference clue: How would you describe how the notes of an organ react in a cathedral?) . . . sepulchral (Restatement clue: "vaults")

3. (b) millennia (Inference clue: How long traditionally has it been since Moses came down from Mt. Sinai with the Ten Commandments?) . . . precepts (Context clue: "the Ten Commandments")

4. (d) transgressions (Restatement clue: "sins") . . . expiate (Inference clue: What was the death of a sacrificial victim in an ancient religion intended to do?)

5. (c) sinecure (Inference clue: What kind of job *don't* you have to be talented to do?) . . . sedulous (Inference clue: What *don't* you have to be to perform a sinecure?)

Two-Word Completions (page 108)

1. (d) grandiose (Inference clue: On what kind of scale would a few lucky "haves" be able to live?) . . . penury (Inference clue: In what state would a pauper be likely to live?)

2. (a) culpable (Inference clue: "the . . . offense") . . . mitigated (Inference clue: "the . . . committed")

3. (b) infraction (Restatement clue: "violation") . . . relegated (Restatement clue: "put there")

4. (c) cadavers (Inference clue: In what do morgues and funeral parlors deal?) . . . squeamish (Contrast clue: "has . . . stomach")

5. (b) odium (Inference clue: With what would history be likely to regard a traitor such as Benedict Arnold?) . . . perfidy (Inference clue: What is Benedict Arnold's villainous act an example of?)

6. (c) pillaged (Inference clue: What would barbarians do to a civilized town they raided?) . . . desecrated (Inference clue: What would they do to its temples?)

Choosing the Right Meaning (page 109)

1. (b) (Inference clue: What kind of a liquid does one usually get when mixing a powder with water?) (a), (c), (d): ws.

2. (d) (Contrast clue: "smooth") (a), (b), (c): ws.

3. (a) (Contrast clue: "cravens") (b), (c): ws; (d): ir.

4. (a) (Inference clue: How was Hathor usually represented?) (c), (d): ws; (b): ir.

5. (c) (Inference clue: What effect does Aurora [the dawn] have on the black skies of night?) (a), (b), (d): ws.

Analogies (page 114)

1. (a) An A is by definition B.
2. (c) A means the same as B.
3. (b) An A is a person who would by definition be likely to B.
4. (c) A means the opposite of B.
5. (a) An A is by definition B.
6. (c) A means the same as B.
7. (d) Someone who is A would possess a great deal of B.
8. (c) Someone who is A pays a great deal of attention to (is concerned about) B.
9. (c) Someone who is A would by definition exhibit B.
10. (c) If you A something, you make it B.

Choosing the Right Meaning (pages 114–115)

1. (c) (Inference clue: What do industrial waste and other contaminants do to water?) (a), (d): ws; (b): ir.

2. (b) (Inference clue: "Sweeps . . . along") (c): ws; (a), (d): ir.

3. (d) (Inference clue: "distilled") (c): ws; (a), (b): ir.

4. (a) (Inference clue: "concrete") (b), (c), (d): ws.

Two-Word Completions (page 115)

1. (b) straitlaced (Inference clue: How would most people characterize the typical Victorian mentality?) . . . expurgated (Inference clue: What did Thomas Bowdler do to the plays of Shakespeare?)

2. (c) anathema (Inference clue: How would you describe a practice that was abhorrent to you?) . . . inveighed (Inference clue: What did the Old Testament prophets do in regard to practices they considered abhorrent?)

3. (d) compensation (Restatement clue: "salary") . . . prerogative (Restatement clue: "privilege")

4. (b) abates (Inference clue: Does a summer thundershower last a long time?) . . . transient (Inference clue: What adjective would describe something that didn't last long?)

5. (a) Scourge (Inference clue: What would you call the instrument of divine retribution?) . . . transgressions (Inference clue: Why would a deity visit divine retribution on human beings?)

Review Units 10–12

Two-Word Completions (page 141)

1. (c) sedentary (Restatement clue: "desk jockey"; Inference clue: What is the nature of an office worker's job?) . . . efficacious (Inference clue: Why is it important for an office worker to make frequent use of a gym?)

2. (d) ostentatious (Restatement clue: "flamboyant") . . . dowdy (Restatement clue: "drab")

3. (c) searing (Restatement clue: "withering") . . . invective (Inference clue: What would a withering political attack be likely to contain?)

4. (b) enthralled (Contrast clue: "find . . . bore") . . . satiated (Restatement clue: "had . . . enough")

5. (a) denizens (Restatement clue: "crew") . . . motley (Restatement clue: "come . . . life")

6. (a) procrastinate (Inference clue: What *aren't* you doing when you take immediate steps to stop something from happening?) . . . pernicious (Inference clue: What kind of effect would a highly dangerous development be likely to have?)

Choosing the Right Meaning (page 142)

1. (a) (Inference clue: What figure is produced by the troop movements indicated?) (b), (c), (d): ir.

2. (b) (Inference clue: What kind of person would the speaker regret having made himself?) (a), (c), (d): ws.

3. (c) (Inference clue: "The funeral . . . tables") (d): ws; (a), (b): ir.

4. (d) (Contrast clue: "sedentary") (b), (c): ws; (a): ir.

CUMULATIVE REVIEW III

Analogies (pages 147–148)

1. (d) A means the same as B.
2. (b) A means the opposite of B.
3. (c) You would use an A in order to B.
4. (d) A means the opposite of B.
5. (a) An A is a person who would *not* be B.
6. (c) Something that was in a state of A would be full of B.
7. (a) A means the opposite of B.
8. (c) A refers to a B that is slow-moving.
9. (d) A means the same as B.
10. (c) If a person has great A, he or she is very B.
11. (c) Someone who is A would be guilty of B.
12. (a) A means the same as B.
13. (d) Something that would A your appetite would be likely to make you feel B.
14. (d) A means the same as B.
15. (a) A means the opposite of B.
16. (b) Someone who performed something with A would *not* be described as B.
17. (b) An A is someone who by definition would be B.
18. (a) You A something with B.
19. (a) An A is a person who by definition would be B.
20. (c) A means the same as B.

Choosing the Right Meaning (pages 148–149)

1. (d) (Inference clue: In what might a bed of flowers lie snugly?) (a), (b), (c): ws.

2. (b) (Inference clue: "pall," "see not"; Restatement clue: "dark") (c): ws; (a), (d): ir.

3. (c) (Inference clue: "meaningless") (a), (d): ws; (b): ir.

4. (b) (Inference clue: "A true . . . Prison") (a), (c), (d): ir.

5. (a) (Inference clue: What would one need to do to the environment after a major oil spill?) (b), (c), (d): ws.

6. (c) (Inference clue: What would one do if one wanted to protect the confidentiality of one's sources?) (a), (b), (d): ws.

Two-Word Completions (page 149)

1. (a) specious (Restatement clue: "faulty") . . . transmute (Inference clue: What did the medieval alchemists attempt to do to base metals?)

2. (a) contraband (Inference clue: What do smugglers deal in?) . . . corroborates (Inference clue: What would incriminating evidence do to a charge brought against a suspect?)

3. (d) astute (Inference clue: What kind of comments would be made by a person of formidable common sense?) . . . redoubtable (Inference clue: More than what amount of common sense would you need to make astute comments?)

4. (c) repudiate (Inference clue: In the old days what were people forced to do if they did not hold orthodox beliefs?) . . . heresy (Inference clue: If they didn't, what would they be charged with?)

5. (d) epitome (Inference clue: What is the lead paragraph in a newspaper article supposed to do?) . . . salient (Inference clue: What kind of ideas would an epitome be likely to contain?)

6. (b) erudition (Inference clue: What would scholarly notes and comments indicate about the person who wrote them?) . . . annotated (Inference clue: What kind of edition contains scholarly notes and comments?)

REVIEW UNITS 13–15

Two-Word Completions (page 175)

1. (a) precocious (Inference clue: How would a person characterize a youngster who had written his first opera at the age of eleven?) . . . prolific (Contrast clue: "negligible")

2. (c) supplications (Restatement clue: "entreaties") . . . adamantly (Inference clue: How would you describe a refusal to yield to entreaty, however tearful?)

3. (d) blatant (Inference clue: What adjective would you use for a display of emotion that was not restrained?) . . . impassivity (Inference clue: With what was a true stoic supposed to react to bad news?)

4. (c) carnage (Restatement clue: "bodies," "the dead") . . . grisly (Inference clue: What sort of task would burying dead soldiers be?)

5. (b) curtail (Inference clue: "Once . . . forever") . . . depleted (Inference clue: "Once . . . forever")

6. (b) thwart (Inference clue: What is protective consumer legislation designed to do in regard to swindlers and con artists?) . . . credulous (Inference clue: On what sort of people do swindlers and con artists prey?)

Choosing the Right Meaning (page 176)

1. (a) (Inference clue: The sense of the sentence and the book it comes from suggest that the context deals with a ship.) (b), (c): ws; (d): ir.

2. (d) (Inference clue: What does a magnet usually do to a piece of electrically charged material?) (a), (b), (c): ws.

3. (c) (Inference clue: What kind of medicine might make one gag?) (b), (d): ws; (a) ir.

4. (b) (Inference clue: What might be sitting on a sideboard?) (a), (c), (d): ir.

CUMULATIVE REVIEW IV _____

Analogies (pages 181–182)

1. (c) A means the opposite of B.
2. (d) By definition B is characterized by A.
3. (c) It is easy to A someone who is B.
4. (b) An A is a statement that is by definition B.
5. (a) An A is a person who would by definition be B.
6. (d) An A is an animal that is proverbially B.
7. (d) Someone who is A would be likely to B.
8. (a) Something that would A would make a person feel B.
9. (c) An A would by definition make a person feel B.
10. (b) If you A something, you add B to it.
11. (b) If something is A, you cannot B it.
12. (c) A means the same as B.
13. (c) A means the same as B.
14. (d) An A is someone who is by nature B.
15. (b) Something that is A lacks B.
16. (a) A means the same as B.
17. (c) A means the same as B.
18. (d) Someone who is A is suffering from B.
19. (b) A indicates that something is decidedly reminiscent of a B.
20. (d) A indicates that there is an excess of B in something.

Choosing the Right Meaning (page 182)

1. (c) (Inference clue: "bloody") (a), (b), (d): ws.

2. (b) (Inference clue: "bars," "captive") (d): ws; (a), (c): ir.

3. (c) (Inference clue: What would a feast do to hunger?) (b), (d): ws (too weak); (a): ir.

4. (b) (Inference clue: What effect would the rocking of a ship have on a person?) (a), (c), (d): ws.

5. (a) (Inference clue: The meaning here must apply to birds.) (c): ws; (b), (d): ir.

Two-Word Completions (page 183)

1. (c) abet (Restatement clue: "aid") . . . culpable (Inference clue: How would you describe someone who had committed a crime?)

2. (d) potpourri (Restatement clue: "assortment") . . . motley (Inference clue: How would you describe the assortment of acts that used to be presented at a vaudeville house?)

3. (b) Contingents (Inference clue: Into what are crack troops usually organized?) . . . foment (Inference clue: What would malcontent firebrands be likely to do in regard to a riot and other disorders?)

4. (d) sartorial (Inference clue: What kind of splendor would a dapper person be likely to have?) . . . slovenly (Contrast clue: "dapper"; Inference clue: How would a person who appeared to have slept in his or her clothes probably look?)

5. (b) nebulous (Restatement clue: "shapeless") . . . dissipated (Restatement clue: "vanished")

6. (a) rejoinder (Inference clue: What wouldn't it be possible to make in regard to an airtight case?) . . . incontrovertible (Inference clue: What kind of evidence would an airtight case be likely to contain?)

Notes

Vocabulary Workshop
Workshop
New Edition

Level F

Jerome Shostak

Series Consultants

Sylvia A. Rendón, Ph.D.
Coord., Secondary Reading
Cypress-Fairbanks I.S.D.
Houston, Texas

Mel H. Farberman
Director of English
 Language Arts, K–12
Bay Shore U.F.S.D.
Bay Shore, New York

John Heath, Ph.D.
Department of Classics
Santa Clara University
Santa Clara, California

Sadlier-Oxford
A Division of William H. Sadlier, Inc.

Reviewers

The publisher wishes to thank for their comments and suggestions the following teachers and administrators, who read portions of the series prior to publication.

Anne S. Crane
Clinician, English Education
Georgia State University
Atlanta, GA

Arlene A. Oraby
Dept. Chair (Ret.), English 6–12
Briarcliff Public Schools
Briarcliff Manor, NY

Patricia M. Stack
English Teacher
South Park School District
South Park, PA

Susan W. Keogh
Curriculum Coordinator
Lake Highland Preparatory
Orlando, FL

Susan Cotter McDonough
English Department Chair
Wakefield High School
Wakefield, MA

Joy Vander Vliet
English Teacher
Council Rock High School
Newtown, PA

Mary Louise Ellena-Wygonik
English Teacher
Hampton High School
Allison Park, PA

Sr. M. Francis Regis Trojano
Sisters of St. Joseph (CSJ)
Educational Consultant
Boston, MA

Karen Christine Solheim
English Teacher
Jefferson High School
Jefferson, GA

Lisa Anne Pomi
Language Arts Chairperson
Woodside High School
Woodside, CA

Keith Yost
Director of Humanities
Tomball Ind. School District
Tomball, TX

Photo Credits

Jack Anthony: 71 *Corbis*/Bettmann: 57, 104; Walker Evans: 90; Owen Franken: 137; Christel Gerstenberg: 157; Morton Beebe: 164. *Getty Images*/Hulton Archive: 27, 97; Taxi/Jim Cummins: 64; Stone/David E. Myers: 116; Bob Parent: 123; Stone/Colin Hawkins: 150; Stone/Chad Slattery: 171. *The Image Works*/© Syracuse Newspapers/Dick Blume: 34; Sean Cayton: 83. *Index Stock Imagery*/Mark Gibson: 41. *The Kobal Collection*/Europa Cinematografica: 184. *The Library of Congress*: 130.

Printed in the United States of America.
ISBN: 0-8215-7111-7
3456789/09 08 07 06 05

PREFACE

For over five decades, VOCABULARY WORKSHOP has proven a highly successful tool for guiding systematic vocabulary growth and developing vocabulary skills. It has also been shown to be a valuable help to students preparing for standardized tests. This New Edition of VOCABULARY WORKSHOP has been prepared in recognition of important changes to these tests, with the introduction of two features designed to address the new emphasis on writing skills, including grammar, and reading skills on those tests.

A new **Vocabulary for Comprehension** section appears in each of the five Reviews. This two-page feature is modeled on the reading sections of standardized tests, and as in those tests, presents reading comprehension questions, including specific vocabulary-related ones, based on a reading passage. (For more on Vocabulary for Comprehension, see page 13.)

Following Vocabulary for Comprehension in each of the Reviews is another new feature called **Grammar in Context**. This one-page exercise is linked to the reading passage that precedes it, referring to a grammar or usage topic illustrated in the passage and then reviewing that topic with a brief explanation and practice questions. (For more on Grammar in Context, see page 16.)

The 15 Units that form the core of VOCABULARY WORKSHOP remain unchanged. Each of the Units comprises a five-part lesson consisting of **Definitions**, **Completing the Sentence**, **Synonyms and Antonyms**, **Choosing the Right Word**, and **Vocabulary in Context**. Together, these exercises provide multiple and varied exposures to the taught words, an approach that has been shown to be consistent with and supportive of research-based findings in vocabulary instruction.

Enrichment and vocabulary-building exercises also remain in the form of **Building with Classical Roots**, **Word Associations**, and **Word Families** in the Reviews, and **Analogies** and **Enriching Your Vocabulary** in the Cumulative Reviews.

In this Level of Vocabulary Workshop you will study 300 key words. The words in this Level, as well as all of the other Levels of this series, have been selected on the following bases: currency and general usefulness; frequency of appearance on recognized vocabulary lists; applicability to, and appearance on, standardized tests; and current grade-level research. In addition to the 300 key words, you will be introduced to hundreds of other words in the form of synonyms, antonyms, and other relatives. Mastery of these words will make you a better reader, a better writer and speaker, and better prepared for the challenges of standardized tests.

CONTENTS

PRONUNCIATION KEY

The pronunciation is indicated for every basic word introduced in this book. The symbols used for this purpose, as listed below, are similar to those appearing in most standard dictionaries of recent vintage. (Pronunciation keys and given pronunciations sometimes differ from dictionary to dictionary.) The author has consulted a large number of dictionaries for this purpose but has relied primarily on *Webster's Third New International Dictionary* and *The Random House Dictionary of the English Language (Unabridged)*.

There are, of course, many English words for which two (or more) pronunciations are commonly accepted. In virtually all cases where such words occur in this book, the author has sought to make things easier for the student by giving just one pronunciation. The only significant exception occurs when the pronunciation changes in accordance with a shift in the part of speech. Thus we would indicate that *project* in the verb form is pronounced prə jekt', and in the noun form, präj' ekt.

It is believed that these relatively simple pronunciation guides will be readily usable by the student. It should be emphasized, however, that the *best* way to learn the pronunciation of a word is to listen to and imitate an educated speaker.

Vowels	ā	lake	e	stress	ü	loot, new
	a	mat	ī	knife	u̇	foot, pull
	â	care	i	sit	ə	jumping, broken
	ä	bark, bottle	ō	flow	ər	bird, better
	au̇	doubt	ô	all, cord		
	ē	beat, wordy	oi	oil		

Consonants	ch	child, lecture	s	cellar	wh	what
	g	give	sh	shun	y	yearn
	j	gentle, bridge	th	thank	z	is
	ŋ	sing	th	those	zh	measure

All other consonants are sounded as in the alphabet.

Stress	The accent mark *follows* the syllable receiving the major stress: en rich'

Abbreviations	*adj.* adjective	*n.* noun	*prep.* preposition
	adv. adverb	*part.* participle	*v.* verb
	int. interjection	*pl.* plural	

See page T21 for information about the Interactive Audio Pronunciation Program.

THE VOCABULARY OF VOCABULARY

There are some interesting and useful words that we use to describe and identify words. The exercises that follow will help you to check and strengthen your knowledge of this "vocabulary of vocabulary."

Denotation and Connotation

The **denotation** of a word is its specific dictionary meaning. Here are a few examples:

Word	Denotation
eminent	distinguished or noteworthy
cumbersome	hard to handle or manage
remember	call to mind

The **connotation** of a word is its **tone**—that is, the emotions or associations it normally arouses in people using, hearing, or reading it. Depending on what these feelings are, the connotation of a word may be *favorable* (*positive*) or *unfavorable* (*negative, pejorative*). A word that does not normally arouse strong feelings of any kind has a *neutral* connotation. Here are some examples of words with different connotations:

Word	Connotation
eminent	favorable
cumbersome	unfavorable
remember	neutral

Exercises   *In the space provided, label the connotation of each of the following words* **F** *for "favorable,"* **U** *for "unfavorable," or* **N** *for "neutral."*

<u>U</u> **1.** perverse   <u>U</u> **3.** lucrative   <u>N</u> **5.** savory

<u>N</u> **2.** liability   <u>F</u> **4.** adieu   <u>F</u> **6.** magnanimous

Literal and Figurative Usage

When a word is used in a **literal** sense, it is being employed in its strict (or primary) dictionary meaning in a situation (or context) that "makes sense" from a purely logical or realistic point of view. For example:

> Yesterday I read an old tale about a knight who slew a *fire-breathing* dragon.

In this sentence, *fire-breathing* is employed literally. The dragon is pictured as breathing real fire.

Sometimes words are used in a symbolic or nonliteral way in situations that do not "make sense" from a purely logical or realistic point of view. We call this nonliteral application of a word a **figurative** or **metaphorical** usage. For example:

> Suddenly my boss rushed into my office, *breathing fire.*

In this sentence *breathing fire* is not being used in a literal sense. That is, the boss was not actually breathing fire out of his nostrils. Rather, the expression is intended to convey graphically that the boss was very angry.

Exercises   In the space provided, write **L** for "literal" or **F** for "figurative" next to each of the following sentences to show how the italicized expression is being used.

__F__ **1.** The years of silence allowed resentment to silently *creep* into their relationship.

__L__ **2.** The ivy vines *crept* over the trestle.

__F__ **3.** "It was *easy as cake*," she said of the math exam.

Synonyms

A **synonym** is a word that has *the same* or *almost the same* meaning as another word. Here are some examples:

eat—consume   clash—conflict
hurt—injure   fire—discharge
big—large   slim—slender

Exercises   In each of the following groups, circle the word that is most nearly the **synonym** of the word in **boldface** type.

1. opaque	**2. salvage**	**3. dilate**	**4. rectify**
a. sturdy	a. garner	a. soften	a. corroborate
b. cubic	b. save	b. enrich	b. subscribe
c. ionic	c. requisition	c. enlarge	c. usurp
d. murky	d. surrender	d. dissolve	d. correct

Antonyms

An **antonym** is a word that means *the opposite* of or *almost the opposite* of another word. Here are some examples:

enter—leave   happy—sad
wild—tame   leader—follower
buy—sell   war—peace

Exercises   In each of the following groups, circle the word that is most nearly the **antonym** of the word in **boldface** type.

1. candid	**2. embroil**	**3. chaos**	**4. immunity**
a. dishonest	a. embargo	a. science	a. untenable
b. alien	b. extricate	b. entropy	b. eminence
c. new	c. entangle	c. order	c. susceptibility
d. accepted	d. enigma	d. imposition	d. boorishness

VOCABULARY STRATEGY: USING CONTEXT

How do you go about finding the meaning of an unknown or unfamiliar word that you come across in your reading? You might look the word up in a dictionary, of course, provided one is at hand. But there are two other useful strategies that you might employ to find the meaning of a word that you do not know at all or that is used in a way that you do not recognize. One strategy is to analyze the **structure** or parts of the word. (See pages 11 and 12 for more on this strategy.) The other strategy is to try to figure out the meaning of the word by reference to context.

When we speak of the **context** of a word, we mean the printed text of which that word is part. By studying the context, we may find **clues** that lead us to its meaning. We might find a clue in the immediate sentence or phrase in which the word appears (and sometimes in adjoining sentences or phrases, too); or we might find a clue in the topic or subject matter of the passage in which the word appears; or we might even find a clue in the physical features of a page itself. (Photographs, illustrations, charts, graphs, captions, and headings are some examples of such features.)

One way to use context as a strategy is to ask yourself what you know already about the topic or subject matter in question. By applying what you have learned before about deserts, for example, you would probably be able to figure out that the word *arid* in the phrase "the arid climate of the desert" means "dry."

The **Vocabulary in Context** exercises that appear in the Units and the **Vocabulary for Comprehension** and the **Choosing the Right Meaning** exercises that appear in the Reviews and Cumulative Reviews both provide practice in using context to determine the meaning of given words.

When you do the various word-omission exercises in this book, look for ***context clues*** built into the sentence or passage to guide you to the correct answer. Three types of context clues appear in the exercises in this book.

A ***restatement clue*** consists of a *synonym* for, or a *definition* of, the missing word. For example:

> "I'm willing to <u>tell</u> what I know about the matter," the reporter
> said, "but I can't _____ my sources."
> a. conceal   b. defend   c. find   (d. reveal)

In this sentence, *tell* is a synonym of the missing word, *reveal*, and acts as a restatement clue for it.

A ***contrast clue*** consists of an *antonym* for, or a phrase that means the *opposite* of, the missing word. For example:

> "I'm trying to <u>help</u> you, <u>not</u> (**assist,** (**hinder**))you!" she exclaimed in annoyance.

In this sentence, *help* is an antonym of the missing word, *hinder*. This is confirmed by the presence of the word *not. Help* thus functions as a contrast clue for *hinder*.

An **inference clue** implies but does not directly state the meaning of the missing word or words. For example:

A utility infielder has to be a very _____
player because he is a veritable jack-of-all-trades on the
_____ diamond.

a. veteran . . . football   c. experienced . . . hockey
b. versatile . . . baseball   d. energetic . . . golf

In this sentence, there are several inference clues: (a) the term *jack-of-all-trades* suggests the word *versatile* because a jack-of-all-trades is by definition versatile; the word *utility* in the term *utility infielder* suggests the same thing; (b) the words *infielder* and *diamond* suggest *baseball* because they are terms employed regularly in that sport. Accordingly, all these words are inference clues because they suggest or imply, but do not directly state, the missing word or words.

Exercises   *Use context clues to choose the word or words that complete each of the following sentences or sets of sentences.*

1. If I don't understand the lesson now, I certainly won't
_____ it after I go home.

a. comprehend   c. disregard
b. deliver   d. enumerate

2. "At our picnic, the neighbor's dog got into the _____
basket and managed to _____ all the sandwiches.

a. silver . . .devour   c. egg . . . hole
b. food . . . eat   d. treasure . . . steal

3. If you provide the car, I will (**pay,** look) for the gas.

VOCABULARY STRATEGY: WORD STRUCTURE

One important way to build your vocabulary is to learn the meaning of word parts that make up many English words. These word parts consist of **prefixes**, **suffixes**, and **roots**, or **bases**. A useful strategy for determining the meaning of an unknown word is to "take apart" the word and think about the parts. For example, when you look at the word parts in the word *invisible,* you find the prefix *in-* ("not") + the root *-vis-* ("see") + the suffix *-ible* ("capable of"). From knowing the meanings of the parts of this word, you can figure out that *invisible* means "not capable of being seen."

Following is a list of common prefixes. Knowing the meaning of a prefix can help you determine the meaning of a word in which the prefix appears.

Prefix	Meaning	Sample Words
bi-	two	bicycle
com-, con-	together, with	compatriot, contact
de-, dis-	lower, opposite	devalue, disloyal
fore-, pre-	before, ahead of time	forewarn, preplan
il-, im-, in-, ir, non-, un-	not	illegal, impossible, inactive, irregular, nonsense, unable
in-, im-	in, into	inhale, import
mid-	middle	midway
mis-	wrongly, badly	mistake, misbehave
re-	again, back	redo, repay
sub-	under, less than	submarine, subzero
super-	above, greater than	superimpose, superstar
tri-	three	triangle

Following is a list of common suffixes. Knowing the meaning and grammatical function of a suffix can help you determine the meaning of a word.

Noun Suffix	Meaning	Sample Nouns
-acy, -ance, -ence, -hood, -ity, -ment, -ness, -ship	state, quality, or condition of, act or process of	adequacy, attendance, persistence, neighborhood, activity, judgment, brightness, friendship
-ant, -eer, -ent, -er, -ian, -ier, -ist, -or	one who does or makes something	contestant, auctioneer, resident, banker, comedian, financier, dentist, doctor
-ation, -ition, -ion	act or result of	organization, imposition, election

Verb Suffix	Meaning	Sample Verbs
-ate	to become, produce, or treat	validate, salivate, chlorinate
-en	to make, cause to be	weaken
-fy, -ify, -ize	to cause, make	liquefy, glorify, legalize

Adjective Suffix	Meaning	Sample Adjectives
-able, -ible	able, capable of	believable, incredible
-al, -ic,	relating to, characteristic of	natural, romantic
-ful, -ive, -ous	full of, given to, marked by	beautiful, protective, poisonous
-ish, -like	like, resembling	foolish, childlike
-less	lacking, without	careless

A **base** or **root** is the main part of a word to which prefixes and suffixes may be added. Many roots come to English from Latin, such as *-socio-,* meaning "society," or from Greek, such as *-logy-,* meaning "the study of." Knowing Greek and Latin roots can help you determine the meaning of a word such as *sociology,* which means "the study of society."

In the **Building with Classical Roots** sections of this book you will learn more about some of these Latin and Greek roots and about English words that derive from them. The lists that follow may help you figure out the meaning of new or unfamiliar words that you encounter in your reading.

Greek Root	Meaning	Sample Word
-astr-, -aster-, -astro-	star	astral, asteroid, astronaut
-auto-	self	autograph
-bio-	life	biography
-chron-, chrono-	time	chronic, chronological
-cosm-, -cosmo-	universe, order	microcosm, cosmopolitan
-cryph-, -crypt-	hidden, secret	apocryphal, cryptographer
-dem-, -demo-	people	epidemic, democracy
-dia-	through, across, between	diameter
-dog-, -dox-	opinion, teaching	dogmatic, orthodox
-gen-	race, kind, origin, birth	generation
-gnos-	know	diagnostic
-graph-, -graphy-, -gram-	write	graphite, autobiography, telegram
-log-, -logue-	speech, word, reasoning	logic, dialogue
-lys-	break down	analysis
-metr-, -meter-	measure	metric, kilometer
-micro-	small	microchip
-morph-	form, shape	amorphous
-naut-	sailor	cosmonaut
-phon-, -phone-, -phono-	sound, voice	phonics, telephone, phonograph
-pol-, -polis-	city, state	police, metropolis
-scop-, -scope-	watch, look at	microscope, telescope
-tele-	far off, distant	television
-the-	put or place	parentheses

Latin Root	Meaning	Sample Word
-cap-, -capt-, -cept-, -cip-	take	capitulate, captive, concept, recipient
-cede-, -ceed-, -ceas-, -cess-	happen, yield, go	precede, proceed, decease, cessation
-cred-	believe	incredible
-dic-, -dict-	speak, say, tell	indicate, diction
-duc-, -duct-, -duit-	lead, conduct, draw	educate, conduct, conduit
-fac-, -fact-, -fect-, -fic-, -fy-	make	faculty, artifact, defect, beneficial, clarify
-ject-	throw	eject
-mis-, -miss-, -mit-, -mitt-	send	promise, missile, transmit, intermittent
-note-, -not-	know, recognize	denote, notion
-pel-, -puls-	drive	expel, compulsive
-pend-, -pens-	hang, weight, set aside	pendulum, pension
-pon-, -pos-	put, place	component, position
-port-	carry	portable
-rupt-	break	bankrupt
-scrib-, -scribe-, -script-	write	scribble, describe, inscription
-spec-, -spic-	look, see	spectator, conspicuous
-tac-, -tag-, -tang-, -teg-	touch	contact, contagious, tangible, integral
-tain-, -ten-, -tin-	hold, keep	contain, tenure, retinue
-temp-	time	tempo
-ven-, -vent-	come	intervene, convention
-vers-, -vert-	turn	reverse, invert
-voc-, -vok-	call	vocal, invoke

VOCABULARY AND READING

Word knowledge is essential to reading comprehension. Quite simply, the more words you know, the easier it is to make sense of what you read. Your growing knowledge of word meanings combined with an ability to read carefully and think about what you read will help you succeed in school and do well on standardized tests, including the new SAT, the ACT, and the PSAT.

The **Vocabulary for Comprehension** exercises in this book will give you the opportunity to put your vocabulary knowledge and critical reading skills to use. Each exercise consists of a nonfiction reading passage followed by comprehension questions. The passages and questions are similar to those that you are likely to find on standardized tests.

Kinds of Questions

The questions on the reading sections of standardized tests are formulated in many different ways, but they are usually only of a small number of kinds, or types— the same ones that appear most frequently in the Vocabulary for Comprehension exercises in this book.

Main Idea Questions generally ask what the passage as a whole is about. Questions about the main idea may begin like this:

- The primary or main purpose of the passage is

- The primary focus of the passage is on

- The passage is best described as

- The passage is primarily concerned with

- The title that best describes the content of the passage is

Often the main idea is stated in the first paragraph of the passage. Sometimes, however, the first paragraph serves as an introduction and the main idea is included later on. When you answer questions about the main idea, you should make sure that the answers you choose reflect the focus of the entire passage and not just part of it. You may also be asked the main idea of a specific paragraph.

Detail Questions focus on important information that is explicitly stated in the passage. Often, however, the correct answer choices do not use the exact language of the passage. They are instead restatements, or paraphrases, of the text. So, for example, the answer to a question about "trash production and disposal" might use the term "waste management."

Vocabulary-in-Context Questions check your ability to use context to identify a word's meaning. All vocabulary-in-context questions include line references so that you can refer back to the passage to see how and in what context the word is used.

Here are some examples:

- **Condone** (line 6) most nearly means
- **Eminent** (line 8) is best defined as
- The meaning of **diffuse** (line 30) is

It is important to use context to check your answer choices, particularly when the vocabulary word has more than one meaning. Among the choices may be two (or more) correct meanings of the word in question. Your task is to choose the meaning that best fits the context.

Inference Questions ask you to make inferences or draw conclusions from the passage. These questions often begin like this:

- It can be inferred from the passage that
- The author implies that
- The passage suggests that
- Evidently the author feels that

The inferences you make and the conclusions you draw must be based on the information in the passage. Your own knowledge and reasoning come into play in understanding what is implied and in reaching conclusions that are logical.

Questions about Tone show your understanding of the author's attitude toward the subject of the passage. Words that describe tone, or attitude, are "feeling" words, for example, *indifferent, ambivalent, scornful, astonished, respectful.* These are typical questions:

- The author's attitude toward . . . is best described as
- The author's perspective is that of . . .
- Which word best describes the author's tone . . .

To determine the tone, it's important to pay attention to the author's choice of words and note your personal reaction. The author's attitude may be positive *(respectful, astonished)*, negative *(scornful)*, or neutral *(indifferent, ambivalent)*.

Questions about Author's Technique focus on the way a text is organized and the language the author uses. These questions ask you to think about structure and function. For example:

- The final paragraph serves to
- What is the function of the phrase . . . ?
- What does the author mean by . . . ?
- The author cites . . . in order to . . . .

To answer the questions, you must demonstrate an understanding of the way the author presents information and develops ideas.

Strategies

Here are some general strategies to help you in reading each passage and answering the questions.

- Read the introduction first. The introduction will provide a focus for the selection.

- Be an active reader. As you read, ask yourself questions about the passage, for example: What is this paragraph about? What does the writer mean here? Why does the writer include this information?

- Refer back to the passage when you answer the questions. In general, the order of the questions mirrors the organization of the passage, and many of the questions include paragraph or line references. It is often helpful to go back and reread before choosing an answer.

- Read carefully, and be sure to base your answer choices on the passage. There are answer choices that make sense, but are not based on the information in the passage. These are true statements, but incorrect answers. The correct answers are either restatements of ideas in the text or inferences that can be made from the text.

- Consider each exercise a learning experience. Keep in mind that your ability to answer the questions correctly shows as much about your understanding of the questions as about your understanding of the passage.

GRAMMAR AND WRITING

In order to write well, so that your meaning and your purpose are clearly understood, you must use words correctly; but, more than that, you must also make sure that what you write is grammatically correct. Knowing the rules of grammar, usage, and mechanics—the conventions of standard English—make your writing not just correct but more powerful and persuasive, too.

As a student you are regularly challenged to write effectively and correctly not only in your English classes but in your social studies, science, and history classes, too. Furthermore, high schools and colleges have raised their expectations for graduates. If you have taken a standardized test recently or are preparing to take one, you know this only too well. The writing and grammar sections of these tests have grown more demanding than ever.

On these grammar sections, questions usually appear in one or two multiple-choice formats. In one, you must decide if a mistake has been made in a sentence and, if one has been made, identify it. In another format, you must decide if an identified word or phrase is incorrect and, if it is incorrect, choose from several options the best way to correct it.

The **Grammar in Context** exercise that appears in each of the five Reviews in this book will provide you with opportunity to review and apply grammar and usage rules that are critical to good writing and that are frequently tested on the multiple-choice parts of standardized tests. In Level F, these topics are:

- Run-on sentences
- *Who* and *Whom*
- Subject-verb agreement
- Misplaced modifier
- Parallel structure

(For the sake of convenience, we sometimes use the term *grammar* to embrace all of the "rules" of English; but it's important to note that grammar, usage, and mechanics each represents a different aspect of writing. Grammar deals mostly with parts of speech and with parts of sentences and their relations. Usage, as the name suggests, concerns the way that words and phrases are used; usage topics would include, for example, irregular verbs, active and passive voice, subject-verb agreement, and double negatives. Mechanics deals with punctuation, capitalization, and spelling.)

There are many reasons to write and speak correctly other than to score well on standardized tests. You are judged by the way you write and speak. Your use of English is evaluated in the writing you do in school, on college applications, and in many different kinds of careers. You should be able to write and speak correctly when the situation calls for it—in a formal writing assignment, on a test, or in an interview. The more you practice standard English, the more comfortable and confident you will become when you write and speak.

WORKING WITH ANALOGIES

A verbal analogy expresses a relationship or comparison between sets of words. Normally, an analogy contains two pairs of words linked by a word or symbol that stands for an equals (=) sign. A complete analogy compares the two pairs of words and makes a statement about them. It asserts that the relationship between the first pair of words is the same as the relationship between the second pair.

In the **Analogies** exercises that appear in the Cumulative Reviews, you will be asked to complete analogies, that is, to choose the pair of words that best matches or parallels the relationship of the key, or given, pair of words. Here are two examples:

1. maple is to **tree** as
    a. acorn is to oak
    b. hen is to rooster
    c. rose is to flower
    d. shrub is to lilac

2. joyful is to **gloomy** as
    a. cheerful is to happy
    b. strong is to weak
    c. quick is to famous
    d. hungry is to starving

In order to find the correct answer to exercise 1, you must first determine the relationship between the two key words, **maple** and **tree**. In this case, that relationship might be expressed as "a maple is a kind (or type) of tree." The next step is to select from choices a, b, c, and d the pair of words that best reflects the same relationship. Clearly, the correct answer is (c); it is the only choice that parallels the relationship of the key words: a rose is a kind (or type) of flower, just as a maple is a kind (or type) of tree. The other choices do not express the same relationship.

In exercise 2, the relationship between the key words can be expressed as "joyful means the opposite of gloomy." Which of the choices best represents the same relationship? The answer, of course, is (b): "strong" means the opposite of "weak."

Here are examples of some other common analogy relationships:

Analogy	Key Relationship
big is to **large** as **little** is to **small**	**Big** means the same thing as **large**, just as **little** means the same thing as **small**.
brave is to **favorable** as **cowardly** is to **unfavorable**	The tone of **brave** is **favorable**, just as the tone of **cowardly** is **unfavorable**.
busybody is to **nosy** as **klutz** is to **clumsy**	A **busybody** is by definition someone who is **nosy**, just as a **klutz** is by definition someone who is **clumsy**.
cowardly is to **courage** as **awkward** is to **grace**	Someone who is **cowardly** lacks **courage**, just as someone who is **awkward** lacks **grace**.
visible is to **see** as **audible** is to **hear**	If something is **visible**, you can by definition **see** it, just as if something is **audible**, you can by definition **hear** it.
liar is to **truthful** as **bigot** is to **fair-minded**	A **liar** is by definition not likely to be **truthful**, just as a **bigot** is by definition not likely to be **fair-minded**.
eyes are to **see** as **ears** are to **hear**	You use your **eyes** to **see** with, just as you use your **ears** to **hear** with.

There are many different kinds of relationships represented in the analogy questions you will find in this book, but the key to solving any analogy is to find and express the relationship between the two key words.

This test contains a sampling of the words that are to be found in the exercises in this Level of VOCABULARY WORKSHOP. It will give you an idea of the types of words to be studied and their level of difficulty. When you have completed all the units, the Final Mastery Test at the end of this book will assess what you have learned. By comparing your results on the Final Mastery Test with your results on the Diagnostic Test below, you will be able to judge your progress.

Synonyms

*In each of the following groups, circle the word or phrase that **most nearly** expresses the meaning of the word in **boldface** type in the given phrase.*

1. a state of **bedlam**
a. discipline b. dreaminess (c. disorder) d. peace

2. an **erudite** study
a. breezy b. prestigious c. dull (d. scholarly)

3. **concoct** a story
a. listen to b. expose (c. make up) d. confirm

4. **transient** interests
a. long-lasting b. ardent c. scholarly (d. temporary)

5. **scurrilous** rumors
(a. abusive) b. well-informed c. false d. interesting

6. **unwieldy** packages
a. valuable (b. bulky) c. light d. unidentified

7. suffer from **ennui**
(a. boredom) b. fever c. tension d. fear

8. an **infraction** of a regulation
(a. violation) b. enactment c. enforcement d. author

9. **impugn** my sincerity
a. praise (b. question) c. describe d. imitate

10. a **propensity** for dangerous pursuits
a. desire (b. inclination) c. distaste d. dream

11. his **torpid** reactions
a. logical b. erratic c. quick (d. sluggish)

12. **commiserate** with us
(a. sympathize) b. eat c. discuss d. travel

13. **precipitated** a crisis in the government
a. foresaw b. prevented c. analyzed (d. caused)

14. nothing but **drivel**
(a. nonsense) b. light rain c. soil d. pollution

15. **abominate** all forms of injustice
a. study (b. loathe) c. abolish d. fear

16. an **anomalous** situation
a. safe   b. dangerous   c. embarrassing   (d. abnormal)

17. **heinous** deeds
a. charitable   (b. wicked)   c. childish   d. effective

18. a **motley** crew
a. frightened   b. musical   (c. variegated)   d. incompetent

19. remain **irresolute**
(a. wavering)   b. determined   c. uncontrolled   d. alert

20. the **epitome** of the scholarly professor
(a. embodiment)   b. career   c. prestige   d. knowledge

21. omit the **lurid** details
a. unimportant   b. repetitious   c. complicated   (d. sensational)

22. **simulate** interest
a. destroy   (b. pretend)   c. create   d. ignore

23. anonymous rumors and **innuendoes**
(a. insinuations)   b. lawsuits   c. editorials   d. compliments

24. **elicit** a response
a. reject   b. deny   c. explain   (d. draw out)

25. **flout** her expressed wishes
(a. ignore)   b. obey   c. back up   d. dislike

26. the **soporific** effect of the drug
(a. narcotic)   b. hallucinogenic   c. stimulant   d. laxative

27. **castigate** the students
a. address   b. appeal to   c. listen   (d. rebuke)

28. **assuage** her feelings
a. arouse   b. redirect   (c. allay)   d. hide

29. an **equitable** arrangement
(a. fair)   b. uncomfortable   c. lucrative   d. tiresome

30. **expurgate** a play
a. analyze   (b. censor)   c. produce   d. develop

Antonyms

*In each of the following groups, circle the word that is **most nearly opposite** in meaning to the word in **boldface** type in the given phrase.*

31. the **grisly** scene that met our eyes
a. curious   (b. delightful)   c. bloody   d. unexpected

32. had a **deleterious** effect on his health
a. harmful   b. puzzling   c. minimal   (d. beneficial)

33. a decidedly **insular** upbringing
a. foreign   b. narrow   (c. cosmopolitan)   d. inferior

34. will certainly **buttress** our case
(a. undermine)   b. clarify   c. clinch   d. strengthen

35. a victim of his own **avarice**
a. simplemindedness   b. greed   (c. generosity)   d. kindness

36. her rather **austere** taste in clothing
a. dreadful   (b. flamboyant)   c. expensive   d. simple

37. abet the culprits
(a. hinder)   b. assist   c. release   d. try

38. a **sleazy** hotel
(a. elegant)   b. quaint   c. sordid   d. modern

39. a **gauche** remark
(a. tactful)   b. silly   c. typical   d. pointed

40. hypothetical situations
a. interesting   b. typical   c. puzzling   (d. actual)

41. a truly **inauspicious** beginning
a. unpromising   b. belated   c. harrowing   (d. propitious)

42. paraphrase the passage
a. consider   (b. quote)   c. edit   d. publish

43. a life of **penury**
a. deprivation   (b. opulence)   c. sacrifice   d. self-denial

44. pretentious claims
a. extravagant   b. meaningless   c. ancient   (d. modest)

45. deplete our grain reserves
a. exhaust   b. commandeer   c. estimate   (d. replenish)

46. a truly **perceptive** critic
(a. undiscriminating)   b. well-known   c. self-appointed   d. shrewd

47. foment an insurrection
a. instigate   b. join   (c. suppress)   d. predict

48. extraneous data
a. accurate   (b. relevant)   c. complete   d. new

49. corroborate their testimony
a. report   b. confirm   c. collect   (d. refute)

50. covert meetings
a. occasional   b. noisy   (c. public)   d. important

Definitions

Note carefully the spelling, pronunciation, part(s) of speech, and definition(s) of each of the following words. Then write the word in the blank space(s) in the illustrative sentence(s) following. Finally, study the lists of synonyms and antonyms given at the end of each entry.

1. approbation
(ap rə bā′ shən)

(*n.*) the expression of approval or favorable opinion, praise; official approval

My broad hint that I had paid for the lessons myself brought smiles of _____ **approbation** _____ from all the judges at the piano recital.

SYNONYMS: commendation, sanction
ANTONYMS: disapproval, condemnation, censure

2. assuage
(ə swāj′)

(*v.*) to make easier or milder, relieve; to quiet, calm; to put an end to, appease, satisfy, quench

Her eyes told me that more than a few well-chosen words would be needed to _____ **assuage** _____ her hurt feelings.

SYNONYMS: mitigate, alleviate, slake, allay
ANTONYMS: intensify, aggravate, exacerbate

3. coalition
(kō ə lish′ ən)

(*n.*) a combination, union, or merger for some specific purpose

The various community organizations formed a _____ **coalition** _____ to lobby against parking laws.

SYNONYMS: alliance, league, federation, combine
ANTONYM: splinter group

4. decadence
(de′ kə dəns)

(*n.*) decline, decay, or deterioration; a condition or period of decline or decay; excessive self-indulgence

Some characterized her love of chocolate as _____ **decadence** because she ate at least two candy bars a day.

SYNONYMS: degeneration, corruption
ANTONYMS: rise, growth, development, maturation

5. elicit
(ē lis′ it)

(*v.*) to draw forth, bring out from some source (such as another person)

My attempt to _____ **elicit** _____ information over the phone was met with a barrage of irrelevant recordings.

SYNONYMS: call forth, evoke, extract, educe
ANTONYMS: repress, quash, squelch, stifle

6. expostulate
(ik späs′ chə lāt)

(*v.*) to attempt to dissuade someone from some course or decision by earnest reasoning

Shakespeare's Hamlet finds it useless to _____ **expostulate** _____ with his mother for siding with his stepfather.

SYNONYMS: protest, remonstrate, complain

7. hackneyed
(hak′ nēd)

(*adj.*) used so often as to lack freshness or originality

The Great Gatsby tells a universal story without being marred by _____ **hackneyed** _____ prose.

SYNONYMS: banal, trite, commonplace, corny
ANTONYMS: new, fresh, novel, original

8. hiatus
(hī ā′ təs)

(*n.*) a gap, opening, break (in the sense of having an element missing)

I was awakened not by a sudden sound but by a _____ **hiatus** _____ in the din of traffic.

SYNONYMS: pause, lacuna
ANTONYMS: continuity, continuation

9. innuendo
(in yü en′ dō)

(*n.*) a hint, indirect suggestion, or reference (often in a derogatory sense)

Those lacking the facts or afraid of reprisals often tarnish an enemy's reputation by use of _____ **innuendo** _____ .

SYNONYMS: insinuation, intimation
ANTONYM: direct statement

10. intercede
(in tər sēd′)

(*v.*) to plead on behalf of someone else; to serve as a third party or go-between in a disagreement

She will _____ **intercede** _____ in the dispute between the two children, and soon they will be playing happily again.

SYNONYMS: intervene, mediate

11. jaded
(jā′ did)

(*adj.*) wearied, worn-out, dulled (in the sense of being satiated by excessive indulgence)

The wilted handclasp and the fast-melting smile mark the _____ **jaded** _____ refugee from too many parties.

SYNONYMS: sated, surfeited, cloyed
ANTONYMS: unspoiled, uncloyed

12. lurid
(lür′ əd)

(*adj.*) causing shock, horror, or revulsion; sensational; pale or sallow in color; terrible or passionate in intensity or lack of restraint

Bright, sensational, and often _____ **lurid** _____ , some old-time movie posters make today's newspaper ads look tame.

SYNONYMS: gruesome, gory, grisly, baleful, ghastly
ANTONYMS: pleasant, attractive, appealing, wholesome

13. meritorious
(mer i tôr′ ē əs)

(*adj.*) worthy, deserving recognition and praise

Many years of _____ **meritorious** _____ service could not dissuade him from feeling that he had not chosen work that he liked.

SYNONYMS: praiseworthy, laudable, commendable
ANTONYMS: blameworthy, reprehensible, discreditable

14. petulant
(pech' ə lənt)

(*adj.*) peevish, annoyed by trifles, easily irritated and upset

An overworked parent may be unlikely to indulge the complaints of a _____petulant_____ child.

SYNONYMS: irritable, testy, waspish
ANTONYMS: even-tempered, placid, serene, amiable

15. prerogative
(prē räg' ə tiv)

(*n.*) a special right or privilege; a special quality showing excellence

She seemed to feel that a snooze at her desk was not an annoying habit but the _____prerogative_____ of a veteran employee.

SYNONYMS: perquisite, perk

16. provincial
(prə vin' shəl)

(*adj.*) pertaining to an outlying area; local; narrow in mind or outlook, countrified in the sense of being limited and backward; of a simple, plain design that originated in the countryside; (*n.*) a person with a narrow point of view; a person from an outlying area; a soldier from a province or colony

The banjo, once thought to be a _____provincial_____ product of the Southern hills, actually came here from Africa.

At first, a _____provincial_____ may do well in the city using charm alone, but charm, like novelty, wears thin.

SYNONYMS: (*adj.*) narrow-minded, parochial, insular, naive
ANTONYMS: (*adj.*) cosmopolitan, catholic, broad-minded

17. simulate
(sim' yə lāt)

(*v.*) to make a pretense of, imitate; to show the outer signs of

Some skilled actors can _____simulate_____ emotions they might never have felt in life.

SYNONYMS: feign, pretend, affect

18. transcend
(tran send')

(*v.*) to rise above or beyond, exceed

A great work of art may be said to _____transcend_____ time, and it is remembered for decades, or even centuries.

SYNONYMS: surpass, outstrip

19. umbrage
(em' brəj)

(*n.*) shade cast by trees; foliage giving shade; an overshadowing influence or power; offense, resentment; a vague suspicion

She hesitated to offer her opinion, fearing that they would take _____umbrage_____ at her criticism.

SYNONYMS: irritation, pique, annoyance
ANTONYMS: pleasure, delight, satisfaction

20. unctuous
(əŋk' chü əs)

(*adj.*) excessively smooth or smug; trying too hard to give an impression of earnestness, sincerity, or piety; fatty, oily; pliable

Her constant inquiring about the health of my family at first seemed friendly, later merely _____unctuous_____.

SYNONYMS: mealymouthed, servile, fawning, greasy
ANTONYMS: gruff, blunt

Completing the Sentence

From the words for this unit, choose the one that best completes each of the following sentences. Write the word in the space provided.

1. I certainly appreciate your praise, but I must say that I can see nothing so remarkably _____**meritorious**_____ in having done what any decent person would do.

2. Since I don't like people who play favorites in the office, I have frequently _____**expostulated**_____ against such behavior with my superiors.

3. Various insects have a marvelous capacity to protect themselves by _____**simulating**_____ the appearance of twigs and other objects in their environment.

4. In the question-and-answer session, we tried to _____**elicit**_____ from the candidates some definite indication of how they proposed to reduce the national debt.

5. I feel that, as an old friend, I have the _____**prerogative**_____ of criticizing your actions without arousing resentment.

6. The only way to defeat the party in power is for all the reform groups to form a(n) _____**coalition**_____ and back a single slate of candidates.

7. Although we tried to express our sympathy, we knew that mere words could do nothing to _____**assuage**_____ her grief.

8. Their tastes have been so _____**jaded**_____ by luxurious living that they seem incapable of enjoying the simple pleasures of life.

9. Of course you have a right to ask the waiter for a glass of water, but is there any need to use the _____**petulant**_____ tone of a spoiled child?

10. His confidence grew as he received clear signs of the _____**approbation**_____ of his superiors.

11. During the brief _____**hiatus**_____ in the music, someone's ringing cell phone split the air.

12. I take no _____**umbrage**_____ at your personal remarks, but I feel you would have been better advised not to make them.

13. The midnight fire in our apartment building cast a(n) _____**lurid**_____, unearthly light on the faces of the firefighters struggling to put it out.

14. The issue of good faith that your conduct raises far _____**transcends**_____ the specific question of whether or not you are responsible for the problem.

15. If you cannot meet the college's entrance requirements, it will be futile to have someone _____**intercede**_____ on your behalf.

16. If you take pride in expressing yourself with force and originality, you should not use so many _____**hackneyed**_____ phrases.

17. In an age when the United States has truly global responsibilities, we cannot afford to have leaders with _____**provincial**_____ points of view.

18. The manager expressed her unfavorable opinion of the job applicant by _____innuendo_____ rather than by direct statement.

19. Weakened militarily, and with a large part of the population living on free "bread and circuses," the once mighty Roman Empire now entered a period of _____decadence_____.

20. Forever humbling himself and flattering others, Dickens' Uriah Heep is famously _____unctuous_____.

Synonyms

*Choose the word from this unit that is **the same** or **most nearly the same** in meaning as the **boldface** word or expression in the given phrase. Write the word on the line provided.*

1. **pause** in the hectic workday .... hiatus
2. **insinuation** not supported by fact .... innuendo
3. **wearied** by too many compliments .... jaded
4. impolite and **peevish** questions .... petulant
5. a **perquisite** of her rank .... prerogative
6. exploding in **annoyance** .... umbrage
7. unceasing and **servile** modesty .... unctuous
8. **feign** a reconciliation .... simulate
9. **alleviate** his worst fears .... assuage
10. seeking the boss's **commendation** .... approbation
11. **gruesome** tales of grave robbers .... lurid
12. **protest** against a course of action .... expostulate
13. to **exceed** one's limitations .... transcend
14. finding strength through an **alliance** .... coalition
15. **mediate** in a dispute .... intercede

Antonyms

*Choose the word from this unit that is **most nearly opposite** in meaning to the **boldface** word or expression in the given phrase. Write the word on the line provided.*

16. the **development** of a civilization .... decadence
17. a **broad-minded** approach to education .... provincial
18. trying to **squelch** suggestions .... elicit
19. a record of **discreditable** actions .... meritorious
20. a series of **novel** magic tricks .... hackneyed

*Circle the **boldface** word that more satisfactorily completes each of the following sentences.*

1. The magnificence of the scene far (**simulated, transcended**) my ability to describe it in words.

2. The most (**meritorious, lurid**) form of charity, according to the ancient Hebrew sages, is to help a poor person to become self-supporting.

3. The American two-party system almost always makes it unnecessary to form a (**hiatus, coalition**) of minority parties to carry on the government.

4. To impress her newly made friends, she (**simulated, assuaged**) an interest in modern art, of which she knew nothing.

5. Apparently mistaking us for the millionaire's children, the hotel manager overwhelmed us with his (**petulant, unctuous**) attentions.

6. I see no point in (**expostulating, simulating**) with a person who habitually refuses to listen to reason.

7. After watching four TV football games on New Year's Day, I was (**jaded, hackneyed**) with the pigskin sport for weeks to come.

8. Anyone who thinks that it is still a gentleman's (**prerogative, hiatus**) to ask a lady to dance didn't attend our Senior Prom.

9. We cannot know today what sort of accent Abraham Lincoln had, but it may well be that there was a decidedly (**meritorious, provincial**) twang in his speech.

10. Who would have thought he would take (**prerogative, umbrage**) at an e-mail from a friend who wanted only to help?

11. My teacher is so accomplished that she can (**simulate, elicit**) some degree of interest and attention from even the most withdrawn children.

12. When the (**umbrage, hiatus**) in the conversation became embarrassingly long, I decided that the time had come to serve the sandwiches.

13. His skillful use of academic jargon and fashionable catchphrases could not conceal the essentially (**hackneyed, meritorious**) quality of his ideas.

14. On the air the star seemed calm, but he privately sent (**petulant, jaded**) notes to those who gave him bad reviews.

15. I truly dislike the kind of sensational popular biography that focuses solely on the more (**lurid, hackneyed**) or scandalous aspects of a superstar's career.

16. How can you accuse me of employing (**umbrage, innuendo**) when I am saying in the plainest possible language that I think you're a crook?

17. If you try to (**elicit, intercede**) in a lovers' quarrel, the chances are that you will only make things worse.

18. Popularity polls seem to be based on the mistaken idea that the basic task of a political leader is to win immediate (**approbation, coalition**) from the people.

19. They try to "prove" the (**umbrage, decadence**) of modern youth by emphasizing everything that is bad and ignoring whatever is good.

20. Perhaps it will (**expostulate, assuage**) your fright if I remind you that everyone must have a first date at some time in his or her life.

*Read the following passage, in which some of the words you have studied in this unit appear in **boldface** type. Then complete each statement given below the passage by circling the letter of the item that is **the same** or **almost the same** in meaning as the highlighted word.*

Screen Time

(Line)

Americans' love of the movies goes back to the early years of the twentieth century, when shabby little theaters charged a nickel to see a film about a **lurid** crime, a **meritorious** deed, or a thrilling chase. These twenty-minute "flickers," as many called them, offered a short but exciting **hiatus** from everyday life. By the

(5) 1920s the movies had become big business, and cities bragged of cinema palaces three stories tall, their lobbies embellished with splendid carpeted stairways, plaster statues, and colorful lighting. Built in the center of town, these theaters showed brand-new, less **hackneyed**, and longer films, which were later shown

(10) at smaller neighborhood theaters and in **provincial** towns.

In the 1930s the Great Depression hit. Banks closed, businesses failed, and ten percent of Americans lost their jobs, while

(15) many others accepted wage cuts and feared they would be next. By now it cost twenty cents to go to the movies, which was more than the price of a loaf of bread. Why should frightened people short of

(20) cash spend money unnecessarily?

Movie-makers came up with clever answers. For many years they had made films in which poor people proved themselves smarter, kinder, or braver

(25) than the rich and **jaded**. To these they now

Hollywood Premiere of "The Robe," 1953

added movies made from novels set in faraway times and places unlike the alarming here and now. Theaters began showing two full-length films for the price of one, added a cartoon, gave away dishes, and awarded money to the holder of the lucky ticket on "bank night." Ticket sales climbed, and going to the movies

(30) every week became an American pastime.

---

1. The meaning of **lurid** (line 2) is
   a. unsolved   c. true
   (b.) ghastly   d. ridiculous

2. Meritorious (line 3) most nearly means
   a. difficult   c. wicked
   (b.) praiseworthy   d. unusual

3. Hiatus (line 4) is best defined as
   a. story   (c.) pause
   b. excerpt   d. lesson

4. The meaning of **hackneyed** (line 8) is
   a. ragged   c. noisy
   b. exciting   (d.) trite

5. Provincial (line 11) most nearly means
   (a.) outlying   c. deserving
   b. prosperous   d. middle-size

6. Jaded (line 25) is best defined as
   a. famous   c. disappointed
   b. notorious   (d.) surfeited

UNIT 2

Definitions

Note carefully the spelling, pronunciation, part(s) of speech, and definition(s) of each of the following words. Then write the word in the blank space(s) in the illustrative sentence(s) following. Finally, study the lists of synonyms and antonyms given at the end of each entry.

1. ameliorate
(ə mēl' yə rāt)

(*v.*) to improve, make better, correct a flaw or shortcoming

A hot meal can _____**ameliorate**_____ the discomforts of even the coldest day.

SYNONYMS: amend, better
ANTONYMS: worsen, aggravate, exacerbate

2. aplomb
(ə pläm')

(*n.*) poise, assurance, great self-confidence; perpendicularity

Considering the family's tense mood, you handled the situation with _____**aplomb**_____.

SYNONYMS: composure, self-possession, levelheadedness
ANTONYMS: confusion, embarrassment, abashment

3. bombastic
(bäm bas' tik)

(*adj.*) pompous or overblown in language; full of high-sounding words intended to conceal a lack of ideas

He delivered a _____**bombastic**_____ speech that did not even address our problems.

SYNONYMS: inflated, highfalutin, high-flown, pretentious
ANTONYMS: unadorned, simple, plain, austere

4. callow
(kal' ō)

(*adj.*) without experience; immature, not fully developed; lacking sophistication and poise; without feathers

They entered the army as _____**callow**_____ recruits and left as seasoned veterans.

SYNONYMS: green, raw, unfledged, inexperienced
ANTONYMS: mature, grown-up, polished, sophisticated

5. drivel
(driv' əl)

(*n.*) saliva or mucus flowing from the mouth or nose; foolish, aimless talk or thinking; nonsense; (*v.*) to let saliva flow from the mouth; to utter nonsense or childish twaddle; to waste or fritter away foolishly

To me, my dream made perfect sense, but when I told it to my friend it sounded like _____**drivel**_____.

Knowing that his time was nearly up, we kept silent and let him _____**drivel**_____ on.

SYNONYMS: (*n.*) balderdash, hogwash, tommyrot; (*v.*) slaver

6. epitome
(i pit' ə mē)

(*n.*) a summary, condensed account; an instance that represents a larger reality

Admitting when you have been fairly defeated is the _____**epitome**_____ of sportsmanship.

SYNONYMS: abstract, digest, model, archetype

7. exhort
(eg zôrt')

(*v.*) to urge strongly, advise earnestly
With dramatic gestures, our fans vigorously ___exhorted___ the team to play harder.
SYNONYMS: entreat, implore, adjure
ANTONYMS: discourage, advise against, deprecate

8. ex officio
(eks ə fish' ē ō)

(*adj., adv.*) by virtue of holding a certain office
The President is the ___ex officio___ commander-in-chief of the armed forces in time of war.

9. infringe
(in frinj')

(*v.*) to violate, trespass, go beyond recognized bounds
If you continue to ___infringe___ on my responsibilities, will you also take the blame for any mistakes?
SYNONYMS: encroach, impinge, intrude, poach
ANTONYM: stay in bounds

10. ingratiate
(in grā' shē āt)

(*v.*) to make oneself agreeable and thus gain favor or acceptance by others (sometimes used in a critical or derogatory sense)
It is not a good idea to ___ingratiate___ oneself by paying cloying compliments.
SYNONYMS: cozy up to, curry favor with
ANTONYMS: alienate, humiliate oneself, mortify oneself

11. interloper
(in' tər lōp ər)

(*n.*) one who moves in where he or she is not wanted or has no right to be, an intruder
The crowd was so eager to see the band perform that they resented the opening singer as an ___interloper___.
SYNONYMS: trespasser, meddler, buttinsky

12. intrinsic
(in trin' sik)

(*adj.*) belonging to someone or something by its very nature, essential, inherent; originating in a bodily organ or part
It had been my father's favorite book when he was my age, but for me it held little ___intrinsic___ interest.
SYNONYMS: immanent, organic
ANTONYMS: extrinsic, external, outward

13. inveigh
(in vā')

(*v.*) to make a violent attack in words, express strong disapproval
You should not ___inveigh___ against the plan with quite so much vigor until you have read it.
SYNONYMS: rail, harangue, fulminate, remonstrate
ANTONYMS: acclaim, glorify, extol

14. lassitude
(las' ə tüd)

(*n.*) weariness of body or mind, lack of energy
On some days I am overcome by ___lassitude___ at the thought of so many more years of schooling.
SYNONYMS: fatigue, lethargy, torpor, languor
ANTONYMS: energy, vitality, animation, liveliness

15. millennium
(*pl.*, **millennia**)
(mə len' ē əm)

(*n.*) a period of one thousand years; a period of great joy

In 1999 an argument raged over whether 2000 or 2001 would mark the beginning of the new _____**millennium**_____ .

SYNONYMS: chiliad, golden age, prosperity, peace
ANTONYMS: doomsday, day of judgment

16. occult
(ə kəlt')

(*adj.*) mysterious, magical, supernatural; secret, hidden from view; not detectable by ordinary means; (*v.*) to hide, conceal; eclipse; (*n.*) matters involving the supernatural

One need not rely on _____**occult**_____ knowledge to grasp why things disappear in a house where two cats live.

Much of his talk about the _____**occult**_____ seems grounded in nothing but trick photography and folklore.

SYNONYMS: (*adj.*) supernatural, esoteric, abstruse, arcane
ANTONYMS: (*adj.*) mundane, common, public, exoteric

17. permeate
(pər' mē āt)

(*v.*) to spread through, penetrate, soak through

The rain _____**permeated**_____ all of my clothing and reduced the map in my pocket to a pulpy mass.

18. precipitate
(*v.*, pri sip' ə tāt; adj., *n.*, pri sip' ət ət)

(*v.*) to fall as moisture; to cause or bring about suddenly; to hurl down from a great height; to give distinct form to; (*adj.*) characterized by excessive haste; (*n.*) moisture; the product of an action or process

Scholars often disagree over which event or events _____**precipitate**_____ an historic moment.

I admit that my outburst was _____**precipitate**_____ .

Too many eggs in this particular pudding will leave a messy _____**precipitate**_____ in the baking pan.

SYNONYMS: (*v.*) provoke, produce; (*adj.*) reckless, impetuous
ANTONYMS: (*adj.*) wary, cautious, circumspect

19. stringent
(strin' jənt)

(*adj.*) strict, severe; rigorously or urgently binding or compelling; sharp or bitter to the taste

Some argue that more _____**stringent**_____ laws against speeding will make our streets safer.

SYNONYMS: stern, rigorous, tough, urgent, imperative
ANTONYMS: lenient, mild, lax, permissive

20. surmise
(sər mīz')

(*v.*) to think or believe without certain supporting evidence; to conjecture or guess; (*n.*) likely idea that lacks definite proof

I cannot be sure, but I _____**surmise**_____ that she would not accept my apology even if I made it on my knees.

The police had no proof, nothing to go on but a suspicion, a mere _____**surmise**_____ .

SYNONYMS: (*v.*) infer, gather; (*n.*) inference, presumption

Completing the Sentence

From the words for this unit, choose the one that best completes each of the following sentences. Write the word in the space provided.

1. They have a great deal to say on the subject, but unfortunately most of it is meaningless _____ drivel _____.

2. The Vice President of the United States, the Secretary of State, and the Secretary of Defense are _____ ex officio _____ members of the National Security Council.

3. That dancer is very talented, but isn't it going rather far to call her "the very _____ epitome _____ of feminine beauty and grace"?

4. Representing an organization of senior citizens, the rally's keynote speaker _____ inveighed _____ vehemently against conditions that rob the elderly of their dignity and independence.

5. "The rash and _____ precipitate _____ actions of that young hothead almost cost us the battle, to say nothing of the war," the general remarked sourly.

6. The mere fact that we cannot explain at the present time how she was hurt doesn't mean that she was the victim of some _____ occult _____ power.

7. After completing those long, grueling exams, I was overwhelmed by a(n) _____ lassitude _____ so great that I felt I would never be able to study again.

8. We do not know what her motives were, but we may _____ surmise _____ that she was mainly concerned for the child's well-being.

9. A good definition of *freedom* is: "The right to do anything you wish as long as you do not _____ infringe _____ on the rights of others."

10. Addressing the school assembly for the first time was a nerve-racking experience, but I managed to deliver my speech with a reasonable amount of _____ aplomb _____.

11. "If you think my training rules are too _____ stringent _____ and confining," the coach said, "then you probably shouldn't be a candidate for the team."

12. We looked up hungrily as the delightful odor of broiled steak and fried onions _____ permeated _____ the room.

13. He tries to give the impression of being a true man of the world, but his conduct clearly shows him to be a(n) _____ callow _____ and somewhat feckless youth.

14. The voters of this city are looking for practical answers to urgent questions and will not respond to that kind of _____ bombastic _____ and pretentious claptrap.

15. Though fossils show that human beings have been on earth a very, very long time, the earliest written records of their activities date back only about five _____ millennia _____.

16. I refuse to accept the idea that conditions in this slum have deteriorated so far that nothing can be done to _____ ameliorate _____ them.

17. How can we have any respect for people who try to _____ ingratiate _____ themselves with their superiors by flattery and favors?

18. This old necklace has little _____intrinsic_____ value, but it means a great deal to me because it belonged to my mother.

19. The people trying to "crash" our dance may think of themselves as merry pranksters, but they are really _____interlopers_____ who would prevent us all from having a good time.

20. The prophets of old fervently _____exhorted_____ the people to amend their lives.

Synonyms

*Choose the word from this unit that is **the same** or **most nearly the same** in meaning as the **boldface** word or expression in the given phrase. Write the word on the line provided.*

1. a **buttinsky** at their reunion   _____interloper_____

2. a stain that **spread through**   _____permeated_____

3. overdramatic, **high-flown** language   _____bombastic_____

4. the **model** of what not to wear   _____epitome_____

5. a smile meant to **curry favor**   _____ingratiate_____

6. to **rail** against a harmless mistake   _____inveigh_____

7. a line delivered with **composure**   _____aplomb_____

8. thought the idea to be **hogwash**   _____drivel_____

9. a **strict** requirement   _____stringent_____

10. seemed to be a logical **presumption**   _____surmise_____

11. to **encroach** on their rights   _____infringe_____

12. to **entreat** the people to resist   _____exhort_____

13. an **inexperienced** trainee   _____callow_____

14. tonight's moderator **by virtue of her job**   _____ex officio_____

15. hints of a **supernatural** presence   _____occult_____

Antonyms

*Choose the word from this unit that is **most nearly opposite** in meaning to the **boldface** word or expression in the given phrase. Write the word on the line provided.*

16. **external** to the whole plan   _____intrinsic_____

17. a notable **energy** in her manner   _____lassitude_____

18. a **cautious** move on the chess board   _____precipitate_____

19. waiting for the **day of judgment**   _____millennium_____

20. swift action to **worsen** the situation   _____ameliorate_____

Choosing the Right Word

*Circle the **boldface** word that more satisfactorily completes each of the following sentences.*

1. I trust that we will have the will to improve what can now be improved and the patience to bear what cannot now be (**ameliorated,** surmised).

2. When the bridge suddenly collapsed in the high winds, the people on it at the time were (**inveighed, precipitated**) to their deaths in the watery abyss below.

3. "Long periods of intense boredom punctuated by short periods of intense fear"—in this famous definition a British general (**epitomized,** infringed) the nature of war.

4. We are all ready and willing to do what must be done; what we need is leadership—not (**exhortation,** aplomb)!

5. Must we continue to listen to all this childish (lassitude, **drivel**)!

6. A sour odor of decay, stale air, and generations of living (**permeated,** precipitated) every corner of the old tenement.

7. She handled a potentially embarrassing situation with cool (drivel, **aplomb**).

8. His message may seem (**bombastic,** callow), but there is a solid framework of practical ideas underlying the rather pompous language.

9. In this situation we cannot act on the basis of what may be (**surmised,** inveighed), but only in accordance with what is definitely known.

10. "I'm sure your every wish will be granted," I assured the demanding child, my tongue firmly in my check, "when and if the (exhortation, **millennium**) ever comes!"

11. It is easy to (**inveigh,** precipitate) against "dirty politics," but less easy to play a positive role, however small, in the political process.

12. In stating that "All men are created equal and endowed . . . with certain inalienable rights," the Declaration of Independence proclaims the (**intrinsic,** callow) value of every human being.

13. After years of fighting for social reforms, she experienced a sort of spiritual (**lassitude,** aplomb) that caused her to withdraw and let other people lead the struggle.

14. Do we need new laws to combat crime, or rather, more (ingratiating, **stringent**) enforcement of the laws we already have?

15. The publisher will take prompt legal action against anyone who (inveighs, **infringes**) on the copyright of this book.

16. I can usually forgive a(n) (**callow,** ex officio) display of feeble jokes and showing off—but not by someone who has passed his 40th birthday!

17. There is evidence that proves that many persons supposed to possess (**occult,** stringent) powers have either been clever frauds or the victims of self-deception.

18. After the unexpected defeat, the members of the team wanted to be alone and regarded anyone who entered the locker room as a(n) (**interloper,** lassitude).

19. The song had a pleasant, (stringent, **ingratiating**) melody that gained it quick popularity and then caused it to be forgotten just as quickly.

20. Because I believe in spreading governmental powers among several officials, I am opposed to having the Mayor serve as (occult, **ex officio**) head of the Board of Education.

*Read the following passage, in which some of the words you have studied in this unit appear in **boldface** type. Then complete each statement given below the passage by circling the letter of the item that is **the same** or **almost the same** in meaning as the highlighted word.*

Speaking Up

(Line)

Most people shiver at the prospect of making a speech, of facing a roomful of strangers and trying to persuade or inform them. Here are some tips that can help the inexperienced to do the job with **aplomb**.

First, remember that you and your audience are all in one room together. You are not an **interloper**, and your audience is not the enemy. The truth is that your listeners (5) will probably like you if you appear to like them. Try your best to put *them* at ease, for by doing so, you can **ameliorate** your own discomfort.

A student debater makes a point

How should you begin? Despite what you may have been told, do not start off with a joke. Telling jokes successfully to strangers takes practice (10) and skill. Besides, any joke you have recently heard is likely to be one that your listeners have also heard. In short, do not start by trying to **ingratiate** yourself. Instead, pay the audience the compliment of being yourself. Try to be (15) simple and direct. By all means smile if you say something funny, but bear in mind that only **callow** speakers laugh aloud at their own wit.

Should the speech be written out word for word? If you are to speak for as long as thirty (20) minutes, it probably should. (For so long a speech, keep the sentences fairly short; strings of long ones will end up sounding **bombastic**.) If your time is brief, you may need only notes you can scan as you move from point to point. (25) Either way, rehearse and rehearse—so you can look often at your audience. Nothing will increase your bravery and put *you* more at ease than looking into friendly faces.

---

1. The meaning of **aplomb** (line 3) is
  a. assistance
  b. poise
  c. applause
  d. victory

2. Interloper (line 5) most nearly means
  a. professional
  b. amateur
  c. intruder
  d. fool

3. Ameliorate (line 7) is best defined as
  a. amend
  b. wipe out
  c. increase
  d. replace

4. The meaning of **ingratiate** (line 14) is
  a. curry favor for
  b. disguise
  c. exaggerate
  d. make fun of

5. Callow (line 18) most nearly means
  a. pale
  b. raw
  c. proud
  d. loud

6. Bombastic (line 23) is best defined as
  a. complicated
  b. odd
  c. silly
  d. highfalutin

Definitions

Note carefully the spelling, pronunciation, part(s) of speech, and definition(s) of each of the following words. Then write the word in the blank space(s) in the illustrative sentence(s) following. Finally, study the lists of synonyms and antonyms given at the end of each entry.

1. abominate
(ə bäm' ə nāt)

(*v.*) to have an intense dislike or hatred for

I _____ **abominate** _____ cruelty yet do not always notice when I have said something cruel without meaning to.

SYNONYMS: loathe, abhor, despise, detest
ANTONYMS: relish, savor, cherish, esteem

2. acculturation
(ə kəl chə rā' shən)

(*n.*) the modification of the social patterns, traits, or structures of one group or society by contact with those of another; the resultant blend

Every immigrant group newly arrived in another country goes through a slow process of _____ **acculturation** _____.

SYNONYM: adaptation

3. adventitious
(ad ven tish' əs)

(*adj.*) resulting from chance rather than from an inherent cause or character; accidental, not essential; (*medicine*) acquired, not congenital

It was no _____ **adventitious** _____ meeting that led to their writing songs together, for in fact they were cousins.

SYNONYMS: extrinsic, incidental, fortuitous
ANTONYMS: essential, intrinsic, inherent, congenital

4. ascribe
(ə skrīb')

(*v.*) to assign or refer to (as a cause or source), attribute

You may _____ **ascribe** _____ these holes to gophers or elves, but I blame the dog from next door.

SYNONYMS: impute, credit, attribute

5. circuitous
(sər kyü' ə təs)

(*adj.*) roundabout, not direct

I followed a _____ **circuitous** _____ path through the woods, not because I feared pursuit, but because I was lost.

SYNONYMS: indirect, meandering, winding
ANTONYMS: straight, direct, as the crow flies

6. commiserate
(kə miz' ə rāt)

(*v.*) to sympathize with, have pity or sorrow for, share a feeling of distress

The family _____ **commiserated** _____ with her after the loss of her old and faithful dog.

SYNONYMS: feel sorry for, empathize
ANTONYM: feel no sympathy for

7. enjoin
(en join')

(v.) to direct or order; to prescribe a course of action in an authoritative way; to prohibit

I _____ **enjoined** _____ them to stop spending so much money or to face the consequences.

SYNONYMS: bid, charge, command, adjure
ANTONYMS: allow, permit

8. expedite
(ek' spə dīt)

(v.) to make easy, cause to progress faster

The pleasant background music did not _____ **expedite** _____ my work but instead, distracted me.

SYNONYMS: accelerate, facilitate, speed up
ANTONYMS: hinder, hamper, impede, obstruct

9. expiate
(ek' spē āt)

(v.) to make amends, make up for; to avert

They seemed more than willing to _____ **expiate** _____ their guilt by whatever means necessary.

SYNONYMS: redeem, make amends for, atone, make reparation

10. ferment
(n., fər' ment;
v., fər ment')

(n.) a state of great excitement, agitation, or turbulence; (v.) to be in or work into such a state; to produce alcohol by chemical action

Caught in the _____ **ferment** _____ of revolution, the young men enlisted with the local militias.

If left for a time, cider will eventually _____ **ferment** _____ .

SYNONYMS: (n.) commotion, turmoil, unrest
ANTONYMS: (n.) peace and quiet, tranquility, placidity

11. inadvertent
(in əd vər' tənt)

(adj.) resulting from or marked by lack of attention; unintentional, accidental

The poor fellow was stronger than he realized, and the damage he did was _____ **inadvertent** _____ .

SYNONYMS: accidental, unconsidered
ANTONYMS: deliberate, intentional, premeditated

12. nominal
(näm' ə nəl)

(adj.) existing in name only, not real; too small to be considered or taken seriously

Because so many of its patients were having financial troubles, the health clinic charged only _____ **nominal** _____ fees.

SYNONYMS: titular, token, trifling, inconsequential
ANTONYMS: real, actual, exorbitant, excessive

13. noncommittal
(nän kə mit' əl)

(adj.) not decisive or definite; unwilling to take a clear position or to say yes or no

We questioned her quietly, carefully, and at length, but her answers remained _____ **noncommittal** _____ .

SYNONYMS: cagey, uninformative, playing it safe, playing it close to the vest
ANTONYMS: positive, definite, committed

14. peculate
(pek′ yü lāt)

(v.) to steal something that has been given into one's trust; to take improperly for one's own use

Investigators discovered that the clerk came up with a scheme to _____ peculate _____ from the company.

SYNONYMS: embezzle, defraud, misappropriate

15. proclivity
(prō kliv′ ə tē)

(n.) a natural or habitual inclination or tendency (especially of human character or behavior)

Curious, patient, and fond of long walks outdoors, she soon displayed a _____ proclivity _____ for nature study.

SYNONYMS: natural bent, penchant, propensity
ANTONYMS: inability or incapacity

16. sangfroid
(säŋ frwä′)

(n.) composure or coolness, especially in trying circumstances

An experienced actor can perform with what seems like limitless _____ sangfroid _____, even when he forgets a line.

SYNONYMS: poise, self-assurance, equanimity
ANTONYMS: excitability, hysteria, flappability

17. seditious
(sə dish′ əs)

(adj.) resistant to lawful authority; having the purpose of overthrowing an established government

Dictators usually begin their reigns by searching out and silencing _____ seditious _____ opinion.

SYNONYMS: mutinous, rebellious, subversive
ANTONYMS: supportive, loyal, faithful, allegiant

18. tenuous
(ten′ yü əs)

(adj.) thin, slender, not dense; lacking clarity or sharpness; of slight importance or significance; lacking a sound basis, poorly supported

My grasp of trigonometry was _____ tenuous _____ until I attended the extra-help sessions.

SYNONYMS: flimsy, insubstantial, vague, hazy
ANTONYMS: strong, solid, substantial, valid

19. vitriolic
(vi trē äl′ ik)

(adj.) bitter, sarcastic; highly caustic or biting (like a strong acid)

Though hurt by his _____ vitriolic _____ language, I had to admit that some of his points were valid.

SYNONYMS: withering, acerbic, mordant
ANTONYMS: bland, saccharine, honeyed, sugary

20. wheedle
(whēd′ əl)

(v.) to use coaxing or flattery to gain some desired end

The spy used charm and flattery in order to _____ wheedle _____ the information from the diplomat.

SYNONYMS: cajole, inveigle, soft-soap, sweet-talk
ANTONYMS: coerce, browbeat, intimidate, strong-arm

Completing the Sentence

From the words for this unit, choose the one that best completes each of the following sentences. Write the word in the space provided.

1. He _____ expiated _____ the crime committed during his youth by a lifetime of service to humanity.

2. Since she seems to have a strong _____ proclivity _____ both for science and for service to others, I think that she should plan to study medicine.

3. We Americans do not believe that honest criticism of our public officials, no matter how severe, should be regarded as _____ seditious _____.

4. Declaring the boycott to be illegal, the judge _____ enjoined _____ the labor union from applying it against the employing firm.

5. Wines from that part of France are produced by _____ fermenting _____ the juice of the luscious grapes that grow on the hillsides.

6. No matter what their other likes or dislikes are, all Americans thoroughly _____ abominate _____ slavery in all its forms.

7. Certain languages such as Afrikaans are the product of _____ acculturation _____, and were created when two societies merged.

8. Some people say that they cannot understand her defeat in the election, but I _____ ascribe _____ it to her failure to discuss the issues in simple, down-to-earth terms.

9. While he remained the _____ nominal _____ leader of the group, the real power passed into the hands of his wily aide.

10. His line of questioning was so _____ circuitous _____ that I began to suspect that he was not sure of what he was trying to prove.

11. He claims to be a close friend of the Senator, but I believe that the connection between them is extremely _____ tenuous _____.

12. The new computerized referral system will greatly _____ expedite _____ the processing of complaints by customers.

13. Only someone who has suffered from bursitis can fully _____ commiserate _____ with me when I am in the throes of an acute attack.

14. Who in the world can hope to match the unshakable _____ sangfroid _____ of the indestructible James Bond in moments of great peril?

15. We must distinguish between the truly basic policies of our political party and those that are _____ adventitious _____ and have little connection with the essential program.

16. Much of the money that the "robber barons" _____ peculated _____ from the public trust was never recovered—or even missed!

17. You could have indicated frankly what you thought was wrong without embittering them with such _____ vitriolic _____ criticism.

18. As charming, clever, and persuasive as you may be, you will certainly not ___wheedle___ me into lending you my tennis racquet.

19. We had hoped to learn his opinion of the new energy program, but he remained completely ___noncommittal___ during the interview.

20. If, as you say, your slamming of the door on the way out was completely ___inadvertent___, you should be more careful in the future.

Synonyms

*Choose the word from this unit that is **the same** or **most nearly the same** in meaning as the **boldface** word or expression in the given phrase. Write the word on the line provided.*

1. charge both sides to negotiate — enjoin

2. speed up the registration procedure — expedite

3. a motive **attributed** to me — ascribed

4. embezzle from the treasury — peculate

5. was **cajoled** into agreeing — wheedled

6. an **acerbic** tone of voice — vitriolic

7. the **adaptation** of American students in Spain — acculturation

8. to **atone** for her unkindness — expiate

9. only **trifling** objections raised — nominal

10. empathize with your disappointment — commiserate

11. the **turmoil** of opening night — ferment

12. arguing a **poorly supported** point — tenuous

13. their leader's **self-assurance** — sangfroid

14. a nasty **penchant** for lying — proclivity

15. a **fortuitous** sequence of events — adventitious

Antonyms

*Choose the word from this unit that is **most nearly opposite** in meaning to the **boldface** word or expression in the given phrase. Write the word on the line provided.*

16. cherish everything about her — abominate

17. a **deliberate** misuse of the money — inadvertent

18. a **definite** statement of intentions — noncommittal

19. a kingdom filled with **loyal** subjects — seditious

20. a **direct** way home — circuitous

Choosing the Right Word

Circle the **boldface** word that more satisfactorily completes each of the following sentences.

1. I was simply unable to follow the (**circuitous,** adventitious) reasoning by which she "proved" that a straight line is not necessarily the shortest distance between two points.

2. Our military is prepared to deal with external aggression, but our best defense against (**sedition,** peculation) at home is the loyalty of the American people.

3. (**Commiseration,** Proclivity) is a noble human emotion, but in itself it is no substitute for vigorous efforts to help other people.

4. Since he has been able to (expiate, **wheedle**) almost anything he wants out of his parents, he is quite unprepared now to face the harsh realities of life.

5. An experienced politician always tries to avoid making (fermented, **inadvertent**) remarks that may offend some voters.

6. Although the Queen is the (**nominal,** adventitious) head of state, the Prime Minister is the real leader of the British government.

7. (**Peculation,** Sedition) was such a common offense among Roman provincial governors that, when asked how they made their fortunes, most simply replied, "In the provinces."

8. His investments proved to be profitable, but they were (**adventitious,** nominal) rather than the result of knowledge and planning.

9. The Biblical prophets (**abominated,** acculturated) idol worship of any kind and railed vehemently against such practices.

10. You are following an all too familiar pattern in (**ascribing,** expediting) your failures to anyone and everyone—except yourself.

11. Although that critic is feared for (noncommittal, **vitriolic**) reviews, I have learned that there is usually a sound basis for her unfavorable judgments.

12. I learned that I would have to make a choice between my strong aversion to hard work and my equally strong (**proclivity,** wheedle) for eating.

13. It is only in my fantasies that I display the (ferment, **sangfroid**) associated with movie heroes who are "as cool as a cucumber."

14. After he had seen the error of his ways, the villain attempted to (**expiate,** enjoin) the dark deeds of his past by acts of kindness and mercy.

15. Experienced lawyers know that the line between literal truth and slight but significant distortion of the facts is often a (seditious, **tenuous**) one.

16. With the deadline fast approaching, the local newspaper office was in a (**ferment,** sedition) of last-minute activity and preparation.

17. They are conscientious objectors to military service because they are (**enjoined,** ascribed) by a deep religious conviction not to take a human life.

18. When I spoke to Mother about going on the Easter trip to Washington, her only reply was a (nominal, **noncommittal**) "We'll see."

19. Modern American society can justly be said to be the end point of the (commiseration, **acculturation**) of diverse groups of immigrants.

20. The worst way I can think of to (**expedite,** ascribe) this program would be to set up a new Committee on (**Expediting,** Ascribing) Programs.

*Read the following passage, in which some of the words you have studied in this unit appear in **boldface** type. Then complete each statement given below the passage by circling the letter of the item that is **the same** or **almost the same** in meaning as the highlighted word.*

Building in Place

(Line)

Frank Lloyd Wright (1867–1959) is widely considered the greatest American architect in history. Few had a greater vision for how Americans should live or a harder time, despite handling professional obstacles with **sangfroid**, in getting others to further that vision by erecting the buildings he had designed. After college,

(5) where he studied engineering, he worked in Chicago for Louis Sullivan, a great architect who shared Wright's belief that American structures should suit the splendid and varied American landscape in which they were built. Wright

(10) **abominated** and eschewed the classical European designs that formed only a **tenuous** connection to the actual lives his clients lived. He loved nature in general and was inspired by the American plains in particular. He designed

(15) Midwestern "prairie houses" that were long and low. Their shapes and surfaces showed that they were a part of the land on which they stood, and this style became known as "organic architecture." Later, when he was asked to

Country club designed by Wright in Maui

(20) design larger buildings such as churches and offices, he used concrete for its thriftiness and glass ceilings for their natural and brilliant sunshine.

Branching out to Nevada, California, Pennsylvania, and elsewhere, he designed hundreds of buildings, and about 500 of them were built. A man of strong opinions, he stuck by his designs and could be **vitriolic** about preserving their integrity. Wright

(25) later went on to design the Imperial Hotel in Tokyo. Determined to match the building to its place, he made it resistant to the **adventitious** menace of earthquakes, a common danger in Japan. Sure enough, a terrible quake destroyed much of Tokyo, but the Imperial Hotel remained standing.

Toward the end of his career, Wright built a school for architects, and though its

(30) **nominal** purpose was design, its real impetus was his vision of life. Of his work he once said, "The mother of art is architecture. Without an architecture of our own we have no soul of our own civilization."

---

1. The meaning of **sangfroid** (line 3) is
a. menace
b. investment
c. bank account
d. composure

2. Abominated (line 10) most nearly means
a. loathed
b. destroyed
c. made fun of
d. tried out

3. Tenuous (line 11) is best defined as
a. permanent
b. vague
c. expensive
d. pretty

4. The meaning of **vitriolic** (line 24) is
a. acerbic
b. loud
c. confusing
d. tricky

5. Adventitious (line 26) most nearly means
a. frequent
b. destructive
c. accidental
d. massive

6. Nominal (line 30) is best defined as
a. popular
b. easy
c. freshman
d. token

REVIEW UNITS 1–3

Visit us at www.sadlier-oxford.com
for interactive puzzles and games.

Vocabulary for Comprehension

*Read the following passage, in which some of the words you have studied in Units 1–3 appear in **boldface** type. Then answer questions 1–12 on page 43 on the basis of what is <u>stated</u> or <u>implied</u> in the passage and in the introductory statement.*

Douglas Corrigan, the legendary pilot who is the subject of this passage, gained celebrity in an unconventional way.

(Line)

Readers of American history know that in 1927 Charles A. Lindbergh made the first solo flight across the Atlantic Ocean in a plane called the
(5) *Spirit of St. Louis.* But how many people know that in 1938 Douglas Corrigan achieved what might be called the first transatlantic hoax?

At 31, Corrigan, a native Texan, was
(10) an airplane mechanic and flight instructor who longed to fly across the Atlantic. To **assuage** this itch, he prepared his 1929 Curtis-Robin monoplane for the journey; but
(15) because of its age and poor condition, federal aviation authorities refused to certify the plane for a transoceanic flight. Even so, Corrigan flew his patched-up plane from California to
(20) New York in the summer of 1938. He then **elicited** permission from the aviation authorities to fly back home to California. Like Lindbergh, Corrigan took off from Long Island. Since his
(25) flight plan showed a return trip to California, his departure **precipitated** no suspicion. As he took off, he must have seemed the very **epitome** of an innocent amateur, for the flight staff at
(30) the Long Island airfield noted that he headed eastward into clouds instead of turning west. This seemed a

circuitous way to begin a trip to Los Angeles!
(35) Twenty-eight hours and thirteen minutes later, an odd-looking plane landed at an airfield in Dublin, Ireland. "I'm Douglas Corrigan," said the pilot. "Just got in from New York.
(40) Where am I?" (The outrage of the American officials, when they heard, can be imagined; but Corrigan continued to play the part of a cheerful, well-meaning amateur.) He
(45) **ascribed** his "mistake" in direction to a remarkably faulty compass and said that the clouds below him had kept him from seeing that he was flying over an ocean rather than the
(50) continental United States.

Within hours of his landing, the story of "Wrong Way" Corrigan circled the world. Though his flight license was suspended for a short time, he
(55) was given a ticker-tape parade upon his return to New York. During a time of economic depression, Corrigan, who thwarted authority with a grin and a wink, captured Americans'
(60) hearts. He stuck by his story—that he had gotten lost on his way to California—for the rest of his life.

1. The primary purpose of the passage is to
   a. describe Corrigan's monoplane
   b. review Corrigan's training for a historic flight
   c. explain how Corrigan earned the sobriquet "Wrong Way"
   d. focus on Corrigan's regret for a mistake
   e. compare Corrigan with Charles Lindbergh

2. The authorities denied Corrigan permission to make a transoceanic flight because
   a. he filed his application too late
   b. his plane was old and in poor condition
   c. the poor weather made flying dangerous
   d. his actions seemed suspicious
   e. he could not pay the required fees

3. The meaning of **assuage** (line 12) is
   a. pay for
   b. begin
   c. increase
   d. allay
   e. aggravate

4. Elicited (line 21) most nearly means
   a. extracted
   b. ignored
   c. pleaded for
   d. inferred
   e. falsified

5. Precipitated (line 26) is best defined as
   a. got rid of
   b. provoked
   c. hurled down
   d. suggested
   e. rained

6. In lines 27–34, the author suggests that
   a. the Long Island flight staff cooperated with Corrigan in his hoax
   b. the flight staff used a faulty compass
   c. Corrigan told the flight staff he would take off heading eastward
   d. the poor weather confused the flight staff
   e. the flight staff mistook Corrigan for an innocent amateur

7. The meaning of **epitome** (line 28) is
   a. model
   b. opposite
   c. imitation
   d. inspiration
   e. picture

8. Circuitous (line 33) most nearly means
   a. silly
   b. dangerous
   c. direct
   d. mysterious
   e. indirect

9. Ascribed (line 45) is best defined as
   a. denied
   b. concealed
   c. described
   d. restricted
   e. attributed

10. The passage implies that none of the following feelings inspired the nickname "Wrong Way" Corrigan EXCEPT
   a. envy
   b. greed
   c. outrage
   d. affectionate approval
   e. disillusionment

11. For the most part, which of the following organizational methods does the writer use?
   a. chronological order
   b. order of importance
   c. comparison and contrast
   d. cause and effect
   e. spatial order

12. The author's attitude toward Corrigan is best described as one of
   a. embarrassment
   b. admiration
   c. annoyance
   d. indifference
   e. hostility

Grammar in Context

If the sentence "As he took off, he must have seemed the very epitome of an innocent amateur, for the flight staff at the Long Island airfield noted that he headed eastward into clouds instead of turning west" (lines 27–32 on page 42) did not contain the conjunction "for" following the comma, it wouldn't be a sentence. It would be a **run-on sentence**.

A **sentence** is a group of words that expresses a complete thought. If a group of words is punctuated as a sentence but lacks a subject, a verb, or both, it is called a **sentence fragment**. A **run-on sentence**, on the other hand, is really two or more sentences masquerading as a single sentence because of incorrect punctuation or the omission of a conjunction. Without the "for" in the example above, only a comma would separate the two independent clauses. This type of error is called a *comma splice*. There are four ways to correct run-ons: (1) Use capitalization and punctuation to create two shorter sentences. (2) Use a comma followed by a conjunction, as the writer of the passage did. (3) Insert a semicolon with a transitional word or phrase followed by a comma. (4) Use a subordinating conjunction to make one of the two sentences a subordinate clause.

On the lines provided, rewrite the items below, correcting sentence fragments and run-on sentences. Write "correct" if the sentence is correct.

Answers may vary; sample answers given.

1. Made the first solo flight across the Atlantic in a plane called the *Spirit of St. Louis.*
   Charles A. Lindbergh made the first solo flight across the Atlantic in a plane called the *Spirit of St. Louis.*

2. Corrigan was a mechanic and flight instructor, he longed to fly across the Atlantic.
   Corrigan was a mechanic and flight instructor; he hoped to fly across the Atlantic.

3. Because Corrigan's monoplane was old and in poor condition.
   Because Corrigan's monoplane was old and in poor condition, the authorities refused to certify it for a transoceanic flight.

4. Because Corrigan listed his destination as California, the authorities allowed him to take off.
   correct

5. The American officials were outraged, Corrigan maintained he had made an honest mistake.
   The American officials were outraged, but Corrigan maintained he had made an honest mistake.

6. Corrigan had thwarted authority with a grin and a wink, perhaps understandably during a time of economic depression, he captured the hearts of Americans.
   Corrigan had thwarted authority with a grin and a wink. Perhaps understandably during a time of economic depression, he captured the hearts of Americans.

Two-Word Completions

Circle the pair of words that best complete the meaning of each of the following passages.

See pages T38–T48 for explanations of answers.

1. "The general's death-defying feats of gallantry in the recent war certainly deserve our _____," the article declared. "But, by the same token, his wanton acts of cruelty _____ our severest censure."
   a. umbrage . . . enjoin
   b. approbation . . . merit
   c. aplomb . . . expiate
   d. sangfroid . . . elicit

2. Though my teaching job entails numerous responsibilities, it also brings with it certain _____, one of which is the right to use school equipment, services, and facilities during the _____ between semesters or the summer break.
   a. prerogatives . . . hiatus
   b. surmises . . . innuendoes
   c. simulations . . . millennia
   d. ameliorations . . . proclivities

3. Though the Prime Minister actually directs the British government, the reigning monarch is the _____ head of state and, by virtue of that position, also the _____ leader of the Anglican Church.
   a. intrinsic . . . occult
   b. tenuous . . . inadvertent
   c. nominal . . . ex officio
   d. adventitious . . . noncommittal

4. While the Roman people remained vigorous and aggressive, their empire flourished. Once they began to sink into a sort of physical and spiritual _____, however, it became feeble and _____.
   a. umbrage . . . petulant
   b. lassitude . . . decadent
   c. aplomb . . . jaded
   d. ferment . . . adventitious

5. "A(n) _____ government will prove workable only so long as its members are able to _____ party differences," the professor remarked. "As soon as they become entangled in factional disputes, the partnership will begin to collapse."
   a. provincial . . . surmise
   b. ex officio . . . abominate
   c. seditious . . . ameliorate
   d. coalition . . . transcend

6. Some Senators favored the new budget proposal and in the warmest terms _____ their colleagues to pass the measure. Others disliked the idea and just as vehemently _____ against its adoption.
   a. wheedled . . . enjoined
   b. assuaged . . . interceded
   c. exhorted . . . inveighed
   d. elicited . . . infringed

Choosing the Right Meaning

Read each sentence carefully. Then circle the item that best completes the statement below the sentence.

See pages T38–T48 for explanations of answers.

"Planets like stars may be occulted; but as a planet shows a disk and does not appear as a mere point, the disappearance is gradual." (Patrick Moore) (2)

1. The best definition for the word **occulted** in line 1 is

a. discovered   b. observed   c. photographed   (d. eclipsed)

I thoroughly enjoyed that particular TV series and was saddened to discover that it was going on hiatus after only six episodes. (2)

2. The best meaning of the word **hiatus** in line 2 is

(a. a break)   b. an opening   c. a passage   d. a gap

Contingents of provincial militiamen regularly fought side by side with British regulars and their native allies in each of the four great wars France and England waged for (2) control of North America.

3. The word **provincial** in line 1 is used to mean

a. Italian local   (b. American colonial)   c. French rural   d. British parochial

Of the one hundred forty-two books of Livy's great *History of Rome*, only thirty-five survive intact; the rest are known solely from epitomes by later writers. (2)

4. In line 2 the word **epitomes** can best be defined as

a. quotations   b. archetypes   (c. summaries)   d. explanations

"Her family has such a long history of deafness that I am forced to regard her difficulties in that area as congenital, not adventitious," the specialist replied. (2)

5. The word **adventitious** in line 2 most nearly means

a. fatal   b. inherent   (c. acquired)   d. fortuitous

Antonyms

*In each of the following groups, circle the word or expression that is most nearly the **opposite** of the word in **boldface** type.*

1. commiserate
a. empathize
b. liberate
c. shackle
(d. feel no sympathy)

2. circuitous
a. dangerous
(b. direct)
c. unusual
d. confusing

3. abominate
a. avoid
b. encourage
c. loathe
(d. relish)

4. ferment
a. passion
(b. tranquility)
c. solitude
d. turmoil

5. ingratiate
a. curry favor
(b. alienate)
c. ungrateful
d. grateful

6. noncommittal
(a. positive)
b. reliable
c. irregular
d. nominal

7. surmise
a. dusk
b. inference
c. indifference
(d. certainty)

8. petulant
a. unruly
(b. even-tempered)
c. beautiful
d. brilliant

9. bombastic
(a. peaceful)
b. illiterate
c. boring
d. unpretentious

11. aplomb
a. skill
(b. awkwardness)
c. assurance
d. nobility

13. provincial
a. selfish
b. unreasonable
(c. worldly)
d. local

15. tenuous
a. logical
b. remote
(c. strong)
d. nonexistent

10. assuage
a. sense
b. record
(c. inflame)
d. soothe

12. sangfroid
a. composure
b. bravery
c. speed
(d. anxiety)

14. seditious
a. violent
(b. loyal)
c. planned
d. subtle

16. hackneyed
a. amiable
b. blunt
(c. original)
d. essential

Word Families

A. *On the line provided, write the word you have learned in Units 1–3 that is related to each of the following nouns.*
EXAMPLE: sedition—**seditious**

1. province, provincialism, provinciality — provincial
2. simulation, simulator — simulate
3. amelioration, ameliorant, ameliorator — ameliorate
4. exhortation, exhorter — exhort
5. vitriol, vitriolization — vitriolic
6. infringement, infringer — infringe
7. bombast — bombastic
8. interceder, intercession — intercede
9. abomination — abominate
10. fermentation, fermenting — ferment
11. petulance — petulant
12. callowness — callow
13. expostulation — expostulate
14. precipitation — precipitate
15. millennia — millennium

B. *On the line provided, write the word you have learned in Units 1–3 that is related to each of the following verbs.*
EXAMPLE: approbate—**approbation**

16. decay — decadence
17. coalesce — coalition
18. acculturate — acculturation
19. merit — meritorious
20. epitomize — epitome

In each of the following groups, circle the word that is best defined or suggested by the given phrase.

1. argue with the referee
(a. expostulate)   b. expiate   c. confer   d. wheedle

2. sensational account of the tragedy
a. circuitous   (b. lurid)   c. adventitious   d. vitriolic

3. encroach on my territory
a. occult   (b. infringe)   c. intercede   d. precipitate

4. inclination for foreign languages
a. aversion   (b. proclivity)   c. genius   d. prerogative

5. commanded our attendance
(a. enjoined)   b. occulted   c. precipitated   d. ameliorated

6. a weary expression
a. nominal   (b. jaded)   c. lurid   d. bombastic

7. plead on her friend's behalf
a. commiserate   b. assuage   c. abominate   (d. intercede)

8. fill the air
a. defray   b. stagnate   c. usurp   (d. permeate)

9. during the last 1000 years
a. famine   b. war   (c. millennium)   d. revolution

10. adopt strict rules
a. jaded   b. inadvertent   c. hackneyed   (d. stringent)

11. stolen from company funds
a. simulated   (b. peculated)   c. cleaved   d. exploited

12. took offense at my remark
a. sangfroid   (b. umbrage)   c. innuendo   d. deliberation

13. urge them to cooperate
a. assuage   (b. exhort)   c. ascribe   d. wheedle

14. the right to change one's mind
a. aplomb   b. proclivity   (c. prerogative)   d. approbation

15. surpass limitations
(a. transcend)   b. permeate   c. salvage   d. ameliorate

16. cutting words
a. decadent   (b. vitriolic)   c. meritorious   d. nominal

17. the result of low standards
(a. decadence)   b. innuendo   c. millennium   d. sedition

18. imitate his diction
(a. simulate)   b. abominate   c. inveigh   d. belittle

19. drew forth our applause
a. expiated   b. transcended   c. wheedled   (d. elicited)

20. credit the painting to Picasso
a. elicit   (b. ascribe)   c. enjoin   d. expedite

Building with Classical Roots

cede, cess, ceas—to happen, yield, go

This root appears in **intercede** (page 22), literally "to go between." The word now means "to ask a favor from one person for another." Other words based on the same root are listed below.

accede	cessation	decease	predecessor
accessory	concession	precedence	recession

From the list of words above, choose the one that corresponds to each of the brief definitions below. Write the word in the blank space in the illustrative sentence below the definition.

1. someone or something that comes before another in time, especially in an office or position ("*one who leaves before*")

Starting today, I will take over from my ____predecessor____.

2. death ("*going away*")

Marcia will inherit the estate after her aunt's ____decease____.

3. priority in order, rank, or importance

Studying for finals must take ____precedence____ over everything else.

4. to give in, agree; to attain ("*to yield to*")

The King's subjects are expected to ____accede____ to all his requests.

5. an admission, anything yielded, a compromise; a franchise

There is always a line at the food ____concession____.

6. something added, a finishing touch; a helper in a crime

Her sister was held by the police as a(n) ____accessory____.

7. a stopping, ceasing

The ambassador called for a ____cessation____ of hostilities.

8. a withdrawal, departure; a period of economic slump

Millions of workers were unemployed during the ____recession____.

From the list of words above, choose the one that best completes each of the following sentences. Write the word in the space provided.

1. This stern new measure will call for a(n) ____cessation____ of all economic assistance to both nations involved in the dispute.

2. In order to reach an agreement, both sides in the dispute will have to make important ____concessions____.

3. The new gymnasium will be an essential part of the community center, not just a(n) ___accessory___ .

4. The ultramodern office building that now occupies the site in no way resembles its stately old ___predecessor___ .

5. A provision was made for the maintenance of the family estate in the event that the ___decease___ of the mother occurred before that of her husband.

6. In a monarchy, the oldest son usually ___accedes___ to the throne on the death of the king.

7. The authorities declared that deliveries of such essentials as food and medical supplies would be given ___precedence___ over all other shipments into the disaster area.

8. After four years of record-high unemployment, the economists admitted that the ___recession___ was more serious than they had anticipated.

Circle the **boldface** word that more satisfactorily completes each of the following sentences.

1. No matter how much that mother coaxed her child, the stubborn little boy would not (**accede,** precede) to her wishes.

2. The terrified public waited forty-eight hours for a (concession, **cessation**) in the tremors that followed the major earthquake.

3. The couple agreed that saving for their children's education would have to take (**precedence,** predecessor) over vacation spending.

4. With the (recession, **decease**) of the last member of the family, the house and property were taken over by a private foundation.

5. Congress narrowly passed a tax reduction bill designed to head off a likely (cessation, **recession**).

6. Because the current director has no respect for her (**predecessor,** accessory), she has reversed all his policies and replaced them with her own.

7. In order to reach a compromise, both sides in the dispute have to be willing to make some major (**concessions,** recessions).

8. In the 1940s and 1950s, hats and gloves were considered essential (**accessories,** predecessors) for well-dressed women.

Definitions

Note carefully the spelling, pronunciation, part(s) of speech, and definition(s) of each of the following words. Then write the word in the blank space(s) in the illustrative sentence(s) following. Finally, study the lists of synonyms and antonyms given at the end of each entry.

1. affable
(af′ ə bəl)

(*adj.*) courteous and pleasant, sociable, easy to speak to

We spent a pleasant afternoon with our _____affable_____ neighbors.

SYNONYMS: genial, amicable, agreeable, cordial
ANTONYMS: surly, cantankerous, dour, inhospitable

2. aggrandize
(ə gran′ dīz)

(*v.*) to increase in greatness, power, or wealth; to build up or intensify; to make appear greater

John D. Rockefeller worked to _____aggrandize_____ his empire by purchasing oil wells, refineries, and pipelines.

SYNONYMS: augment, amplify, enhance, exalt
ANTONYMS: reduce, decrease, diminish

3. amorphous
(ə môr′ fəs)

(*adj.*) shapeless, without definite form; of no particular type or character; without organization, unity, or cohesion

The _____amorphous_____ body of the amoeba was fascinating to watch under the microscope.

SYNONYMS: formless, unstructured, nebulous, inchoate
ANTONYMS: definite, well-defined, clear-cut

4. aura
(ôr′ ə)

(*n.*) that which surrounds (as an atmosphere); a distinctive air or personal quality

What people thought was her _____aura_____ of mystery was actually a mask for her shyness.

SYNONYMS: ambience, atmosphere

5. contraband
(kän′ trə band)

(*n.*) illegal traffic, smuggled goods; (*adj.*) illegal, prohibited

Three jeweled combs from the 17th century were among the _____contraband_____ seized by the police.

SYNONYMS: (*adj.*) illicit, bootleg, unlawful
ANTONYMS: (*adj.*) legal, lawful, licit

6. erudite
(er′ yü dīt)

(*adj.*) scholarly, learned, bookish, pedantic

For my paper, I would like to find an _____erudite_____ history of the subject written in a clear and unbiased manner.

SYNONYMS: profoundly educated, well-read
ANTONYMS: ignorant, uneducated, illiterate

7. gossamer
(gäs′ ə mər)

(*adj.*) thin, light, delicate, insubstantial; (*n.*) a very thin, light cloth

Ghosts are often depicted in literature as wearing _____ **gossamer** _____ clothing that makes them seem all the more ethereal.

The book was so old that each finely printed page seemed only the weight of _____ **gossamer** _____ .

SYNONYMS: (*adj.*) filmy, diaphanous, sheer, airy, feathery, gauzy
ANTONYMS: (*adj.*) thick, dense, solid, massive

8. infer
(in fər′)

(*v.*) to find out by reasoning; to arrive at a conclusion on the basis of thought; to hint, suggest, imply

I can _____ **infer** _____ nothing from his odd behavior.

SYNONYMS: gather, deduce, presume, guess, speculate

9. inscrutable
(in skrü′ tə bəl)

(*adj.*) incapable of being understood; impossible to see through physically

I could not tell by her _____ **inscrutable** _____ smile whether she was pleased or only amused with me.

SYNONYMS: impenetrable, incomprehensible, enigmatic
ANTONYMS: comprehensible, intelligible, penetrable

10. insular
(in′ syə lər)

(*adj.*) relating to, characteristic of, or situated on an island; narrow or isolated in outlook or experience

You seem too sophisticated to hold such _____ **insular** _____ opinions.

SYNONYMS: narrow-minded, parochial, provincial
ANTONYMS: catholic, cosmopolitan, liberal

11. irrevocable
(i rev′ ə kə bəl)

(*adj.*) incapable of being changed or called back

We tend to think of court verdicts as _____ **irrevocable** _____ , but they are often overturned by higher courts.

SYNONYMS: irreversible, unrecallable, unalterable
ANTONYMS: reversible, changeable

12. propensity
(prə pen′ sə tē)

(*n.*) a natural inclination or predilection toward

Queen Elizabeth I showed a strong _____ **propensity** _____ for putting off decisions in the hopes that they would resolve themselves.

SYNONYMS: natural bent, proclivity, penchant
ANTONYMS: natural incapacity or inability

13. querulous
(kwer′ ə ləs)

(*adj.*) peevish, complaining, fretful

Some flight attendants dread a _____ **querulous** _____ airline passenger more than they do rough weather.

SYNONYMS: petulant, touchy, cranky, irritable
ANTONYMS: uncomplaining, stoical, serene, placid

14. remonstrate
(ri män′ strāt)

(*v.*) to argue or plead with someone against something, protest against, object to

Slowly, carefully, keeping his voice down, he argued with the caller as one might _____remonstrate_____ with a child.

SYNONYMS: reason against, expostulate

15. repudiate
(ri pyü′ dē āt)

(*v.*) to disown, reject, or deny the validity of

He was forced to _____repudiate_____ a statement he had made before he'd had all the information.

SYNONYMS: disavow, abjure, renounce
ANTONYMS: avow, affirm, aver, avouch

16. resilient
(ri zil′ yənt)

(*adj.*) able to return to an original shape or form; able to recover quickly

The development of lightweight, _____resilient_____ plastics revolutionized the design of many durable goods.

SYNONYMS: springy, elastic, buoyant, bouncy
ANTONYMS: rigid, stiff, inflexible, unyielding

17. reverberate
(ri vər′ bə rāt)

(*v.*) to re-echo, resound; to reflect or be reflected repeatedly

From the construction site, the noise of bulldozers and dump trucks _____reverberated_____ across the valley.

SYNONYMS: rumble, thunder, boom, echo

18. scurrilous
(skər′ ə ləs)

(*adj.*) coarsely abusive, vulgar or low (especially in language), foul-mouthed

Days passed and unrest grew, and soon the rebels began a _____scurrilous_____ attack on their absent leader.

SYNONYMS: obscene, filthy, abusive, vituperative
ANTONYMS: decorous, seemly, tasteful, dignified

19. sedulous
(sej′ ə ləs)

(*adj.*) persistent, showing industry and determination

No one could say that he was lazy, for he was a careful, _____sedulous_____ copier of other people's work.

SYNONYMS: assiduous, tireless, indefatigable
ANTONYMS: lackadaisical, listless, indolent, otiose

20. sleazy
(slē′ zē)

(*adj.*) thin or flimsy in texture; cheap; shoddy or inferior in quality or character; ethically low, mean, or disreputable

The old lady made her clothes at home in order to avoid the _____sleazy_____ goods sold in the general store.

SYNONYMS: inferior, cheesy, tawdry, tatty
ANTONYMS: superior, first-rate, quality, sturdy

Completing the Sentence

From the words for this unit, choose the one that best completes each of the following sentences. Write the word in the space provided.

1. The program he suggested was so barren of guiding ideas and specific proposals that I felt justified in referring to it as _____**amorphous**_____ .

2. This jacket is made of a material so _____**resilient**_____ that it sheds wrinkles and keeps its shape even when one has worn it for days.

3. Under the latest regulations, any shipment of arms to those countries is illegal and may be seized as _____**contraband**_____ .

4. His attempts to discredit her by belittling her ability and character were nothing more than _____**scurrilous**_____ abuse.

5. The commitment you have made is _____**irrevocable**_____ without the consent of the other party to the agreement.

6. The sharp crack of the rifle shot _____**reverberated**_____ through the hills.

7. On his combat uniform he wore absolutely no insignia of rank, but he was surrounded with an unmistakable _____**aura**_____ of authority.

8. He used his admittedly remarkable talents only to _____**aggrandize**_____ himself, not to benefit the society that was so kind to him.

9. I am not going to _____**repudiate**_____ the ideas and standards by which I have guided my life just because they have become unpopular.

10. As my opponent cited facts and figures without once referring to notes, I became aware of how _____**erudite**_____ she was.

11. The drops of dew sparkled like diamonds on the _____**gossamer**_____ threads of the spider web.

12. Since our efforts to _____**remonstrate**_____ with the factory managers about pollution of the lake have been ineffective, we are now considering legal action.

13. He is really insufferable when he gets into one of those _____**querulous**_____ moods in which nothing in the world pleases him.

14. If you happen to have a(n) _____**affable**_____ seatmate on a long airplane flight, you may find yourself talking more freely about personal matters than you would under other circumstances.

15. He tried in vain to guess what surprise he might expect next from that _____**inscrutable**_____ power, Lady Luck.

16. Am I to _____**infer**_____ from what you just said that you were not present at the scene of the accident?

17. While tsarist Russia's vast territories were almost purely continental, the British Empire included numerous _____**insular**_____ possessions.

18. Because of his _____propensity_____ for gossiping, we tried not to let him learn anything about our personal affairs.

19. _____Sleazy_____ dives full of disreputable and dangerous-looking characters have given the waterfront areas of many cities a bad reputation.

20. Perhaps she had less native ability than some of her classmates, but her powers of concentration and _____sedulous_____ study program enabled her to finish first in the class.

Synonyms

*Choose the word from this unit that is **the same** or **most nearly the same** in meaning as the **boldface** word or expression in the given phrase. Write the word on the line provided.*

1. expostulate with a noisy neighbor _____remonstrate_____

2. had a festive **ambience** _____aura_____

3. said her decision was **irreversible** _____irrevocable_____

4. resound from wall to wall _____reverberate_____

5. answer with an **enigmatic** smile _____inscrutable_____

6. only a **nebulous** idea of his future _____amorphous_____

7. disavow an earlier promise _____repudiate_____

8. a relaxed, **agreeable** companion _____affable_____

9. to **surmise** from her expression _____infer_____

10. scholarly study of the topic _____erudite_____

11. a **tawdry** appearance _____sleazy_____

12. prevailed due to **assiduous** preparation _____sedulous_____

13. springy as a trampoline _____resilient_____

14. smuggling **illicit** drugs _____contraband_____

Antonyms

*Choose the word from this unit that is **most nearly opposite** in meaning to the **boldface** word or expression in the given phrase. Write the word on the line provided.*

15. a **serene** little boy of four _____querulous_____

16. a **cosmopolitan** awareness of culture _____insular_____

17. a **tasteful** account of her private life _____scurrilous_____

18. his **natural incapacity** for meanness _____propensity_____

19. a **thick** morning mist on the garden _____gossamer_____

20. intended to **diminish** her fame _____aggrandize_____

Choosing the Right Word

*Circle the **boldface** word that more satisfactorily completes each of the following sentences.*

1. The musical composition, with no melodic pattern and no well-defined structure of development, seemed (**amorphous,** querulous) to my ear.

2. The minister said that Cain's question, "Am I my brother's keeper?" has continued to (**reverberate,** infer) through the ages.

3. What we really resent is not sensible criticism but nagging that is petty, capricious, and (**querulous,** affable).

4. Since he seems to have no moral standards whatsoever, it would probably be futile to (infer, **remonstrate**) with him about his outrageous behavior.

5. The language he used in his bitter attack on us was so (amorphous, **scurrilous**) that I hesitate even to repeat it.

6. What a pleasure to talk about old times with so (**affable,** erudite) a companion!

7. The pitiful derelict's only protection against the elements was a cheap overcoat made out of some kind of (resilient, **sleazy**) material that wouldn't keep the cold out in a heat wave.

8. I think that nothing in Shakespeare is lighter or more delightful than the (**gossamer,** aggrandized) wit and fancy of *A Midsummer Night's Dream.*

9. I tried to make some sense out of the strange orders he had given us, but his plan and purpose remained utterly (erudite, **inscrutable**).

10. Your (**propensity,** repudiation) for spending more than you can afford will lead to only one result—bankruptcy!

11. Throughout his career, the man has emphasized the (**aggrandizement,** inscrutability) of wealth and power at the expense of other values.

12. Am I to (remonstrate, **infer**) from your statement that there would be no point in further negotiations?

13. Lucy finally completed her (querulous, **erudite**) term paper, in which she quoted from more than a hundred sources.

14. Carefully avoiding any attempt at originality, he has fashioned his style on (**sedulous,** scurrilous) mimicry of other, more talented writers.

15. On the Sabbath, the entire village is immersed in a(n) (propensity, **aura**) of religious devotion that is difficult to convey to outsiders.

16. When we arrived home we were tired and depressed, but the (gossamer, **resilient**) spirit of youth made things look brighter the next morning.

17. Our determination never to yield to force or the threat of force is firm and (amorphous, **irrevocable**)!

18. We cannot bar foreign influences from our shores, and we cannot treat unfamiliar ideas as (aura, **contraband**)!

19. To limit the free expression of unpopular ideas is to (**repudiate,** infer) the basic spirit of the Bill of Rights.

20. In an age when the world has become a "global village," we cannot afford leaders with (**insular,** sedulous) outlooks.

Vocabulary in Context

*Read the following passage, in which some of the words you have studied in this unit appear in **boldface** type. Then complete each statement given below the passage by circling the letter of the item that is **the same** or **almost the same** in meaning as the highlighted word.*

Fast Talk

(Line)

Slang is a set of informal words or phrases used mainly for speaking rather than writing. Some slang terms are original and unique, while others are given the meaning of a word that already exists. Either way the chief point of slang is to amuse one's listeners with something new, odd, or clever.

(5)   Slang perseveres because it makes us feel **affable** and at home. In its **aura** we know we belong to some group, large or small, that understands it. (In this way, **scurrilous** slang works all too well.) Those outside the group may regard such talk as a form of **contraband** language, a somewhat snobbish secret code. Still

(10)   others become bored by it, for it lives by constant use, like other habits.

Oddly enough, most slang words are not **resilient**. They change their meaning or go stale and are quietly forgotten. Above all,

(15)   slang is a game that anyone can play at any time. For instance, *Money* has coined countless slang terms at various times, such as *lettuce*, *cabbage*, and *bread*. One who supports you with

(20)   money can be called your *meal ticket*. In England in the 1740s the slang for *complete* happened to be *cool*. In the 1940s American jazz musicians such as Duke Ellington (right) took up *cool* to mean

Ellington (1899–1974) at the keyboard.

(25)   *relaxed*, *restrained*, or *not emotional*. Since then the word has been used at various times to mean *not **reverberating*** or *soft* or simply *good*.

Every language has its slang, some of it unkind, most of it harmless. Not much of it is timeless, however, and some of this year's words will soon be showing their age.

---

1. The meaning of **affable** (line 5) is
  a. amusing   c. genial
  b. careless   d. calm

2. Aura (line 5) most nearly means
  a. protection   c. sound
  b. atmosphere   d. spotlight

3. Scurrilous (line 7) is best defined as
  a. abusive   c. mysterious
  b. old-fashioned   d. surprising

4. The meaning of **contraband** (line 8) is
  a. familiar   c. puzzling
  b. illicit   d. second

5. Resilient (line 13) most nearly means
  a. important   c. good
  b. likeable   d. elastic

6. Reverberating (line 26) is best defined as
  a. re-echoing   c. replaying
  b. repeating   d. listening

Definitions

Note carefully the spelling, pronunciation, part(s) of speech, and definition(s) of each of the following words. Then write the word in the blank space(s) in the illustrative sentence(s) following. Finally, study the lists of synonyms and antonyms given at the end of each entry.

1. amnesty
(am′ nə stē)

(*n.*) a general pardon for an offense against a government; in general, any act of forgiveness or absolution

Many political prisoners were freed under the _____ amnesty _____ granted by the new regime.

2. autonomy
(ô tän′ ə mē)

(*n.*) self-government, political control

Even after the thirteen colonies gained _____ autonomy _____ from England, many Americans clung to English traditions.
SYNONYM: home rule
ANTONYMS: dependence, subjection, colonial status

3. axiomatic
(ak sē ə mat′ ik)

(*adj.*) self-evident, expressing a universally accepted principle or rule

One should not accept the idea that the camera never lies as an _____ axiomatic _____ truth.
SYNONYM: taken for granted
ANTONYMS: questionable, dubious, controversial

4. blazon
(blāz′ ən)

(*v.*) to adorn or embellish; to display conspicuously; to publish or proclaim widely

They will _____ blazon _____ the results of the election across the Internet and every television set in the land.
SYNONYMS: broadcast, trumpet
ANTONYMS: hide, conceal, cover up, bury

5. caveat
(kav′ ē at)

(*n.*) a warning or caution to prevent misunderstanding or discourage behavior

The well known Latin phrase "_____ caveat _____ emptor" means "Let the buyer beware."
SYNONYMS: admonition, word to the wise

6. equitable
(ek′ wə tə bəl)

(*adj.*) fair, just, embodying principles of justice

He did more work, so a sixty-forty split of the profits seemed an _____ equitable _____ arrangement.
SYNONYMS: right, reasonable, evenhanded
ANTONYMS: unjust, unfair, one-sided, disproportionate

7. extricate
(ek′ strə kāt)

(*v.*) to free from entanglements or difficulties; to remove with effort

The ring must have slid off my finger as I was trying to _____ extricate _____ the fish from the net.

SYNONYMS: disentangle, extract, disengage
ANTONYMS: enmesh, entangle, involve

8. filch
(filch)

(v.) to steal, especially in a sneaky way and in petty amounts

If you _____ **filch** _____ pennies from the cash drawer, you are unlikely, after a while, to be satisfied with only pennies.

SYNONYMS: pilfer, purloin, swipe

9. flout
(flaủt)

(v.) to mock, treat with contempt

She chose to ignore my advice, not because she wanted to _____ **flout** _____ my beliefs, but because she had strong opinions of her own.

SYNONYMS: scoff at, sneer at, snicker at, scorn
ANTONYMS: obey, honor, revere, uphold

10. fractious
(frak' shəs)

(adj.) tending to be troublesome; unruly, quarrelsome, contrary; unpredictable

It seems as if even the smoothest-running organizations contain one or two _____ **fractious** _____ elements.

SYNONYMS: refractory, recalcitrant, peevish
ANTONYMS: docile, tractable, cooperative

11. precept
(prē' sept)

(n.) a rule of conduct or action

Many religions follow the _____ **precept** _____ that it is important to treat others as you, yourself, would like to be treated.

SYNONYMS: principle, maxim

12. salutary
(sal' yə ter ē)

(adj.) beneficial, helpful; healthful, wholesome

The cute new puppy had a _____ **salutary** _____ effect on her health.

SYNONYMS: salubrious, curative
ANTONYMS: detrimental, deleterious, pernicious

13. scathing
(skā' thiŋ)

(adj.) bitterly severe, withering; causing great harm

Sometimes a carefully reasoned discussion does more to change people's minds than a _____ **scathing** _____ attack.

SYNONYMS: searing, harsh, ferocious, savage
ANTONYMS: bland, mild

14. scourge
(skərj)

(v.) to whip, punish severely; (n.) a cause of affliction or suffering; a source of severe punishment or criticism

Jonathan Swift used wit to _____ **scourge** _____ the British government for its cruel treatment of Ireland.

Competing teams consider my daughter the _____ **scourge** _____ of the soccer field.

SYNONYMS: (*v.*) flog, beat; (*n.*) bane, plague, pestilence
ANTONYMS: (*n.*) godsend, boon, blessing

15. sepulchral
(sə pəl′ krəl)

(*adj.*) funereal, typical of the tomb; extremely gloomy or dismal

My sister announced in a severe and _____sepulchral_____ tone of voice that we were out of cookies.

SYNONYMS: doleful, lugubrious, mortuary

16. soporific
(säp ə rif′ ik)

(*adj.*) tending to cause sleep, relating to sleepiness or lethargy; (*n.*) something that induces sleep

He claimed that the musical, despite its energy, was _____soporific_____ and that he had slept through the entire second act.

Shakespeare's Juliet drinks a _____soporific_____ so as to appear to be dead—a trick she is soon to regret.

SYNONYMS: (*n.*) narcotic, anesthetic
ANTONYMS: (*adj.*) stimulating; (*n.*) stimulant, stimulus

17. straitlaced
(strāt′ lāst)

(*adj.*) extremely strict in regard to moral standards and conduct; prudish, puritanical

Travelers may find people overseas _____straitlaced_____ in some ways but surprisingly free in others.

SYNONYMS: highly conventional, overly strict, stuffy
ANTONYMS: lax, loose, indulgent, permissive, dissolute

18. transient
(tran′ shənt)

(*adj.*) lasting only a short time, fleeting; (*n.*) one who stays only a short time

His bad mood was _____transient_____, and by the time he'd finished his breakfast, he was smiling.

Many farm hands lived the lives of _____transients_____ during the Great Depression.

SYNONYMS: (*adj.*) impermanent, ephemeral, evanescent
ANTONYMS: (*adj.*) permanent, imperishable, immortal

19. unwieldy
(ən wēl′ dē)

(*adj.*) not easily carried, handled, or managed because of size or complexity

We loaded the truck with the chairs and the coffee table, but the grand piano was too _____unwieldy_____ .

SYNONYMS: cumbersome, bulky, clumsy, impractical
ANTONYMS: manageable, easy to handle

20. vapid
(vap′ id)

(*adj.*) dull, uninteresting, tiresome; lacking in sharpness, flavor, liveliness, or force

While critics called the movie _____vapid_____, I thought the performers were very compelling.

SYNONYMS: insipid, lifeless, colorless
ANTONYMS: zesty, spicy, savory, colorful, lively

**Completing
the Sentence**

*From the words for this unit, choose the one that best
completes each of the following sentences. Write the
word in the space provided.*

1. Her approach to the problem seems to have been guided by the time-honored
_____ **precept** _____ that "Force is the remedy for nothing."

2. Since the close of World War II, almost 100 former colonies have gained full
_____ **autonomy** _____ and joined the family of nations.

3. She has made so many contradictory promises to so many people that I don't see
how she can _____ **extricate** _____ herself from the situation.

4. Shivers went up and down our spines as, in a(n) _____ **sepulchral** _____ voice, the
teacher spoke to us of ghosts, vampires, and the "living dead."

5. It is _____ **axiomatic** _____ that democracy, more than any other form of
government, calls for the active participation of all the people in public affairs.

6. The decision was a disappointment to me, but after thinking it over, I had to agree
that it was _____ **equitable** _____ .

7. The new government, seeking to restore normal conditions, declared a(n)
_____ **amnesty** _____ for all political prisoners.

8. It was Lincoln who said: "Fondly do we hope, fervently do we pray, that this mighty
_____ **scourge** _____ of war may speedily pass away."

9. The standards of behavior generally accepted in Victorian times would probably be
rejected today as excessively _____ **straitlaced** _____ .

10. I tried to warn them of the dangers involved in such an undertaking, but all my
_____ **caveats** _____ and admonitions fell on deaf ears.

11. The carton was not heavy, but it was so _____ **unwieldy** _____ that it took four of
us to carry it to the shed.

12. Even the most talented actors could not breathe life and credibility into the
_____ **vapid** _____ lines of that silly play.

13. Who would have thought that the new treasurer could sink so low as to _____ **filch** _____
money from the club's petty cash fund?

14. My teacher's criticism of my term paper was so _____ **scathing** _____ that after
reading it I felt thoroughly crushed.

15. It became clear that the squad of policemen would be unable to control the small
but _____ **fractious** _____ crowd of angry protesters.

16. His fame as a football star proved to be _____ **transient** _____ , and he found
himself just another young man looking for a job.

17. Failures are always unpleasant, but if you learn from them, they may have a(n)
_____ **salutary** _____ effect on your future career.

18. Any unit of government—national or local—that _____ flouts _____ sound economic principles is headed for disaster.

19. The fighter planes of World War II sometimes had the pictures of famous movie stars, like Betty Grable, _____ blazoned _____ on the fuselage.

20. The _____ soporific _____ effect of his droning lectures surpasses that of any sleeping pill now in use.

Synonyms

*Choose the word from this unit that is **the same** or **most nearly the same** in meaning as the **boldface** word or expression in the given phrase. Write the word on the line provided.*

1. guided by stern **principles** _____ precepts _____

2. a **doleful** atmosphere during the service _____ sepulchral _____

3. eager to **scoff at** the unknown _____ flout _____

4. a **warning** regarding possible difficulties _____ caveat _____

5. too **cumbersome** to carry home _____ unwieldy _____

6. **pardon** for the former rebels _____ amnesty _____

7. working toward a **reasonable** treaty _____ equitable _____

8. **disengage** the cat from the tree _____ extricate _____

9. to **purloin** some coins from petty cash _____ filch _____

10. an argumentative, **refractory** congress _____ fractious _____

11. **ephemeral** as a rainbow _____ transient _____

12. **flog** the oxen unmercifully _____ scourge _____

13. an **insipid** little five-note tune _____ vapid _____

14. unruffled by his **savage** tone _____ scathing _____

Antonyms

*Choose the word from this unit that is **most nearly opposite** in meaning to the **boldface** word or expression in the given phrase. Write the word on the line provided.*

15. a **dubious** motto to live by _____ axiomatic _____

16. the **detrimental** effects of sunshine _____ salutary _____

17. **subjection** of the small nation _____ autonomy _____

18. the **indulgent** grandmother _____ straitlaced _____

19. medicine that acted as a **stimulant** _____ soporific _____

20. to **conceal** the famous trademark _____ blazon _____

Choosing the Right Word

*Circle the **boldface** word that more satisfactorily completes each of the following sentences.*

1. I didn't expect the play to be particularly stimulating, but I certainly never anticipated its overwhelmingly (**equitable, soporific**) power

2. How easy it is for a nation to become trapped in an inflationary price rise; how difficult to (**blazon, extricate**) itself from the upward spiral!

3. Instead of brooding about past wrongs, I suggest that you declare a personal (**amnesty, caveat**) and start thinking about the future.

4. I intend to be guided by the simple (**scourges, precepts**) that have proven their value over long periods of human experience.

5. Unabridged dictionaries often alert the reader to common mistakes in the use of a word by including brief (**caveats, scourges**).

6. The ghost of Hamlet's father whispered in (**sepulchral, salutary**) tones the story of his tragic death.

7. Appointed by the Governor to be Commissioner of Investigations, she soon became the (**scourge, autonomy**) of dishonest and incompetent officials.

8. You may regard her ideas as (**salutary, straitlaced**), but I think that they reflect good thinking and sound values.

9. Today our intricate network of mass communications can (**blazon, flout**) news of national importance across the country in a matter of minutes.

10. We had many talented players, but the (**fractious, scathing**) behavior of a few individuals impaired our team spirit and led to a losing season.

11. The rules of the club proved so (**equitable, unwieldy**) that it was all but impossible to carry on business.

12. I now know that *Gulliver's Travels*, far from being a "children's book," is a work of mature and (**scathing, vapid**) satire.

13. Some sadly misguided individuals seem to go through life trying to (**filch, blazon**) petty advantages from everyone they encounter.

14. Arriving at (**equitable, fractious**) arrangements in human affairs often requires sound judgment, as well as good intentions.

15. The Judeo-Christian tradition teaches that material things are (**transient, fractious**), while spiritual values are eternal.

16. Young people who consider themselves nonconformists often go to extremes in their determination to (**blazon, flout**) the conventions.

17. Isn't it strange that the basic ideas that some economists regard as (**sepulchral, axiomatic**) are rejected by others as absolutely false!

18. Young people, tired of being controlled by parents, teachers, and others, often have a strong impulse to gain (**amnesty, autonomy**).

19. In spite of the tremendous sales of that novel, I found it to be mediocre and (**vapid, salutary**) in every respect.

20. Few things are more (**salutary, unwieldy**) for a young person than an occasional painful reminder that life is not a bowl of cherries.

*Read the following passage, in which some of the words you have studied in this unit appear in **boldface** type. Then complete each statement given below the passage by circling the letter of the item that is **the same** or **almost the same** in meaning as the highlighted word.*

A Very Heavy Hitter

(Line)

Though he grew to be only 5′ 7″, the first baseball commissioner of the United States was named after a mountain. Kenesaw Mountain Landis (1866–1949) was named after the Georgia peak where his father was wounded in the Civil War. From boyhood, Kenesaw was said to have lived as if watching humanity from on high and laying down the law. Not surprisingly, he became a Chicago judge in 1905 before he was forty years old.   (5)

He ruled his courtroom with a king's **autonomy**, and when John D. Rockefeller, head of Standard Oil and the richest man in America, declined to testify in a case against his

Bat meets ball

own company, Landis forced him to appear. The clashing of wills between   (10) these powerful men was **blazoned** across headlines nationwide.

Landis always loved power, but he may have loved baseball more. A devoted fan at Chicago games, he   (15) called baseball "remarkable for the hold it has on the people, and equally remarkable for its cleanness." But by 1919 gamblers' schemes and warring team owners had so **flouted** that   (20) cleanness that Chicago White Sox players deliberately lost the World Series in return for bribes. Officials appointed Landis as baseball commissioner, with the job of saving the honor of the game. The owners expected to be treated gently, but Landis was **equitable** in his   (25) reforms, and a **scourge** to all sides.

Players suspected of taking bribes were barred for life with no hope of an **amnesty**. Trades were canceled, star players suspended. Owners had to give up investments in race tracks, and fought Landis for years before they could schedule games at night. For two decades, Landis ruled. When he died in 1944 he was   (30) known to all in baseball as "the judge."

---

1. The meaning of **autonomy** (line 7) is
  a. snobbery
  c. home rule
  b. meanness
  d. whim

2. Blazoned (line 11) most nearly means
  a. set fire to
  c. praised
  b. denounced
  d. trumpeted

3. Flouted (line 20) is best defined as
  a. mocked
  c. showed off
  b. observed
  d. misunderstood

4. The meaning of **equitable** (line 25) is
  a. surprising
  c. slow
  b. quick
  d. reasonable

5. Scourge (line 26) most nearly means
  a. bane
  c. favorite
  b. comfort
  d. instructor

6. Amnesty (line 28) is best defined as
  a. transfer
  c. apology
  b. general absolution
  d. explanation

Definitions

Note carefully the spelling, pronunciation, part(s) of speech, and definition(s) of each of the following words. Then write the word in the blank space(s) in the illustrative sentence(s) following. Finally, study the lists of synonyms and antonyms given at the end of each entry.

1. anomalous
(ə năm' ə ləs)

(*adj.*) abnormal, irregular, departing from the usual

Feeling protective of my friend but knowing of his difficulties placed me in an _____**anomalous**_____ position.

SYNONYMS: exceptional, atypical, unusual, aberrant
ANTONYMS: normal, regular, customary, typical, ordinary

2. aspersion
(ə spər' zhən)

(*n.*) a damaging or derogatory statement; the act of slandering or defaming

Think twice before casting _____**aspersions**_____ on his honesty, for he might be telling the truth.

SYNONYMS: innuendo, calumny, denigration
ANTONYMS: endorsement, testimonial, praise

3. bizarre
(bi zär')

(*adj.*) extremely strange, unusual, atypical

Years from now I will look at this picture and wonder what sort of _____**bizarre**_____ costume I was wearing.

SYNONYMS: grotesque, fantastic, outlandish
ANTONYMS: normal, typical, ordinary, expected

4. brusque
(brəsk)

(*adj.*) abrupt, blunt, with no formalities

His request for a large loan for an indefinite length of time was met with a _____**brusque**_____ refusal.

SYNONYMS: curt, tactless, ungracious, gruff, rough
ANTONYMS: gracious, tactful, courteous, diplomatic

5. cajole
(kə jōl')

(*v.*) to coax, persuade through flattery or artifice; to deceive with soothing thoughts or false promises

With a smile, a joke, and a second helping of pie, she would _____**cajole**_____ him into doing what she wanted.

SYNONYMS: wheedle, inveigle, soft-soap, sweet-talk
ANTONYMS: coerce, force, strong-arm

6. castigate
(kas' tə gāt)

(*v.*) to punish severely; to criticize severely

After he _____**castigated**_____ the unruly children, they settled down to study quietly.

SYNONYMS: chastise, rebuke, censure, upbraid
ANTONYMS: reward, honor, praise, laud

7. contrive
(kən trīv')

(v.) to plan with ingenuity, invent; to bring about as the result of a scheme or plan

She can _____ **contrive** _____ wonderful excuses; but when she tries to offer them, her uneasiness gives her away.

SYNONYMS: think up, devise, concoct, fabricate

8. demagogue
(dem' ə gäg)

(n.) a leader who exploits popular prejudices and false claims and promises in order to gain power

Often a show of angry concern conceals the self-serving tactics of a _____ **demagogue** _____ .

SYNONYMS: rabble-rouser, firebrand

9. disabuse
(dis ə byüz')

(v.) to free from deception or error, set right in ideas or thinking

He thinks that all women adore him, but my sister will probably _____ **disabuse** _____ him of that idea.

SYNONYMS: undeceive, enlighten, set straight
ANTONYMS: deceive, delude, pull wool over one's eyes

10. ennui
(än wē')

(n.) weariness and dissatisfaction from lack of occupation or interest, boredom

Some people seem to confuse sophistication with _____ **ennui** _____ .

SYNONYMS: languor, world-weariness, listlessness
ANTONYMS: enthusiasm, liveliness, excitement, intensity

11. fetter
(fet' ər)

(n.) a chain or shackle placed on the feet (often used in plural); anything that confines or restrains; (v.) to chain or shackle; to render helpless or impotent

The old phrase "chain gang" refers to prisoners made to work, each joined to the next by linked _____ **fetters** _____ .

It is said that good inventors do not _____ **fetter** _____ themselves with conventional thinking.

SYNONYMS: (n.) bond, restraint; (v.) bind, hamper
ANTONYMS: (v.) free, liberate, emancipate

12. heinous
(hā' nəs)

(adj.) very wicked, offensive, hateful

A town so peaceful, quiet, and law-abiding was bound to be horrified by so _____ **heinous** _____ a crime.

SYNONYMS: evil, odious, abominable, outrageous
ANTONYMS: excellent, wonderful, splendid

13. immutable
(i myü' tə bəl)

(adj.) not subject to change, constant

Scientists labored to discover a set of _____ **immutable** _____ laws of the universe.

SYNONYMS: unchangeable, unalterable, fixed, invariable
ANTONYMS: changeable, inconstant, variable, fickle

14. insurgent
(in sər′ jənt)

(*n.*) one who rebels or rises against authority; (*adj.*) rising in revolt, refusing to accept authority; surging or rushing in or on

George Washington and his contemporaries were
_____ insurgents _____ against Britain.

The army was confident that they could crush the
_____ insurgent _____ forces.

SYNONYMS: (*adj.*) revolutionary, rebellious, mutinous
ANTONYMS: (*adj.*) loyalist, loyal, faithful

15. megalomania
(meg ə lō mā′ nē ə)

(*n.*) a delusion marked by a feeling of power, wealth, talent, etc., far in excess of reality

Sudden fame and admiration can make people feel unworthy—or it can bring on feelings of _____ megalomania _____.

SYNONYM: delusions of grandeur
ANTONYMS: humility, modesty, self-abasement

16. sinecure
(si′ nə kyür)

(*n.*) a position requiring little or no work; an easy job

The office of Vice President of the United States was once considered little more than a _____ sinecure _____.

SYNONYMS: "no-show" job, cushy job, "plum"

17. surreptitious
(sər əp tish′ əs)

(*adj.*) stealthy, secret, intended to escape observation; made or accomplished by fraud

The movie heroine blushed when she noticed the
_____ surreptitious _____ glances of her admirer.

SYNONYMS: furtive, covert, clandestine, concealed
ANTONYMS: open, frank, aboveboard, overt

18. transgress
(tranz gres′)

(*v.*) to go beyond a limit or boundary; to sin, violate a law

The penitent citizens promised to never again
_____ transgress _____ the laws of the land.

SYNONYMS: overstep, exceed, trespass, err
ANTONYMS: obey, toe the line

19. transmute
(tranz myüt′)

(*v.*) to change from one nature, substance, or form to another

To _____ transmute _____ distrust into friendship along that war-torn border will take more than wise politicians and just laws.

SYNONYMS: transform, convert, translate, metamorphose
ANTONYMS: maintain unchanged, preserve

20. vicarious
(vī kâr′ ē əs)

(*adj.*) performed, suffered, or otherwise experienced by one person in place of another

In search of _____ vicarious _____ excitement, we watched movies of action and adventure.

SYNONYMS: surrogate, substitute, imagined, secondhand
ANTONYMS: real, actual, firsthand

Completing the Sentence

From the words for this unit, choose the one that best completes each of the following sentences. Write the word in the space provided.

1. The _____**surreptitious**_____ way in which they planned the undertaking shows that they were aware of its illegal character.

2. Is there any other crime in history as _____**heinous**_____ as the attempt of the Nazis to annihilate so-called "inferior" racial groups?

3. Although the _____**insurgents**_____ were defeated by the government's forces, a small group escaped into the mountains, where they kept the spirit of rebellion alive.

4. Although most of us lead a quiet, humdrum sort of life, we can all get a(n) _____**vicarious**_____ thrill from the achievements of our astronauts.

5. The Emancipation Proclamation issued by Abraham Lincoln once and for all broke the _____**fetters**_____ that bound Southern blacks to a life of servitude and humiliation.

6. I find it hard to understand how they were able to _____**contrive**_____ such an elaborately underhanded scheme in so short a time.

7. His endless talk about himself and his interests is truly unexcelled for producing _____**ennui**_____ in others.

8. Wearing _____**bizarre**_____ masks at Halloween is a tradition that goes back many centuries.

9. Resorting to rather farfetched promises, I finally _____**cajoled**_____ Tina into going to the prom with me.

10. At the very outset of the term, I urged you to _____**disabuse**_____ yourself of the idea that you can pass this course without hard, regular work.

11. The one fact about nature that seems completely _____**immutable**_____ is that everything is subject to change.

12. His conceit is so great and so immune to the lessons of experience that this must be considered a kind of _____**megalomania**_____.

13. Anyone who refers to my job as a(n) _____**sinecure**_____ should spend just one day in my place!

14. The alchemists of the Middle Ages, who were both skilled magicians and primitive chemists, hoped to _____**transmute**_____ base metals into gold.

15. The speaker's blatant appeal to the emotions of the crowd smacked more of the _____**demagogue**_____ than the true leader of the people.

16. Since he had always been quiet and retiring, we were amazed when he stood up at the meeting and _____**castigated**_____ the chairperson for failing to give everyone a chance to speak.

17. Can you imagine anything as _____**anomalous**_____ as a successful drama coach who has never acted on the stage!

18. In his determination to be blunt and honest, he has _____transgressed_____ the limits of good taste.

19. Rude questions call for _____brusque_____ answers, and mine is "No!"

20. I welcome honest criticism, but I deeply resented their _____aspersions_____ on my sincerity and good faith.

Synonyms

*Choose the word from this unit that is **the same** or **most nearly the same** in meaning as the **boldface** word or expression in the given phrase. Write the word on the line provided.*

1. abominable treatment of prisoners of war _____heinous_____

2. an unwarranted **denigration** against my friend _____aspersion_____

3. trying to **restrain** our imaginations _____fetter_____

4. the fear-mongering of a **rabble-rouser** _____demagogue_____

5. undeceive him of that belief _____disabuse_____

6. wish to **rebuke** the vandals _____castigate_____

7. the disposition of a **revolutionary** _____insurgent_____

8. the cleverest plan we could **devise** _____contrive_____

9. an **atypical** position _____anomalous_____

10. inveigle a pay raise _____cajole_____

11. a truly **outlandish** set of circumstances _____bizarre_____

12. a woman of **unalterable** habits _____immutable_____

13. a scandal involving **"no-show" jobs** _____sinecures_____

14. convert ambition into action _____transmute_____

15. sensed **furtive** movements in the darkness _____surreptitious_____

Antonyms

*Choose the word from this unit that is **most nearly opposite** in meaning to the **boldface** word or expression in the given phrase. Write the word on the line provided.*

16. his usual **gracious** reply _____brusque_____

17. the **excitement** of the ninth inning _____ennui_____

18. the **modesty** of the real genius _____megalomania_____

19. obey the week-night curfew _____transgress_____

20. experienced **actual** thrills at the race _____vicarious_____

Choosing the Right Word

Circle the **boldface** word that more satisfactorily completes each of the following sentences.

1. A favorite ploy of the (**anomalous, demogogue**) is to appoint a convenient scapegoat upon whom a misguided populace can vent its anger.

2. By casting (**sinecures, aspersions**) on the ability and character of others, you reveal the misgivings you have about yourself.

3. The task of education, said the speaker, is to (**transgress, transmute**) the primitive selfishness of the child into socially useful modes of behavior.

4. His conduct after his mother's death was so (**anomalous, brusque**) that I must conclude he was not in full possession of his faculties.

5. With the innumerable activities open to a young person like you, I can't understand why you should suffer from (**ennui, megalomania**).

6. I cannot understand how she was able to (**disabuse, contrive**) a meeting between two people who had refused to have anything to do with each other.

7. If, as they now claim, they were not aware of the illegal character of their undertaking, why did they plan it so (**cajolingly, surreptitiously**)?

8. The President complained that government bureaucracy was hobbling his programs with (**fetters, aspersions**) of red tape.

9. He's so tight with his money that it's just about impossible to (**cajole, transmute**) a nickel out of him, no matter how worthy the cause.

10. Her description of the Western frontier was so vivid that I seemed to be (**vicariously, surreptitiously**) experiencing the realities of pioneer life.

11. In *Gulliver's Travels* and other writings, Jonathan Swift (**cajoled, castigated**) the human race for its follies and wickedness.

12. Her opinion of her own importance is so grotesquely exaggerated that we have come to regard her as a (**megalomaniac, demagogue**).

13. He may have kept within the letter of the law, but there is no doubt that he has (**cajoled, transgressed**) the accepted moral code.

14. For ancient Romans, fleeing from the battlefield was the most (**heinous, immutable**) act of cowardice a soldier could commit.

15. The institutions of our society, far from being (**immutable, anomalous**), are in the process of change at this very moment.

16. A(n) (**insurgent, heinous**) group at the convention refused to accept the choices of the regular party leaders.

17. Have you ever heard of anything as (**bizarre, brusque**) as an experimental technique to test the intelligence of cows!

18. What hurt my feelings was not so much his refusal to give me a job as the (**brusque, vicarious**) way in which he told me that he had nothing for me.

19. Although her new position bore a high-sounding title, it was really little more than a(n) (**insurgent, sinecure**).

20. Although she is well into middle age, my aunt Sally seems unable to (**cajole, disabuse**) herself of the idea that she is still a teenager.

*Read the following passage, in which some of the words you have studied in this unit appear in **boldface** type. Then complete each statement given below the passage by circling the letter of the item that is **the same** or **almost the same** in meaning as the highlighted word.*

Kudzu

(Line)

Some readers may recognize kudzu as the name of a comic strip, but Southerners know it as a fact of nature too **bizarre** to be funny. This galloping vine, nearly impossible to kill, grows from a finger-like shoot that winds around any stump, car, shed, tree, house, or barn that stands in its way. In one day's time, kudzu

(5) (pronounced "kəd-zü") can grow up to twelve inches. All too soon, its trunk is the width of a one-quart milk bottle, and its leaves are as large as this book. Its flowers bloom purple and fragrant; its root can weigh

(10) well over two hundred pounds.

This **insurgent** weed, long common in Asia, was welcomed here in the late nineteenth century as a pretty porch decoration.

(15) Then the U.S. Government spread kudzu in the South to prevent soil erosion and to make cheap grazing for livestock. But the vine soon eluded the **fetters** of farm

(20) work, and in that damp, warm climate made its **surreptitious** way across seven million acres,

Kudzu covering a house in rural Georgia

mainly in North and South Carolina, Mississippi, Georgia, and Alabama. Now, neither farmers nor state governments can afford the labor needed to chop off the trunks

(25) and dig up the roots. Scientists put their hope in certain kinds of plant-eating beetles but must first make certain that the hungry little creatures will not **transgress** the bounds of their assignment and start new troubles of their own.

Whatever solution is **contrived** for the kudzu problem, it cannot be applied too soon. The vine has hitchhiked, flown, or wiggled through the mail to Massachusetts,

(30) New York, New Jersey, and Connecticut. Should it manage to acclimate itself to the cold Northern winter, it will stretch out and make itself at home there, too.

---

1. The meaning of **bizarre** (line 2) is
a. common
b. commercial
c. widespread
d. strange *(circled)*

2. Insurgent (line 11) most nearly means
a. huge
b. widespread
c. mutinous *(circled)*
d. sweet-smelling

3. Fetters (line 19) is best defined as
a. assignments
b. weariness
c. restraints *(circled)*
d. complications

4. The meaning of **surreptitious** (line 21) is
a. furtive *(circled)*
b. awkward
c. speedy
d. deliberate

5. Transgress (line 26) most nearly means
a. misunderstand
b. overstep *(circled)*
c. trample
d. consume

6. Contrived (line 28) is best defined as
a. devised *(circled)*
b. forbidden
c. attempted
d. praised

REVIEW UNITS 4-6

Visit us at www.sadlier-oxford.com
for interactive puzzles and games.

Vocabulary for Comprehension

*Read the following passage, in which some of the words you have studied in Units 4–6 appear in **boldface** type. Then answer questions 1–12 on page 73 on the basis of what is <u>stated</u> or <u>implied</u> in the passage and in the introductory statement.*

In this passage, the writer discusses the unlikely beginnings of one of today's most popular sports: basketball.

(Line)

Strange as it may seem, basketball was invented in the 1890s as an alternative to calisthenics and indoor marching at a YMCA school in

(5) Massachusetts. James Naismith, the physical education instructor at the school, noticed that his students, who played baseball in the spring and football in the fall, were not

(10) adequately challenged by indoor marching during New England's long, cold winters. Students' wintertime confinement, coupled by a lack of physical exertion, had a **soporific**

(15) effect. Naismith resolved to invent a new and **salutary** alternative.

To Naismith, it was **axiomatic** that the ideal team sport involved a ball and some sort of goal. But the new game,

(20) which would be played on a hard gym floor, had to be gentler than football. He chose a basket as a goal because the ball had to be dropped into it rather than hurled straight at it. To prevent

(25) **fractious** scuffles and to keep the defense from ganging up on the offense, Naismith placed the goals up beyond an average person's grasp.

In 1892 Naismith's first game was

(30) played by his entire eighteen-member gym class. But this proved too **unwieldy**, and the number of players on each side was later reduced and

standardized to five. The sport proved

(35) fortuitous for Naismith. During the first women's basketball game, he met a teacher named Maude Sherman, whom he later married.

Colleges, including Vassar,

(40) Vanderbilt, and Yale, swiftly adopted the sport, and the YMCA formed several leagues of its own. Despite the benefits it offered, some **castigated** the game for being too

(45) rough; and a few YMCAs stuck to a schedule of good old-fashioned push-ups and marching instead. Basketball enthusiasts who still wanted to play the game simply rented dance halls or

(50) armories to compete in and charged admission in order to pay the rent. Professional basketball was born as a result of these admission fees; and in 1896, players in Trenton, New Jersey,

(55) were paid for the first time, $15 apiece, to compete in a game.

1. The meaning of **soporific** (line 14) is
   a. stimulating
   b. exceptional
   c. debilitating
   d. sleep inducing
   e. frustrating

2. Salutary (line 16) is best defined as
   a. deleterious
   b. unsanitary
   c. healthful
   d. exciting
   e. lucrative

3. Which of the following best describes the main purpose of the first paragraph (lines 1–16)?
   a. to explain why Naismith invented basketball
   b. to discuss why basketball was first played in New England
   c. to survey Naismith's career as a physical education instructor
   d. to explain why Naismith chose a basket as a goal
   e. to list reasons for the success of basketball as a sport

4. Axiomatic (line 17) most nearly means
   a. ridiculous
   b. inconvenient
   c. self-evident
   d. meaningless
   e. redundant

5. Which of the following best describes the writer's organizational method in paragraph 2 (lines 17–28)?
   a. chronological order
   b. order of impression
   c. comparison and contrast
   d. order of importance
   e. cause and effect

6. The meaning of **fractious** (line 25) is
   a. unruly
   b. hilarious
   c. confused
   d. unnecessary
   e. frequent

7. Which of the following inferences is supported by the passage?
   a. Women as well as men played basketball in the sport's early days.
   b. For some time after the sport's invention, only men played basketball.
   c. Many YMCAs refused to form basketball leagues.
   d. Basketball soon became more popular than football at many colleges.
   e. Basketball had no appeal to professional athletes.

8. Unwieldy (line 32) most nearly means
   a. rowdy
   b. cumbersome
   c. boring
   d. confusing
   e. dangerous

9. According to the passage, the standard number of players on each team is
   a. four
   b. five
   c. seven
   d. nine
   e. eighteen

10. Castigated (line 44) is best defined as
   a. praised
   b. rebuked
   c. attended
   d. closed down
   e. disapproved of

11. Which of the following best describes the author's tone in the passage?
   a. factual
   b. humorous
   c. indignant
   d. persuasive
   e. critical

12. Which would be the most appropriate form of publication for the passage?
   a. a newspaper editorial
   b. an encyclopedia entry
   c. a Ph.D. dissertation in history
   d. a specialty sports magazine
   e. a widely circulated e-mail

Grammar in Context

The pronouns **who** and **whom** can be used in two ways: (1) to form a question ("Who was the inventor of basketball?") and (2) to introduce a subordinate clause ("During the first women's basketball game, he met a teacher named Maude Sherman, whom he later married," lines 35–38 on page 72). Do not confuse *who* and *whom* or their related forms *whoever* and *whomever*. The pronoun's form depends on its use in the question or in the subordinate clause. *Who* is used as the subject of a verb or as a predicate nominative. *Whom* is used as the direct object of a verb or as the object of a preposition. Although *who* is sometimes used instead of *whom* in informal situations ("Who did you see?"), the distinction between *who* and *whom* should be maintained in formal speaking and writing ("Whom did you see?").

When deciding between *who* and *whom*, as well as between *whoever* and *whomever*, be careful not to be misled by words outside the subordinate clause or by parenthetical expressions such as "she thinks" or "they believe." For example, in the sentence "A prize will go to whoever shoots the most free throws during the season," *whoever* is the subject of the verb "shoots" in the subordinate clause. In the sentence "Naismith is the man who, historians think, deserves the credit for the game's invention," *who* is the subject of the verb "deserves."

On the lines provided, rewrite each of the sentences below, correcting errors in the use of who, whom, whoever, *and* whomever. *Write "correct" if the sentence is correct.*

1. When we were asked whom invented basketball, we wondered whom it could be.
   When we were asked who invented basketball, we wondered who it could be.

2. Naismith's students, whom played football in the fall, needed a winter sport.
   Naismith's students, who played football in the fall, needed a winter sport.

3. Some critics, to whom basketball seemed too rough, stuck to good old-fashioned push-ups.
   correct

4. Enthusiasts whom still wanted to play the game rented dance halls or armories.
   Enthusiasts who still wanted to play the game rented dance halls or armories.

5. In 1896, whomever wanted to compete in the first professional game was paid $15 apiece.
   In 1896, whoever wanted to compete in the first professional games was paid
   $15 apiece.

6. Whom do you suppose will win the play-offs this season?
   Who do you suppose will win the play-offs this season?

Two-Word Completions

Circle the pair of words that best complete the meaning of each of the following passages.

See pages T38–T48 for explanations of answers.

1. Rubber's remarkable _____ to resume its original shape makes it one of the world's most _____ materials.
   a. aura . . . fractious
   b. propensity . . . resilient
   c. autonomy . . . erudite
   d. ennui . . . gossamer

2. Only the sound of my footsteps _____ through the empty hallway disturbed the _____ silence in which the deserted office building was enveloped. "It's as quiet as a tomb in here at night," I thought as I made my way to the exit.
   a. transgressing . . . gossamer
   b. exacting . . . anomalous
   c. reverberating . . . sepulchral
   d. transmuting . . . bizarre

3. When I returned from lunch earlier than I had planned, I surprised a little sneak thief _____ attempting to _____ a few dollars from the petty cash drawer.
   a. brusquely . . . admonish
   b. irrevocably . . . wheedle
   c. rapidly . . . cajole
   d. surreptitiously . . . filch

4. "The American legal system is not _____, nor are our laws _____," the Chief Justice observed. "Like everything else in this fluid world of ours, they change and develop over time."
   a. anomalous . . . autonomous
   b. transient . . . resilient
   c. immutable . . . irrevocable
   d. axiomatic . . . inscrutable

5. He is usually so courteous and _____ that I was completely taken aback by his unaccountably _____ and surly reply to my question.
   a. affable . . . brusque
   b. fractious . . . scurrilous
   c. equitable . . . erudite
   d. straitlaced . . . querulous

6. "It took months of _____ effort and astute planning on my part to _____ this company from the mess in which I found it," the new owner smugly boasted. "If I hadn't worked like a dog, the firm would still be in financial hot water."
   a. amorphous . . . cajole
   b. sedulous . . . extricate
   c. immutable . . . contrive
   d. irrevocable . . . disabuse

Read each sentence carefully. Then circle the item that best completes the statement below the sentence.

See pages T38–T48 for explanations of answers.

No one who has seen *Cool Hand Luke* will ever forget the shocking scenes of Paul Newman and the other convicts on that Georgia chain gang, fettered together more like animals than human beings. (2)

1. In line 2 the word **fettered** can best be defined as

a. shackled   b. roped   c. tied   d. linked

In small-town America one hundred years ago, the boardinghouse catered to long-term visitors, while the hotel met the needs of mere transients. (2)

2. The best definition of the word **transients** in line 2 is

a. traveling salespeople   c. people just passing through
b. tourists on holiday   d. displaced persons

The practice of scourging ordinary seamen severely for even petty offenses lasted well into the 19th century in both the British and the American navies. (2)

3. The word **scourging** in line 1 can best be defined as

a. flogging   b. reprimanding   c. punishing   d. fining

Smaller and smaller images of the chandeliers and candelabras forever reverberated in the mirrors that encrusted the wall of the great central reception hall. (2)

4. The best meaning for the word **reverberated** in line 1 is

a. thundered   b. were reflected   c. resounded   d. were enlarged

The fog that morning was so inscrutable that traffic officials were warning drivers not to proceed until it lifted. (2)

5. In line 1 the word **inscrutable** most nearly means

a. incapable of being understood   c. unable to distinguish
b. unlikely to cause harm   d. impossible to see through

**Antonyms**

In each of the following groups, circle the word or expression that is most nearly the **opposite** of the word in **boldface** type.

1. erudite
a. uninformed
b. wordy
c. brief
d. relevant

2. soporific
a. adequate
b. long-winded
c. disorganized
d. stimulating

3. aspersions
a. praise
b. advice
c. slander
d. rumors

4. insular
a. cosmopolitan
b. bigoted
c. old-fashioned
d. provincial

5. ennui
a. adiposity
b. depression
c. excitement
d. uncertainty

6. repudiate
a. reject
b. accept
c. publish
d. amend

7. vapid
a. foreign
b. dull
c. prize-winning
d. meaningful

8. autonomy
a. dependence
b. freedom
c. stability
d. financial ruin

9. affable
a. talkative
b. unfriendly *(circled)*
c. long-standing
d. faithful

10. transient
a. selfish
b. permanent *(circled)*
c. passing
d. innocent

11. surreptitious
a. hasty
b. brief
c. open *(circled)*
d. unexpected

12. heinous
a. noble *(circled)*
b. cruel
c. inadvertent
d. wicked

13. sleazy
a. colorful
b. well made *(circled)*
c. inexpensive
d. dingy

14. irrevocable
a. considered
b. hasty
c. minor
d. reversible *(circled)*

15. querulous
a. agreeable *(circled)*
b. loud
c. hostile
d. complaining

16. scathing
a. complimentary *(circled)*
b. bitter
c. ungrammatical
d. unjustified

Word Families

A. *On the line provided, write the word you have learned in Units 4–6 that is related to each of the following nouns.*
EXAMPLE: reverberation—**reverberate**

1. affability — affable
2. erudition, eruditeness — erudite
3. inscrutability, inscrutableness — inscrutable
4. querulousness — querulous
5. remonstration, remonstrance, remonstrator — remonstrate
6. resilience, resiliency — resilient
7. scurrilousness, scurrility — scurrilous
8. inference, inferrer — infer
9. insularity, insularism, insulation, insulator — insular
10. cajolery, cajolement, cajoler — cajole
11. autonomist — autonomy
12. transiency, transience — transient
13. castigation — castigate
14. transmutation — transmute
15. anomaly, anomalousness — anomalous
16. cajolery — cajole

B. *On the line provided, write the word you have learned in Units 4–6 that is related to each of the following verbs.*
EXAMPLE: contrive—**contrivance**

17. insulate — insular
18. extract — extricate
19. scathe — scathing
20. asperse — aspersion

In each of the following groups, circle the word that is best defined or suggested by the given phrase.

1. living through another
a. affable   b. salutary   c. vicarious   d. sleazy

2. a buoyant spirit
a. resilient   b. vapid   c. transgressive   d. insurgent

3. political prisoners set free
a. ennui   b. sinecure   c. scourge   d. amnesty

4. a curt reply
a. resilient   b. vapid   c. brusque   d. straitlaced

5. a leader who exploits
a. demagogue   b. scourge   c. soporific   d. caveat

6. rebuke the students
a. flout   b. castigate   c. repudiate   d. flatten

7. "We hold these truths to be self-evident"
a. affable   b. bizarre   c. contraband   d. axiomatic

8. transform his experiences into fiction
a. transgress   b. reverberate   c. transmute   d. remonstrate

9. a fair distribution of wealth
a. salutary   b. scathing   c. equitable   d. inscrutable

10. belligerent rebel forces
a. insurgent   b. contraband   c. erudite   d. surreptitious

11. the victim of an inflated ego
a. sinecure   b. aura   c. megalomania   d. demagogue

12. plot a deception
a. contrive   b. scourge   c. extricate   d. transmute

13. bypass outdated conventions
a. transgress   b. infer   c. disabuse   d. extricate

14. a tendency to boast
a. anathema   b. propensity   c. precept   d. caveat

15. disregard advice
a. infer   b. flout   c. blazon   d. reverberate

16. shatter an illusion
a. transmute   b. repudiate   c. fetter   d. disabuse

17. healthy atmosphere of the park
a. aura   b. demagogue   c. ennui   d. aspersion

18. an abnormal set of circumstances
a. gossamer   b. anomalous   c. inscrutable   d. amorphous

19. formless creatures
a. bizarre   b. amorphous   c. affable   d. erudite

20. display conspicuously
a. cajole   b. blazon   c. filch   d. repudiate

Building with Classical Roots

grad, gress—to step, walk

This root appears in **transgress** (page 67), literally, "to step beyond." The word now means "to go beyond a limit or bound" or "to violate a command or law." Other words based on the same root are listed below.

aggressive	digress	gradient	regress
congress	egress	gradualism	retrograde

From the list of words above, choose the one that corresponds to each of the brief definitions below. Write the word in the blank space in the illustrative sentence below the definition.

1. a policy of approaching a desired end by slight degrees

The moderates advocate a policy of _____**gradualism**_____.

2. attacking, taking the first step in an attack or quarrel; energetic, forceful (*"walking toward"*)

Most wild animals are not _____**aggressive**_____ toward humans.

3. moving backward, contrary to the usual or normal order; tending toward a worse state

They resisted the _____**retrograde**_____ tendencies of the small but vocal faction.

4. to move backward; to decline, grow worse

Their reading skills will _____**regress**_____ if they do not study over the summer.

5. an exit; a going out (*"walking out"*)

We could not find a means of _____**egress**_____.

6. a part (as of a road or path) that slopes upward or downward

The climbers struggled up the dangerously steep _____**gradient**_____.

7. a meeting (especially of persons or minds)

We were invited to attend a(n) _____**congress**_____ of medical workers.

8. to turn aside, get off the main topic (*"to step away"*)

She tried not to _____**digress**_____ from her speech.

From the list of words above, choose the one that best completes each of the following sentences. Write the word in the space provided.

1. Since their property does not border the road, their neighbor's private driveway is their only means of _____**egress**_____.

2. In her view, social problems in the community are too pressing to be dealt with through a policy of _____**gradualism**_____.

3. Since time was so limited, the moderator refused to allow the panel discussion to _____digress_____, even for a moment, from the topic.

4. A business concern either progresses or _____regresses_____; it never stands still.

5. The road spiraled around the mountain with a moderate _____gradient_____, making it passable even during stormy weather.

6. We had hoped that the UN could prevent _____aggressive_____ nations from trampling on the rights of their neighbors.

7. After the first month of the term, I was considered an excellent math student, but then I began a(n) _____retrograde_____ movement that carried me to the bottom of the class.

8. A special _____congress_____ of religious leaders from all over the world will be held in London next month.

---

*Circle the **boldface** word that more satisfactorily completes each of the following sentences.*

1. Sometimes an older child will (**digress**, **regress**) in behavior when a new baby brother or sister seems to be getting all the parents' attention.

2. The radicals attacked the (**gradualism**, **congress**) of their opponents and accused them of caving in to established interests.

3. The purpose of a fire drill is to ensure the orderly (**regress**, **egress**) of the occupants from a building in case of fire.

4. The newspaper editorial condemned the (**retrograde**, **aggressive**) thinking of those who wished to halt all spending on space exploration.

5. Her competitive nature made her a(n) (**aggressive**, **retrograde**) opponent on the basketball court.

6. All the attendees at a recent (**gradient**, **congress**) of writers agreed to protest against attempts to ban books or limit freedom of speech.

7. While on vacation, we often like to (**regress**, **digress**) from the interstate highways and take some of the more picturesque back roads.

8. The (**gradient**, **gradualism**) of the road going up the mountain makes it a dangerous drive in icy conditions.

Analogies

In each of the following, circle the item that best completes the comparison.

See pages T38–T48 for explanations of answers.

1. aggrandize is to **bigger** as
a. ascribe is to larger
b. contrive is to smaller
c. ameliorate is to better
d. flout is to shorter

2. meritorious is to **heinous** as
a. amorphous is to shapeless
b. puzzling is to inscrutable
c. immutable is to permanent
d. bland is to scathing

3. intermediary is to **intercede** as
a. interloper is to intrude
b. proponent is to repudiate
c. demagogue is to conciliate
d. stalwart is to adjudicate

4. propensity is to **proclivity** as
a. hiatus is to continuity
b. aura is to atmosphere
c. aspersion is to remark
d. approbation is to disapproval

5. remonstrate is to **expostulate** as
a. abominate is to intercede
b. castigate is to precipitate
c. wheedle is to cajole
d. ingratiate is to commiserate

6. lassitude is to **tired** as
a. sangfroid is to excited
b. resilience is to annoyed
c. ennui is to wearied
d. aplomb is to mortified

7. tenuous is to **strength** as
a. vitriolic is to rancor
b. transient is to permanence
c. equitable is to fairness
d. stringent is to durability

8. provincial is to **insular** as
a. occult is to esoteric
b. inadvertent is to deliberate
c. salutary is to baneful
d. fractious is to docile

9. querulous is to **fret** as
a. affable is to bellyache
b. petulant is to fuss
c. bizarre is to gripe
d. noncommittal is to complain

10. vapid is to **flavor** as
a. sedulous is to industry
b. intrinsic is to value
c. hackneyed is to novelty
d. brusque is to brevity

Choosing the Right Meaning

Read each sentence carefully. Then circle the item that best completes the statement below the sentence.

See pages T38–T48 for explanations of answers.

On the retreat from Moscow, Napoleon's once invincible Grand Armée degenerated into an amorphous mass of frightened fugitives, thanks to the Cossacks and the Russian winter. (2)

1. The word **amorphous**, as used in line 2, most nearly means
a. lacking substance
b. lacking character
c. lacking cohesion
d. lacking limits

For certain types of wheel-thrown ceramics, a fine, unctuous clay is best; for others, a less malleable medium is preferable. (2)

2. The word **unctuous** in line 1 may best be defined as
a. servile   b. dry   c. smug   d. plastic

ICBMs and other types of guided missiles are unfortunately much too fractious to allow for testing anywhere near populated areas, however thinly inhabited. (2)

3. The best definition for the word **fractious** in line 1 is

(a. unpredictable)   b. explosive   c. quarrelsome   d. expensive

"That particular artist is so eclectic," the critic admitted, "that it is impossible
to track down absolutely all the tenuous influences on his work." (2)

4. The best meaning for the word **tenuous** in line 2 is

a. unusual   (b. vague)   c. flimsy   d. various

"Or like stout Cortez when with eagle eyes
He star'd at the Pacific—and all his men (2)
Looked at each other with a wild surmise—
Silent, upon a peak in Darien." (4)
    (Keats, "On First Looking into Chapman's Homer," 11–14)

5. The word **surmise** in line 3 most nearly means

a. smile of recognition   c. peal of laughter
(b. flash of intuition)   d. yawn of boredom

Two-Word Completions

*Circle the pair of words that best complete the meaning
of each of the following sentences.*

See pages T38–T48 for explanations of answers.

1. The flames from the tire factory bathed the whole neighborhood in a(n)
_____ glow and the stench of burning rubber _____ the air.

a. vapid . . .transmuted   c. sleazy . . . transcended
(b. lurid . . . permeated)   d. amorphous . . . simulated

2. The sonorous notes of the mighty organ _____ through the
_____ vaults and cavernous expanses of the cathedral like the
distant roar of thunder.

(a. reverberated . . . sepulchral)   c. expostulated . . . surreptitious
b. blazoned . . . unctuous   d. debased . . . circuitous

3. Though _____ have passed since the day Moses brought them
down from the top of Mt. Sinai, the _____ contained in the Ten
Commandments are still revered by many throughout the world.

a. epitomes . . . caveats   c. addenda . . . coalitions
(b. millennia . . . precepts)   d. umbrages . . . archetypes

4. In many ancient religions, the _____ of an entire community would
periodically be placed on the head of a single sacrificial animal, so that the death of
one might _____ the sins of all.

a. innuendoes . . . fetter   c. aspersions . . . expedite
b. surmises . . . enjoin   (d. transgressions . . . expiate)

5. If the job you have is nothing more than a(n) _____, you don't
have to be a particularly _____ or talented worker to handle it.

a. hiatus . . . erudite   (c. sinecure . . . sedulous)
b. prerogative . . . noncommittal   d. anathema . . . soporific

Enriching Your Vocabulary

Read the passage below. Then complete the exercise at the bottom of the page.

Living Latin

While some might consider Latin a "dead language" because it is no longer spoken in the modern world, most scholars can attest to the fact that Latin has contributed many roots, conjugations, and phrases to the English language. We can determine the meanings of some Latin expressions based on the familiar word roots that appear in other Anglicized words. For example, the phrase *e pluribus unum* appears on American money. Recognizing the *e* prefix as in *e*ject as meaning *out* or *from*, the *plur* root as in *plur*al as meaning *many*, and the *un* root as in *un*ited as meaning *one*, we can figure out the meaning of this phrase representing American democracy: out of many, one.

Alumni and *alumnae* come from the Latin for "stepchild."

The forms of other Latin phrases may not be as easily recognizable, yet these words play a significant role in our lexicon. For example, *ex officio* (Unit Two) means "by virtue of holding a certain office"; a play's producer may distribute parts *ex officio* as the head of the production. *Ex post facto* means "after the fact." *Habeas corpus* refers to the need for absolute proof. And of course, where would our lists be without the popular abbreviation *etc.*, short for *et cetera*, meaning, "and other things"?

With or without a dictionary, select the item in the box below that completes each sentence.

alma mater	modus operandi	pro tempore
de facto	persona non grata	status quo

1. The football player donated a large sum to his _____alma mater_____.

2. The burglar's ____modus operandi____ included climbing in a second story window.

3. After I decided not to sign the petition to plant more trees on our block, I became ____persona non grata____ in our neighborhood.

4. The governor decided to maintain the _____status quo_____ and not raise taxes.

5. Until we hire a new principal, the assistant principal will be the principal _pro tempore_.

6. While the monarchy of England plays a ceremonial role, the _____de facto_____ head of government is the prime minister.

 **Definitions**

Note carefully the spelling, pronunciation, part(s) of speech, and definition(s) of each of the following words. Then write the word in the blank space(s) in the illustrative sentence(s) following. Finally, study the lists of synonyms and antonyms given at the end of each entry.

1. austere
(ô stēr′)

(*adj.*) severe or stern in manner; without adornment or luxury, simple, plain; harsh or sour in flavor

The _____ **austere** _____ clothing and conduct of the Puritans expressed their religious humility.

SYNONYMS: forbidding, rigorous, puritanical, ascetic, unadorned, subdued
ANTONYMS: mild, indulgent, luxurious, flamboyant

2. beneficent
(bə nef′ ə sənt)

(*adj.*) performing acts of kindness or charity; conferring benefits, doing good

From them I learned that purely _____ **beneficent** _____ acts can require as much hard work as a nine-to-five job.

SYNONYMS: humanitarian, magnanimous, charitable
ANTONYMS: selfish, cruel, harmful, deleterious

3. cadaverous
(kə dav′ ər əs)

(*adj.*) pale, gaunt, resembling a corpse

Weak from hunger and _____ **cadaverous** _____ in appearance, the rescued captives were carried from the plane.

SYNONYMS: corpselike, wasted, haggard, emaciated, ghastly
ANTONYMS: robust, portly, rosy, the picture of health

4. concoct
(kän käkt′)

(*v.*) to prepare by combining ingredients, make up (as a dish); to devise, invent, fabricate

He _____ **concocts** _____ a savory stew with fresh herbs and vegetables from the garden.

SYNONYMS: create, fashion, rustle up

5. crass
(kras)

(*adj.*) coarse, unfeeling; stupid

We feel that the positions of our representative show a _____ **crass** _____ indifference to our problems.

SYNONYMS: crude, vulgar, tasteless, oafish, obtuse
ANTONYMS: refined, elegant, tasteful, polished, brilliant

6. debase
(di bās′)

(*v.*) to lower in character, quality, or value; to degrade, adulterate; to cause to deteriorate

Every time a new rule is introduced in a popular sport, there are fans who say it will _____ **debase** _____ the game.

SYNONYMS: cheapen, corrupt, demean, depreciate
ANTONYMS: elevate, uplift, improve, enhance

7. desecrate
(des′ ə krāt)

(*v.*) to commit sacrilege upon, treat irreverently; to contaminate, pollute

The search continues for the vandals who __desecrated__ the cemetery.

SYNONYMS: profane, defile, violate
ANTONYMS: revere, honor, venerate, consecrate

8. disconcert
(dis kən sərt′)

(*v.*) to confuse; to disturb the composure of

They had hoped to __disconcert__ him with an unexpected question, but he was well prepared.

SYNONYMS: upset, rattle, ruffle, faze, perturb
ANTONYMS: relax, calm, put at ease

9. grandiose
(gran′ dē ōs)

(*adj.*) grand in an impressive or stately way; marked by pompous affectation or grandeur, absurdly exaggerated

In how many stories, I wonder, does an ambitious villain become the victim of __grandiose__ plans?

SYNONYMS: majestic, bombastic, highfalutin
ANTONYMS: simple, modest, unaffected, humble

10. inconsequential
(in kän sə kwen′ shəl)

(*adj.*) trifling, unimportant

Feel free to ignore the __inconsequential__ details, provided that you know exactly which ones they are.

SYNONYMS: trivial, negligible, petty, paltry
ANTONYMS: important, essential, crucial, vital

11. infraction
(in frak′ shən)

(*n.*) a breaking of a law or obligation

His uncle paid a fine for his __infraction__ of the local recycling regulations.

SYNONYMS: violation, transgression, breach, offense

12. mitigate
(mit′ ə gāt)

(*v.*) to make milder or softer, to moderate in force or intensity

I had hoped to __mitigate__ her anger by offering an apology.

SYNONYMS: lessen, relieve, alleviate, diminish
ANTONYMS: aggravate, intensify, irritate, exacerbate

13. pillage
(pil′ ij)

(*v.*) to rob of goods by open force (as in war), plunder; (*n.*) the act of looting; booty

The commanding officer warned his troops not to __pillage__ the conquered city.

__Pillage__ and murder became a fact of life in Europe during the Dark Ages.

SYNONYMS: (*v.*) ravage, sack, loot; (*n.*) booty

14. prate
(prāt)

(v.) to talk a great deal in a foolish or aimless fashion

He would _____ prate _____ endlessly about the past but say nothing useful about our present dilemma.

SYNONYMS: chatter, prattle, blab, blabber, palaver
ANTONYMS: come to the point, not waste words

15. punctilious
(pəŋk til′ ē əs)

(adj.) very careful and exact, attentive to fine points of etiquette or propriety

The clerk was so _____ punctilious _____ in obeying court rules that I had to remind him why I was there.

SYNONYMS: precise, scrupulous, exacting, fussy, finicky
ANTONYMS: careless, negligent, lax, perfunctory

16. redoubtable
(ri daủ′ tə bəl)

(adj.) inspiring fear or awe; illustrious, eminent

As a ruler he was _____ redoubtable _____ but, like all such rulers, not much loved.

SYNONYMS: formidable, fearsome, awesome, august
ANTONYMS: laughable, risible, contemptible

17. reprove
(ri prüv′)

(v.) to find fault with, scold, rebuke

She _____ reproved _____ her staff for having followed orders blindly.

SYNONYMS: chide, chastise, upbraid, reproach
ANTONYMS: praise, commend, laud, pat on the back

18. restitution
(res tə tü′ shən)

(n.) the act of restoring someone or something to the rightful owner or to a former state or position; making good on a loss or damage

They made _____ restitution _____ for the damage to the car but never fully regained the friendship of its owner.

SYNONYMS: compensation, reimbursement, redress, restoration

19. stalwart
(stôl′ wərt)

(adj.) strong and sturdy; brave; resolute; (n.) a brave, strong person; a strong supporter; one who takes an uncompromising position

She became as _____ stalwart _____ on the basketball court as she was quick at mathematical puzzles.

The enemy had broken through our first line but was repulsed by the _____ stalwarts _____ defending the gates.

SYNONYMS: (adj.) sturdy, stout, intrepid, valiant; (n.) mainstay
ANTONYMS: (adj.) weak, infirm, irresolute, vacillating

20. vulnerable
(vəl′ nər ə bəl)

(adj.) open to attack; capable of being wounded or damaged; unprotected

Those brave enough to have opposed the dictator's rise now found themselves in a _____ vulnerable _____ position.

SYNONYMS: defenseless, exposed, unguarded
ANTONYMS: invincible, protected, safe, secure

Completing the Sentence

From the words for this unit, choose the one that best completes each of the following sentences. Write the word in the space provided.

1. Though most of our players were the equals of theirs, the awesome size of their _____**redoubtable**_____ center filled us with apprehension.

2. I became desperately tired of listening to him _____**prate**_____ about how important he was, how much money he had, and so forth.

3. Who can ever forget those pictures showing the _____**cadaverous**_____ faces of the people who had been in concentration camps!

4. Whenever she serves as chairperson, she is so _____**punctilious**_____ that she insists on observing every fine point of parliamentary procedure.

5. I found that beneath his rather _____**austere**_____ manner and appearance there was a warm, sympathetic person.

6. An official who is responsible for shaping vital national policies should not waste time and energy on such _____**inconsequential**_____ matters.

7. Even a so-called minor _____**infraction**_____ of the traffic laws may lead to a serious accident.

8. At a time when we need a modest, low-cost housing program, how can we be expected to accept such a(n) _____**grandiose**_____ scheme?

9. His work on behalf of the homeless was merely the latest in a long line of _____**beneficent**_____ undertakings.

10. Is there any way that we can make _____**restitution**_____ for the terrible wrong we have done them?

11. Fond remembrances of happy days of family life intensified rather than _____**mitigated**_____ her grief.

12. They _____**desecrated**_____ the funeral service by talking loudly during the ceremonies, laughing, and generally showing a complete lack of respect.

13. Before they arrived home from the party, they _____**concocted**_____ an elaborate story that they hoped would excuse their being two hours late.

14. It is hard to forgive the _____**crass**_____ selfishness with which they took most of the food supplies for their own use.

15. Our democracy, I believe, is more _____**vulnerable**_____ to decay from within than it is to attack from the outside.

16. Though she looked rather frail, her _____**stalwart**_____ spirit made her a tireless crusader for women's rights.

17. We are, I trust, long past the time when it was considered quite "natural" for newly elected officials to _____**pillage**_____ the city treasury.

18. She has _____debased_____ her considerable talents by writing books that are designed to appeal to the lowest tastes.

19. I'm telling you this not to _____reprove_____ you for having made a mistake but to prevent the mistake from being repeated.

20. He went right on with his speech, refusing to be _____disconcerted_____ by the heckling of a few loudmouths.

Synonyms

*Choose the word from this unit that is **the same** or **most nearly the same** in meaning as the **boldface** word or expression in the given phrase. Write the word on the line provided.*

1. not **perturbed** by the noise _____disconcerted_____

2. **vulgar** appeal for money _____crass_____

3. to **chatter** boringly about the weather _____prate_____

4. **compensation** for his misdeeds _____restitution_____

5. **diminish** the horror of the crime _____mitigate_____

6. **fabricate** an excuse _____concoct_____

7. exaggerating **trivial** flaws _____inconsequential_____

8. a **breach** of our agreement _____infraction_____

9. **exposed** to wind and high water _____vulnerable_____

10. **loot** the museum of valuables _____pillage_____

11. to **demean** our group's reputation _____debase_____

12. an **intrepid** and faithful sidekick _____stalwart_____

13. an **ascetic** life of plain food and little sleep _____austere_____

14. was **reproached** for his mistakes _____reproved_____

15. happy results from **magnanimous** choices _____beneficent_____

Antonyms

*Choose the word from this unit that is **most nearly opposite** in meaning to the **boldface** word or expression in the given phrase. Write the word on the line provided.*

16. a **robust** specimen _____cadaverous_____

17. her **unaffected** delivery of Shakespeare's lines _____grandiose_____

18. **honor** this ritual of the tribe _____desecrate_____

19. **laughable** as a challenger _____redoubtable_____

20. **negligent** in filling out the form _____punctilious_____

Choosing the Right Word

*Circle the **boldface** word that more satisfactorily completes each of the following sentences.*

1. That sum may seem (**inconsequential,** vulnerable) to you, but to me it is a great deal of money.

2. By concentrating on personal gain, he has (**debased,** disconcerted) both himself and the high office to which he was elected.

3. The starving children shown in the TV special looked more like (**cadavers,** stalwarts) than living creatures.

4. Whenever I go to a concert, I seem to spend half my time shushing the (**crass,** austere) boors who chitchat while the orchestra is playing.

5. As (**restitution,** infraction) for the damage he had caused to the family car, Phil promised to clean and polish it regularly for a full year.

6. Since my next paycheck was not to be had until the first of the month, I reconciled myself to living (**austerely,** inconsequentially) until then.

7. The woman is known and loved throughout the community for her many (redoubtable, **beneficent**) acts on behalf of all types of unfortunates.

8. The principal (disconcerted, **reproved**) the entire student body for their discourteous behavior toward the guest speaker at the school assembly.

9. His (**grandiose,** beneficent) schemes for world conquest collapsed in a nightmare of military defeat and internal revolt.

10. In her clumsy efforts to be recognized as an "intellectual," she (**prates,** desecrates) endlessly about matters she does not really understand.

11. All the power of Great Britain could not shake the American colonists in their (**stalwart,** beneficent) opposition to measures that they considered unfair and tyrannical.

12. She is such a (**redoubtable,** crass) foe of the trite phrase that her students tremble lest her wrath descend on them for using a cliché.

13. The sale of so many great works of art to foreign collectors is, in my eyes, little more than (**pillage,** mitigation) of our cultural heritage.

14. The master chef has (debased, **concocted**) a dessert that is so rich that it will be a menace to weight watchers throughout the country.

15. He is so (**punctilious,** austere) about every detail that it is said he irons his shoelaces before wearing them.

16. Her self-confidence is so unshakeable that she is simply not (grandiose, **vulnerable**) to "put-down" remarks that would annoy other people.

17. The fact that he did everything possible to help the poor child after the accident tends to (**mitigate,** desecrate) his responsibility for the tragedy.

18. It is a (**desecration,** restitution) of the memory of Lincoln to involve his name in defense of such a racist policy.

19. Although his conduct may not have violated any law, I consider it a gross (cadaver, **infraction**) of conventional ethical standards.

20. The conductor of the orchestra was so (desecrated, **disconcerted**) by the noisy audience that he stopped the performance and asked for quiet.

*Read the following passage, in which some of the words you have studied in this unit appear in **boldface** type. Then complete each statement given below the passage by circling the letter of the item that is **the same** or **almost the same** in meaning as the highlighted word.*

Walker Evans: Life As It Is

(Line)

In the 1920s still cameras were considered mere gadgets. They took only black-and-white pictures and one used them to record weddings or to let friends see how fast the children were growing. Almost no one encouraged Walker Evans, a shy young Midwesterner, in his belief that photography could be an art. (5)

The few older photographers who shared Evans' view chose foreign locations or poetical subjects in which billowing mists or sharply contrasted tones made the viewer marvel that a photo could so dramatically resemble a painting. But Evans thought (10) that imitating paintings **debased** photography. He wanted to show life as we ourselves commonly see it— but show it more clearly than we usually see. As with this photo of a cotton harvest worker in Alabama (left), Evans learned to find the wonderful within the ordinary. (15)

In 1936 Evans was hired to go South with the writer James Agee to produce a magazine article on tenant farmers, the largest group of abjectly poor workers in the nation. Other articles had presented these farmers as nobly heroic or pitifully **vulnerable**, (20) or as **cadaverous** scarecrows dramatic in their poverty, posed with lighting to match. Evans photographed them as he found them, **austere**, likeable people doing their best with the little they had. No contrived drama **mitigated** their terrible, (25)

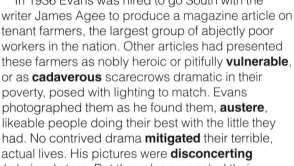

Hale County, Alabama, Summer 1936

actual lives. His pictures were **disconcerting** because they were so clear and obviously true. But they also respected their subjects, and this aura of respect made them unforgettable.

Though Evans died in 1975, his honest and evocative photographs of American life serve as a testament to the art of the camera. (30)

---

1. The meaning of **debased** (line 11) is
  a. glorified   c. depreciated
  b. strained   d. broke

2. Vulnerable (line 20) most nearly means
  a. defenseless   c. funny
  b. hungry   d. poor

3. Cadaverous (line 21) is best defined as
  a. waving   c. comical
  b. emaciated   d. menacing

4. The meaning of **austere** (line 23) is
  a. unhappy   c. unadorned
  b. busy   d. relaxed

5. Mitigated (line 25) most nearly means
  a. diminished   c. broadcast
  b. hid   d. saved

6. Disconcerting (line 26) is best defined as
  a. puzzling   c. interesting
  b. enlightening d. upsetting

Definitions

Note carefully the spelling, pronunciation, part(s) of speech, and definition(s) of each of the following words. Then write the word in the blank space(s) in the illustrative sentence(s) following. Finally, study the lists of synonyms and antonyms given at the end of each entry.

1. acrimonious
(ak rə mō′ nē əs)

(*adj.*) stinging, bitter in temper or tone

She whirled to face me when I spoke, and her answer startled me by its _____**acrimonious**_____ bluntness.

SYNONYMS: biting, caustic, rancorous, hostile, peevish
ANTONYMS: gentle, warm, mild, friendly, cordial

2. bovine
(bō′ vīn)

(*adj.*) resembling a cow or ox; sluggish, unresponsive

After I told him what had happened, he sat there with a _____**bovine**_____ expression and said nothing.

SYNONYMS: stolid , dull, slow, stupid
ANTONYMS: alert, sharp, bright, keen, quick

3. consternation
(kän stər nā′ shən)

(*n.*) dismay, confusion

His father looked at the mess with _____**consternation**_____, hardly knowing what to say first.

SYNONYMS: shock, amazement, bewilderment, dismay
ANTONYMS: calm, composure, aplomb

4. corpulent
(kôr′ pyə lənt)

(*adj.*) fat; having a large, bulky body

Though she had grown _____**corpulent**_____ with the years, the opera singer's voice and her way with a song were the same.

SYNONYMS: overweight, heavy, obese, stout, portly
ANTONYMS: slender, lean, spare, gaunt, emaciated

5. disavow
(dis ə vaủ′)

(*v.*) to deny responsibility for or connection with

The suspect stubbornly continued to _____**disavow**_____ any part in the kidnapping plot.

SYNONYMS: disown, disclaim, retract, abjure
ANTONYMS: acknowledge, admit, grant, certify

6. dispassionate
(dis pash′ ə nət)

(*adj.*) impartial; calm, free from emotion

Being a neighbor but not quite a family friend, he was called in to give a _____**dispassionate**_____ view of our plan.

SYNONYMS: unbiased, disinterested, cool, detached
ANTONYMS: committed, engaged, partial, biased

7. dissension
(di sen′ shən)

(*n.*) disagreement, sharp difference of opinion

The political party was torn by _____ **dissension** _____ and finally split into two wings.

SYNONYMS: strife, discord, contention
ANTONYMS: agreement, accord, harmony

8. dissipate
(dis′ ə pāt)

(*v.*) to cause to disappear; to scatter, dispel; to spend foolishly, squander; to be extravagant in pursuit of pleasure

As chairman he is fair and open, but he _____ **dissipates** _____ his energies on trivial things.

SYNONYMS: disperse, strew, diffuse, waste
ANTONYMS: gather, collect, conserve, husband

9. expurgate
(ek′ spər gāt)

(*v.*) to remove objectionable passages or words from a written text; to cleanse, purify

According to the unwritten law of journalism, the editor alone has the right to _____ **expurgate** _____ the article.

SYNONYMS: purge, censor, bowdlerize

10. gauntlet
(gônt′ lət)

(*n.*) an armored or protective glove; a challenge; two lines of men armed with weapons with which to beat a person forced to run between them; an ordeal

In the Middle Ages, a knight threw down his _____ **gauntlet** _____ as a challenge, and another knight picked it up only if he accepted.

SYNONYMS: dare, provocation, trial, punishment

11. hypothetical
(hī pə thet′ ə kəl)

(*adj.*) based on an assumption or guess; used as a provisional or tentative idea to guide or direct investigation

Science is not based on _____ **hypothetical** _____ assumptions, but on proven facts.

SYNONYMS: assumed, supposed, conjectural, conditional
ANTONYMS: actual, real, tested, substantiated

12. ignoble
(ig nō′ bəl)

(*adj.*) mean, low, base

Most people will agree that a noble purpose does not justify _____ **ignoble** _____ means.

SYNONYMS: inferior, unworthy, dishonorable, sordid
ANTONYMS: admirable, praiseworthy, lofty, noble

13. impugn
(im pyün′)

(*v.*) to call into question; to attack as false

You can _____ **impugn** _____ the senator's facts, but you cannot accuse her of concealing her intentions.

SYNONYMS: challenge, deny, dispute, query, question
ANTONYMS: confirm, prove, verify, validate

14. intemperate
(in tem′ pər ət)

(*adj.*) immoderate, lacking in self-control; inclement

Experience taught her to control her _____intemperate_____ outbursts of anger.

SYNONYMS: excessive, extreme, unrestrained, inordinate
ANTONYMS: moderate, restrained, cool and collected

15. odium
(ō′ dē əm)

(*n.*) hatred, contempt; disgrace or infamy resulting from hateful conduct

Those eager to heap _____odium_____ on the fallen tyrant learned that he had escaped in the night.

SYNONYMS: abhorrence, opprobrium, shame, ignominy
ANTONYMS: esteem, admiration, approbation

16. perfidy
(pər′ fə dē)

(*n.*) faithlessness, treachery

Rulers in Shakespeare's plays often find themselves armed against enemies but not against the _____perfidy_____ of their friends.

SYNONYMS: betrayal, disloyalty, treason, duplicity
ANTONYMS: faithfulness, loyalty, steadfastness

17. relegate
(rel′ ə gāt)

(*v.*) to place in a lower position; to assign, refer, turn over; to banish

Even if they _____relegate_____ him to a mere clerical job, he is determined to make his presence felt.

SYNONYMS: transfer, consign, demote, exile
ANTONYMS: promote, elevate, advance, recall

18. squeamish
(skwē′ mish)

(*adj.*) inclined to nausea; easily shocked or upset; excessively fastidious or refined

If I am called _____squeamish_____ for disliking the horror movie, what do we call those who say that they liked it?

SYNONYMS: nauseated, queasy, delicate, oversensitive, priggish

19. subservient
(səb sər′ vē ənt)

(*adj.*) subordinate in capacity or role; submissively obedient; serving to promote some end

The officers were taught to be respectful of but not blindly _____subservient_____ to their superior's wishes.

SYNONYMS: secondary, servile, obsequious, useful
ANTONYMS: primary, principal, bossy, domineering

20. susceptible
(sə sep′ tə bəl)

(*adj.*) open to; easily influenced; lacking in resistance

The trouble with being _____susceptible_____ to flattery is that you can never be sure that the flatterer is sincere.

SYNONYMS: vulnerable, receptive, impressionable
ANTONYMS: resistant, immune

Completing the Sentence

From the words for this unit, choose the one that best completes each of the following sentences. Write the word in the space provided.

1. We have had enough of high-powered, excited oratory; what we need now is a(n) _____**dispassionate**_____ examination of the facts.

2. Although she seems rather plodding in her behavior and rarely becomes excited, I think it is unfair to call her "_____**bovine**_____."

3. She is a person of such fine moral standards that she seems incapable of a(n) _____**ignoble**_____ act.

4. Instead of using all their forces in one concerted attack on the enemy, they _____**dissipated**_____ their strength in minor engagements.

5. The job of cleaning up the field and the stands after the big game was _____**relegated**_____ to the freshmen.

6. Our discussion that day was a(n) _____**hypothetical**_____ one, based on the possibility—still far from definite—that I would take the job.

7. Far from presenting a unified front, the party is torn by all kinds of strife and _____**dissension**_____.

8. I am not trying to _____**impugn**_____ his truthfulness, but I still do not see how the facts support his claims.

9. Now that these ugly facts about his business dealings have come to light, I must _____**disavow**_____ my support of his candidacy.

10. Vigorous debate is fine, but is there any real need for such unrestrained and _____**acrimonious**_____ name-calling?

11. He is so _____**susceptible**_____ to flattery that with a few complimentary words I can get him to do almost anything I want.

12. Though her overall position seemed to be sensible, her language was so unrestrained and _____**intemperate**_____ that people wouldn't support her.

13. Anyone as _____**squeamish**_____ as that trainee will have trouble accustoming himself to the sights, sounds, and smells of hospital work.

14. Because Vidkun Quisling cooperated with the Nazis, his name has become a symbol of _____**perfidy**_____ in his home country of Norway.

15. The _____**odium**_____ for this tragic failure does not belong to any individual or small group but to the community as a whole.

16. To the _____**consternation**_____ of the people in the stands, the lion leaped out of the cage and bounded toward the exit.

17. Thomas Bowdler _____**expurgated**_____ certain words from Shakespeare's plays because he felt that they were unfit to "be read aloud in a family."

18. Under the American form of government, all branches of the military are clearly _____subservient_____ to the civilian authority.

19. The bold candidate threw down the _____gauntlet_____ and dared her opponent to face her in a televised debate.

20. People with a tendency toward being _____corpulent_____ must wage a lifelong struggle against rich foods.

Synonyms

*Choose the word from this unit that is **the same** or **most nearly the same** in meaning as the **boldface** word or expression in the given phrase. Write the word on the line provided.*

1. standing before us in **bewilderment** _____consternation_____

2. to **disown** any credit for herself _____disavow_____

3. deciding to **bowdlerize** the passage _____expurgate_____

4. unwilling to **question** his honor _____impugn_____

5. setting aside her **conjectural** motive _____hypothetical_____

6. the brutal **challenge** he endured _____gauntlet_____

7. a **dishonorable** end to a shadowy life _____ignoble_____

8. feeling **queasy** at the very thought _____squeamish_____

9. **consigned** to the highest bleachers _____relegated_____

10. not a hint of **duplicity** in him _____perfidy_____

11. a show of **unrestrained** scorn _____intemperate_____

12. a **stolid**, faithful devotion _____bovine_____

13. to deliberately **waste** her wealth _____dissipate_____

14. give a **detached** account _____dispassionate_____

15. his **caustic** way of speaking _____acrimonious_____

Antonyms

*Choose the word from this unit that is **most nearly opposite** in meaning to the **boldface** word or expression in the given phrase. Write the word on the line provided.*

16. a slow, **gaunt** old man _____corpulent_____

17. the **esteem** attached to that name _____odium_____

18. a family vacation marked by **harmony** _____dissension_____

19. quite **immune** to outside influences _____susceptible_____

20. an intern's **domineering** manner _____subservient_____

Choosing the Right Word

*Circle the **boldface** word that more satisfactorily completes each of the following sentences.*

1. A certain amount of disagreement is healthy in any organization, but in our club (**dissension,** perfidy) has almost become a way of life.

2. I noticed with some distaste how her usually overbearing manner became (**susceptible, subservient**) when our employer joined the group.

3. If we are going to be required to perform a(n) (**expurgated,** relegated) version of the play, then I think it is not worth doing.

4. Imagine our (**consternation,** dissension) when the brakes failed and we headed full speed toward the busy intersection!

5. Students who have been well trained in the social sciences should not be (**susceptible,** ignoble) to the cheap fallacies of racism.

6. The estate he had inherited from his father was (**dissipated,** disavowed) in a long series of impractical and/or mismanaged business enterprises.

7. Try your best to subdue your natural reluctance and make a (squeamish, **dispassionate**) decision that will be in your son's best interests.

8. My Spanish friend finds it hard to understand the (**odium,** dissension) attached to bullfighting in most non-Hispanic countries.

9. Their (susceptible, **bovine**) stares and obvious inability to understand the seriousness of the situation made me doubt their mental capacity.

10. Though I was annoyed by the child's behavior, the father's outburst of anger seemed to me deplorably (**intemperate,** bovine).

11. I am not ordinarily a (corpulent, **squeamish**) person, but the sight of that terrible automobile accident haunted me for weeks.

12. By reference to (**hypothetical,** ignoble) cases, you may be able to clarify the difference between "murder" and "manslaughter" for the law students.

13. It is not for me to (expurgate, **impugn**) his motives, but how could anyone except an overambitious scoundrel have misled his friends in that way?

14. Aren't you going a little far when you accuse me of (consternation, **perfidy**) because I didn't vote for you in the beauty contest?

15. The retiring coach said he no longer had the stomach to run the (**gauntlet,** odium) of critics who assailed him after every loss.

16. There is often a thin line between the kind of debate that is spirited and useful and that which is (**acrimonious,** hypothetical) and nonproductive.

17. Not too long ago in our society, a (**corpulent,** bovine) body was generally admired as a sign of prosperity and physical vigor.

18. When Mr. Kummer saw my pathetically inept efforts to prepare a banana split, I was (impugned, **relegated**) to the ranks of the unemployed.

19. The prisoner attempted to (**disavow,** dissipate) his confession on the grounds that he had not been informed of his legal rights.

20. Far from being (**ignoble,** dispassionate), her failure after making a valiant effort may serve as an inspiration to young people.

*Read the following passage, in which some of the words you have studied in this unit appear in **boldface** type. Then complete each statement given below the passage by circling the letter of the item that is **the same** or **almost the same** in meaning as the highlighted word.*

Monster in the Lake

(Line)

Mysteries become more popular the older they get, and the so-called mystery of the Loch Ness Monster is at least fifteen hundred years old. The creature, called everything from a fish to a dragon, was reportedly seen by a monk in 565 A.D., in a lake in Scotland (the "loch," to the Scots) that she has ever

(5) since been said to inhabit. For some reason, the **hypothetical** "Nessie" is always referred to as "she." Her size can only be guessed at, but the loch itself is 788 feet deep and twenty-three miles long.

For centuries, local people kept the mystery alive, but not until 1933 did newspapers cause

(10) **consternation** among the general public by publishing reports of "Nessie" sightings. Shortly thereafter, hunters, scientists, and tourists began arriving to see if she existed. One popular theory said that Nessie was a kind of

(15) dinosaur left over from another age. Such talk was like a **gauntlet** thrown down to scientists, who had repeatedly examined the stories of sightings and the photographs said to show Nessie's hump, flippers, and head (right). So

(20) far, most such pictures have been proven to be large logs or floating tree stumps, waves made by boats, rocks seen at a distance, or deer out swimming. Small submarines have searched the water, and thirty motorboats once lined up

A "sighting" of the Loch Ness Monster?

(25) from shore to shore and scanned the length of the loch with equipment to detect objects under water. They discovered no monster. Those **susceptible** to the legend said Nessie was hiding in a cave.

Arguments over Nessie have at times been **acrimonious**. Nonbelievers **relegate** her to a folk tale. Still, all agree that the local tourist trade has never

(30) been better.

---

1. The meaning of **hypothetical** (line 5) is
  a. secret   c. huge
  (b.) conjectural   d. ancient

2. Consternation (line 10) most nearly means
  a. mockery   (c.) shock
  b. boredom   d. happiness

3. Gauntlet (line 16) is best defined as
  (a.) provocation   c. clue
  b. joke   d. explanation

4. The meaning of **susceptible** (line 27) is
  a. suspicious   c. profiting
  b. amused   (d.) receptive

5. Acrimonious (line 28) most nearly means
  a. entertaining   c. long
  (b.) rancorous   d. illegal

6. Relegate (line 29) is best defined as
  (a.) consign   c. raise
  b. compare   d. describe

Definitions

Note carefully the spelling, pronunciation, part(s) of speech, and definition(s) of each of the following words. Then write the word in the blank space(s) in the illustrative sentence(s) following. Finally, study the lists of synonyms and antonyms given at the end of each entry.

1. abate
(ə bāt')

(*v.*) to make less in amount, degree, etc.; to subside, become less; to nullify; to deduct, omit

We stood on the dock on that moonless night, waiting for the storm to _____ **abate** _____.

SYNONYMS: diminish, decrease, subside, let up
ANTONYMS: intensify, increase, magnify, wax

2. adulation
(aj ə lā' shən)

(*n.*) praise or flattery that is excessive

Athletes have little choice but to enjoy the sometimes puzzling _____ **adulation** _____ of their fans.

SYNONYMS: adoration, idolization, hero-worship
ANTONYMS: ridicule, derision, scorn, odium

3. anathema
(ə nath' ə mə)

(*n.*) an object of intense dislike; a curse or strong denunciation (often used adjectivally without the article)

The author's views on bringing up children are _____ **anathema** _____ to my dad but a delight to my mother.

SYNONYMS: malediction, imprecation, abomination
ANTONYMS: benediction, blessing

4. astute
(ə stüt')

(*adj.*) shrewd, crafty, showing practical wisdom

The _____ **astute** _____ management of money is a valuable skill but may not by itself make a good executive.

SYNONYMS: shrewd, acute, sagacious, judicious, wily
ANTONYMS: obtuse, doltish, empty-headed, dumb

5. avarice
(av' ər is)

(*n.*) a greedy desire, particularly for wealth

Her career exhibited both the miser's ever-growing _____ **avarice** _____ and the miser's diminishing charm.

SYNONYMS: cupidity, rapacity, acquisitiveness

6. culpable
(kəl' pə bəl)

(*adj.*) deserving blame, worthy of condemnation

It was the inspectors' _____ **culpable** _____ neglect of duty that left such old buses in service.

SYNONYMS: guilty, delinquent, peccant, blameworthy
ANTONYMS: blameless, innocent, laudable, meritorious

7. dilatory
(dil′ ə tôr ē)

(*adj.*) tending to delay or procrastinate, not prompt; intended to delay or postpone

She hired an assistant because, on her own, she was always _____ dilatory _____ in paying her bills.

SYNONYMS: stalling, slow, tardy, laggard
ANTONYMS: prompt, punctual, speedy, expeditious

8. egregious
(i grē′ jəs)

(*adj.*) conspicuous, standing out from the mass (used particularly in an unfavorable sense)

Whoever allowed that man on a stage is guilty of an _____ egregious _____ blunder.

SYNONYMS: glaring, flagrant, blatant
ANTONYMS: unnoticeable, paltry, piddling

9. equivocate
(i kwiv′ ə kāt)

(*v.*) to speak or act in a way that allows for more than one interpretation; to be deliberately vague or ambiguous

I won't soon give my vote to a candidate who shows such a marked tendency to _____ equivocate _____ .

SYNONYMS: to talk out of both sides of one's mouth, palter, hedge
ANTONYM: to speak one's mind plainly

10. evanescent
(ev ə nes′ ənt)

(*adj.*) vanishing, soon passing away; light and airy

Looking back, I see that the magic of that summer was _____ evanescent _____ .

SYNONYMS: ephemeral, transient, transitory
ANTONYMS: everlasting, immortal, imperishable

11. irresolute
(ir ez′ ə lüt)

(*adj.*) unable to make up one's mind, hesitating

In *Hamlet*, the prince is _____ irresolute _____ about whether to obey his father's ghost or to go on as if nothing has happened.

SYNONYMS: indecisive, vacillating, wavering
ANTONYMS: determined, decisive, unwavering

12. nebulous
(neb′ yə ləs)

(*adj.*) cloudlike, resembling a cloud; cloudy in color, not transparent; vague, confused, indistinct

By the time everyone present had expressed an opinion, the original idea had become somewhat _____ nebulous _____ .

SYNONYMS: hazy, fuzzy, cloudy, vague, murky, opaque, indeterminate
ANTONYMS: definite, distinct, clear, sharply focused

13. novice
(näv′ is)

(*n.*) one who is just a beginner at some activity requiring skill and experience (also used adjectivally)

You must be patient and realize that all his mistakes are typical of a _____ novice _____ in this line of work.

SYNONYMS: neophyte, tyro, trainee, apprentice
ANTONYMS: veteran, past master, pro, expert

14. penury
(pen′ yə rē)

(*n.*) extreme poverty; barrenness, insufficiency

We never seem to tire of stories of people who go from _____ penury _____ to sudden wealth.

SYNONYMS: destitution, want, indigence
ANTONYMS: affluence, abundance, luxury, opulence

15. pretentious
(prē ten′ shəs)

(*adj.*) done for show, striving to make a big impression; claiming merit or position unjustifiably; making demands on one's skill or abilities, ambitious

Talking about one's wealth is thought to be _____ pretentious _____ and in poor taste.

SYNONYMS: inflated, ostentatious, affected
ANTONYMS: unassuming, unaffected, modest

16. recapitulate
(rē ka pich′ ə lāt)

(*v.*) to review a series of facts; to sum up

Don't bother to _____ recapitulate _____ the plot of the book; instead, tell me if you liked it.

SYNONYMS: review, summarize, sum up, go over

17. resuscitate
(ri səs′ ə tāt)

(*v.*) to revive, bring back to consciousness or existence

We need someone who can _____ resuscitate _____ our neighborhood council and thus perk up the community spirit.

SYNONYMS: revitalize, reanimate, restore, reactivate

18. slovenly
(sləv′ ən lē)

(*adj.*) untidy, dirty, careless

Her room was in a _____ slovenly _____ state, and it took her an entire Saturday to clean it.

SYNONYMS: unkempt, slatternly, slipshod, lax
ANTONYMS: neat, tidy, careful, meticulous

19. supposition
(səp ə zish′ ən)

(*n.*) something that is assumed or taken for granted without conclusive evidence

Guided by a _____ supposition _____ that turned out to be false, they made some disastrous decisions.

SYNONYMS: assumption, presumption, hypothesis

20. torpid
(tôr′ pid)

(*adj.*) inactive, sluggish, dull

We all felt _____ torpid _____ after that long, dull lecture.

SYNONYMS: sluggish, lethargic, otiose, languid
ANTONYMS: energetic, dynamic, vigorous

Completing the Sentence

From the words for this unit, choose the one that best completes each of the following sentences. Write the word in the space provided.

1. I don't think I'd call such a(n) _____**egregious**_____ grammatical mistake a minor "slip of the pen."

2. It will mean more to him to gain the approval of the few people who can appreciate his work than to receive the _____**adulation**_____ of the crowd.

3. He holds forth in great detail on what is wrong with our city government, but the remedies he suggests are exceedingly _____**nebulous**_____ .

4. Her mind, _____**torpid**_____ as a result of hours of exposure to the bitter cold, was not alert enough to sense the impending danger.

5. Since he was a(n) _____**novice**_____ at bridge, the three veteran players hoped to find someone more suitable to fill out their table.

6. Using the most up-to-date equipment, the firefighters worked tirelessly to _____**resuscitate**_____ the victim of smoke inhalation.

7. The study of history teaches us that a hunger for land, like other kinds of _____**avarice**_____ , is the cause of a great many wars.

8. Your brilliant plan is based on one false _____**supposition**_____ —that I am willing to work without pay.

9. The _____**penury**_____ she had experienced in her childhood and youth made her keenly aware of the value of money.

10. Sure, it's great to be a big-league ballplayer, but bear in mind that the years of stardom are brief and _____**evanescent**_____ .

11. I told my friend that dress for the party was casual, but he showed up looking, in my opinion, just plain _____**slovenly**_____ .

12. Does he use all those quotations as a means of clarifying his meaning, or simply as a(n) _____**pretentious**_____ display of his learning?

13. I was so _____**irresolute**_____ about whether to go out for basketball or for swimming that I ended up going out for neither.

14. As her anger slowly _____**abated**_____ , she realized that such childish outbursts of emotion would do nothing to help solve her problems.

15. I was impressed by the _____**astute**_____ way our hostess guided the conversation away from topics that might be embarrassing to her guests.

16. Since I truly loathe people who think they are "above the common herd," any form of snobbery is absolutely _____**anathema**_____ to me.

17. Although she tried to _____**equivocate**_____ , we insisted on a simple "yes" or "no" answer.

18. When you are _____ dilatory _____ in returning a book to the library, you are preventing someone else from using it.

19. After giving us extremely detailed instructions for more than an hour, she briefly _____ recapitulated _____ and then sent us out on our assignments.

20. How can you consider him _____ culpable _____ when the accident was caused by a landslide that no one could have foreseen or prevented?

Synonyms

*Choose the word from this unit that is **the same** or **most nearly the same** in meaning as the **boldface** word or expression in the given phrase. Write the word on the line provided.*

1. driven by a limitless **cupidity** _____ avarice

2. guilty of **flagrant** rudeness _____ egregious

3. a delicate and **transitory** beauty _____ evanescent

4. **sum up** your requirements _____ recapitulate

5. ashamed of a **slipshod** job _____ slovenly

6. struggle along in **destitution** _____ penury

7. **revive** the dull party _____ resuscitate

8. made **sluggish** by the heat _____ torpid

9. a maddeningly **murky** explanation _____ nebulous

10. demonstrated **shrewd** understanding _____ astute

11. a reasonable **presumption** _____ supposition

12. the clumsiness of a **neophyte** _____ novice

13. the hurricane's wind **subsided** _____ abated

14. **vacillating** over a choice _____ irresolute

15. a last, muttered **imprecation** _____ anathema

Antonyms

*Choose the word from this unit that is **most nearly opposite** in meaning to the **boldface** word or expression in the given phrase. Write the word on the line provided.*

16. a **laudable** decision to walk away _____ culpable

17. ready to meet the **scorn** of the crowd _____ adulation

18. a **prompt** reckoning of their losses _____ dilatory

19. **speak plainly** on important subjects _____ equivocate

20. an **unassuming** house near the city limits _____ pretentious

Choosing the Right Word

*Circle the **boldface** word that more satisfactorily completes each of the following sentences.*

1. What do you think of the concept that when a crime is committed, society is often as (**culpable,** astute) as the criminal?

2. The heat in the room, the quiet drone of the fly at the window, and the bright sunlight put me into a (**torpid,** slovenly) state.

3. As a result of (**irresolution,** egregiousness) when that novel was first submitted, the publishing house lost the biggest best-seller of the year.

4. What she calls her "philosophy of life" seems to me a hodgepodge of childish fallacies and (**nebulous,** dilatory) generalizations.

5. As the election drew nearer, the candidates went from reasonable discussion to quarrelsomeness to (**anathematizing,** recapitulating) each other.

6. The glory of this perfect spring day sems to be all the more precious because it is so (torpid, **evanescent**).

7. Biologists have a theory that every plant or animal in the course of its development (abates, **recapitulates**) all the stages of its evolution.

8. Only a (penury, **novice**) at golf would have tried to use a driver when hitting into such a strong wind.

9. In everyone's life, a situation may arise that calls for a basic moral choice to be made, without compromise or (abatement, **equivocation**).

10. Is it any wonder that a 17-year-old star athlete becomes smug when she receives such (recapitulation, **adulation**) from the entire school?

11. Since he is known to be a multimillionaire, it seems almost (culpable, **pretentious**) of him, in an inverted sense, to drive around in a small, battered, inexpensive car.

12. He is completely indifferent to wealth and luxurious living; his (anathema, **avarice**) is directed instead toward fame and prestige.

13. Sportswriters attribute the success of the pennant-winning team largely to the (**astute,** evanescent) managing of old Buck Coakley.

14. In the densely populated and underdeveloped countries we visited, we saw the depths to which people can be reduced by (**penury,** anathema).

15. The (**slovenly,** pretentious) physical appearance of the report was matched by its careless writing and disorganized content.

16. They say that school spirit at Central High is dead, but I am confident that it can be (**resuscitated,** equivocated) if the right methods are used.

17. When the results of her mistakes became public knowledge, she gained a well-deserved reputation for being an (astute, **egregious**) blunderer.

18. In playing chess, she deliberately uses (**dilatory,** nebulous) tactics to make her opponent impatient and tense.

19. You may be right in your belief that she won't let us use her car, but remember that this is still only a(n) (anathema, **supposition**).

20. As soon as the hurricane (**abated,** equivocated), rescue teams rushed out to help people in the devastated area.

Vocabulary in Context

*Read the following passage, in which some of the words you have studied in this unit appear in **boldface** type. Then complete each statement given below the passage by circling the letter of the item that is **the same** or **almost the same** in meaning as the highlighted word.*

A Writer Finds Her Way

(Line)

Edith Wharton (1862–1937) faced some interesting hurdles in becoming the important writer of fiction that she aspired to be. She was female at a time when the rich trained their daughters to be pretty hostesses on the lookout to marry wealthy men. Luckily, young Edith and her family lived in Europe for a time, and she was encouraged to read books. From both experiences, (5) she saw that life could be led in other ways.

Back in America, she published some stories and poems that received little attention. Soon she did indeed marry a rich banker. In redecorating their mansion, Wharton discovered that she had (10) **astute** judgment regarding furnishings and, with her designer, published a popular book on interior design. But she was learning that the pleasures of glittering society parties were **evanescent**. It was a prosperous time; Mark (15) Twain had called it "the Gilded Age." New York seemed full of **novice** millionaires. Wharton thought many **egregious** in their **avarice**, in their **pretentious** tastes, and, above all, in their lack of human kindness. (20)

She began to publish stories and novels, witty and powerful, in which she showed high society as it had never been shown before. Wharton used her friend and contemporary Henry James as her literary role model, but, though she shared (25)

Wharton in her early twenties

his thematic concerns, her style was all her own. In 1921 Wharton became the first woman to be awarded the Pulitzer Prize for a novel.

Quite a few of Wharton's stories and novels have been adapted as plays, films, and TV series. Three recent films are "The House of Mirth," "Ethan Frome," and "The Age of Innocence." (30)

---

1. Astute (line 11) most nearly means
a. profitable
c. sagacious
b. expensive
d. forceful

2. Evanescent (line 15) most nearly means
a. transitory
c. lasting
b. deceiving
d. childish

3. Novice (line 17) is best defined as
a. modest
c. neophyte
b. witty
d. famous

4. The meaning of **egregious** (line 18) is
a. secret
c. amusing
b. blatant
d. unsolvable

5. Avarice (line 18) most nearly means
a. cupidity
c. rudeness
b. curiosity
d. competitiveness

6. Pretentious (line 19) is best defined as
a. ostentatious
c. bad
b. picky
d. wonderful

Visit us at www.sadlier-oxford.com for interactive puzzles and games.

REVIEW UNITS 7–9

Vocabulary for Comprehension

Read the following passage, in which some of the words you have studied in Units 7–9 appear in boldface type. Then answer questions 1–12 on page 106 on the basis of what is stated or implied in the passage and in the introductory statement.

This passage discusses some aspects of elephants' behavior, especially the ways in which they communicate.

(Line)

At first look, the counting of elephants would seem no harder than the counting of slow-moving trucks. But garnering information about the

(5) population density of elephants has proved to be no easy task for scientists from Cornell University. It is believed that half of the close-knit elephant families in Southern Africa live in

(10) dense and tangled forests, and counting these **corpulent** creatures raises several interesting questions.

A full-grown elephant must eat 500 pounds of leaves a day. This means

(15) that family members, though deeply devoted, spend much time apart— far apart, so as not to **pillage** one another's lunch. How do they keep in touch? And how many humans would

(20) it take to hack through a jungle trying to count an unknown number of widely separated subjects?

Fortunately, these royal families of the southern forest do keep in touch,

(25) and not only by the high-pitched, trumpetlike blasts we've heard in the movies. Some years ago, scientists discovered that elephants also make sounds too deep for human ears to

(30) detect. Although these rumblings are apparently **nebulous**, they are not **inconsequential** in meaning. They seem to keep widely scattered family members moving in the same

(35) direction and headed toward the same destination. They also seem to signal comfort to a strayed elephant calf whose elders are coming to retrieve it. While the high-pitched call is absorbed

(40) by trees or **dissipated** into the air, the deep call is able to travel much greater distances. Are these low rumblings a sophisticated form of communication, or even language? The Cornell team

(45) hopes to find out.

Meanwhile, the scientists mount recording devices in many parts of the forest, converting the inaudible elephant sounds to visual signs on

(50) computer disks. The team determines how long each call took to reach each recorder and eventually charts both the number of elephants in an area and the course of their movements.

(55) As for decoding the calls, this process may be greatly helped when cameras join the recording devices in the forest. Researchers hope that when they **recapitulate** both the

(60) "soundless" calls and the visual records of the elephants' actions, clues will emerge as to what these sociable creatures are saying.

1. The primary purpose of the passage is to
a. explain the obstacles to an accurate census of elephants
b. show how animal behavior experts employ sophisticated technology
c. explore how members of elephant families keep in touch in dense forests
d. prove that elephants possess language
e. highlight that elephants are an endangered species

2. According to the passage, counting elephants accurately is difficult because of
a. their habitat
b. their aggressiveness
c. their shyness
d. their close resemblance to one another
e. their eating habits

3. The meaning of **corpulent** (line 11) is
a. sociable
b. invisible
c. affectionate
d. long-lived
e. portly

4. The writer includes the rhetorical question in lines 19–22 most probably to
a. emphasize how difficult it is to count elephants
b. demonstrate expertise on the topic
c. imply that no current census is accurate
d. question the ability of humans to survive in a dense forest
e. show that elephants are poorly understood

5. **Pillage** (line 17) most nearly means
a. loot
b. step on
c. spoil
d. rub against
e. share

6. According to the passage, scientists have discovered that elephants stay in contact by
a. creating large piles of stones
b. emitting rumbling sounds too deep for human ears to detect
c. scraping bare patches on the forest floor

d. pulling down large trees at regular intervals
e. using their trunks to signal one another

7. The meaning of **nebulous** (line 31) is
a. indistinct
b. strange
c. sonorous
d. surprising
e. menacing

8. **Inconsequential** (line 32) is best defined as
a. unfriendly
b. pleasant
c. trivial
d. frequent
e. important

9. Which of the following statements can be inferred from the passage?
a. Elephant numbers are declining in Southern Africa.
b. Elephants are gradually migrating from dense forests to more open habitats.
c. Elephants live in close-knit groups.
d. Elephants are loners by nature.
e. Elephants make deep rumbling sounds to frighten away predators.

10. **Dissipated** (line 40) most nearly means
a. diffused
b. mixed up
c. corrupted
d. enhanced
e. blocked

11. **Recapitulate** (line 59) is best defined as
a. review
b. record
c. reorganize
d. preserve
e. match

12. In the passage, the author's perspective is that of a(n)
a. expert in animal behavior
b. science teacher
c. fundraiser for wildlife conservation
d. science writer
e. interested amateur

Grammar in Context

Correct writing requires **subject-verb agreement**. In the sentence "But garnering information about the population density of elephants has proved to be no easy task for scientists at Cornell University (lines 4–7 on page 105), the singular verb "has proved" agrees with the singular subject "garnering."

Note that the number of the subject (singular or plural) is not affected by a phrase or clause that follows it. Singular subjects joined by *or* or *nor* take a singular verb. When a singular subject and a plural subject are joined by *or* or *nor*, the verb agrees with the subject nearer to it. Collective noun subjects such as *family* and *team* take singular verbs when the noun refers to the group as a unit; they take plural verbs when the noun refers to the parts or members of the group. A verb should always agree with its subject, not its predicate nominative.

Special problems in agreement arise with indefinite pronoun subjects. The following indefinite pronouns are always singular: *anyone*, *each*, *either*, *everyone*, *neither*, *no one*, *nothing*, *one*, and *someone*. The following indefinite pronouns are always plural: *both*, *few*, *many*, and *several*. The following indefinite pronouns may be singular or plural: *all*, *any*, *most*, *none*, and *some*. A noun in a prepositional phrase usually offers a clue to the number of the pronoun. For example, in the sentence "All of the study area contains good elephant habitat," "all" is singular. But in the sentence "All of the full-grown elephants eat 500 pounds of leaves a day," "all" is plural.

Choose the verb in parentheses that agrees with the subject of each of the following sentences, and write it on the line provided.

1. An accurate census of the elephants in that area (**have, has**) not been an easy task.
has

2. Neither a strayed elephant calf nor the elders coming to retrieve it (**remains, remain**) out of touch.
remain

3. A team from Cornell (**plan, plans**) to convert the inaudible elephant sounds to visual records.
plans

4. An elephant herd moving in the same general direction (**coordinates, coordinate**) their movements.
coordinate

5. In addition to recording devices, one requirement for decoding the elephants' calls (**is, are**) high-resolution cameras.
is

6. Researchers have found that an elephant family (**spend, spends**) much of its time apart.
spends

7. Some of the elephants' deep calls (**are, is**) monitored by recording devices in the dense forest.
are

Two-Word Completions

Circle the pair of words that best complete the meaning of each of the following passages.

See pages T38–T48 for explanations of answers.

1. Though a few lucky "haves" are able to provide themselves with all the comforts of life on a truly _____ scale, the bulk of the people in many third-world countries seem to live like paupers in the most extreme state of _____ and neglect.
   a. egregious . . . avarice
   b. crass . . . dissension
   c. redoubtable . . . perfidy
   d. grandiose . . . penury

2. "Those who circumvent the law are often as _____ as those who actually break it," the lawyer remarked. "The seriousness of such an offense is rarely _____ by the fact that, technically, no crime has been committed."
   a. culpable . . . mitigated
   b. crass . . . abated
   c. vulnerable . . . impugned
   d. susceptible . . . disavowed

3. For a minor _____ of the rules of a hockey game, the offending player is _____ to the penalty box, or "sin bin," for two minutes. For a more serious violation, he is put there for five.
   a. anathema . . . recapitulated
   b. infraction . . . relegated
   c. supposition . . . disavowed
   d. dissension . . . debased

4. A person has to have a strong stomach to work in a funeral parlor or morgue. Handling _____ is definitely not a job for the _____.
   a. modicums . . . slovenly
   b. novices . . . redoubtable
   c. cadavers . . . squeamish
   d. concoctions . . . acrimonious

5. The _____ of history forever attaches itself to the name of Benedict Arnold for his villainous act of _____ during the American Revolution.
   a. acrimony . . . beneficence
   b. odium . . . perfidy
   c. consternation . . . equivocation
   d. anathema . . . restitution

6. In A.D. 267, a band of barbarous Heruli raided the ancient Greek religious center at Delphi. For several days they _____ the town and _____ its temples. Then they rode off, laden with booty.
   a. relegated . . . dissipated
   b. resuscitated . . . debased
   c. pillaged . . . desecrated
   d. disconcerted . . . expurgated

Choosing the Right Meaning

Read each sentence carefully. Then circle the item that best completes the statement below the sentence.

See pages T38–T48 for explanations of answers.

A teaspoonful of "Roach-Rout" powder, mixed with a quart of water, produces a nebulous, strong-smelling liquid that is highly toxic to cockroaches. (2)

1. The best meaning for the word **nebulous** in line 2 is

a. fuzzy   (b. cloudy)   c. vague   d. confused

The grapes from that region produce a full-bodied wine with a decidedly austere flavor—quite the opposite of the smooth, fruity, but somewhat watery vintages (2) characteristic of other parts of the country.

2. The word **austere** in line 1 is used to mean

a. solemn   b. plain   c. subdued   (d. harsh)

Not surprisingly, the tyrant's much-touted troop of stalwarts, once on the battlefield, proved utter cravens, turning and fleeing at the mere sound of gunfire. (2)

3. In line 1 the word **stalwarts** most nearly means

(a. valiants)   b. supporters   c. loyalists   d. bullies

Among their many gods the ancient Egyptians were particularly attached to the bovine Hathor, the goddess of love and mirth and the personification of the sky. (2)

4. The best meaning for the word **bovine** in line 2 is

(a. represented as a cow)   c. sluggish and unresponsive
b. represented as a sheep   d. dim-witted

"Aurora's rosy fingers gently stroke the sky
And dissipate the inky vestiges of Night." (2)
    (A.E. Glug, "Prating in the Prater," 77–78)

5. The word **dissipate** in line 2 may best be defined as

a. squander   b. carouse   (c. dispel)   d. waste

Antonyms

*In each of the following groups, circle the word or expression that is most nearly the **opposite** of the word in **boldface** type.*

1. adulation
a. protection
b. admiration
(c. hostility)
d. patronage

2. pretentious
a. proud
b. self-respecting
(c. self-effacing)
d. unpleasant

3. inconsequential
a. foolish
(b. significant)
c. clever
d. minor

4. dissension
a. fighting
b. discussion
c. discipline
(d. agreement)

5. austere
a. obscure
(b. self-indulgent)
c. simple
d. wholesome

6. abates
a. passes
(b. intensifies)
c. rends
d. occurs

7. grandiose
(a. modest)
b. intricate
c. unselfish
d. far-ranging

8. debase
(a. elevate)
b. examine
c. criticize
d. dress

9. beneficial
a. humanitarian
b. harmful
c. well-planned
d. constructive

11. stalwart
a. uninformed
b. weak
c. armed
d. redoubtable

13. slovenly
a. conspicuous
b. well-groomed
c. unattractive
d. vulgar

15. culpable
a. meritorious
b. criminal
c. bizarre
d. deliberate

10. egregious
a. laughable
b. conspicuous
c. unnoticeable
d. unpredictable

12. intemperate
a. restrained
b. bitter
c. eloquent
d. irrational

14. disavow
a. accept
b. reject
c. pay for
d. be ashamed of

16. disconcert
a. reassure
b. ignore
c. mortify
d. announce

A. *On the line provided, write the word you have learned in Units 7–9 that is related to each of the following nouns.*
EXAMPLE: grandiosity—**grandiose**

1. austerity, austereness   austere

2. recapitulation   recapitulate

3. irresolution, irresoluteness   irresolute

4. evanescence   evanescent

5. culpability   culpable

6. nebula   nebulous

7. astuteness   astute

8. abatement   abate

9. resuscitation, resuscitator   resuscitate

10. torpidity   torpid

11. relegation   relegate

12. dissent, dissenter   dissension

13. dissipation   dissipate

14. beneficence, beneficiary   beneficent

B. *On the line provided, write the word you have learned in Units 7–9 that is related to each of the following verbs.*
EXAMPLE: dissipate—**dissipation**

15. evanesce   evanescent

16. adulate   adulation

17. suppose   supposition

18. pretend   pretentious

19. hypothecate, hypothesize   hypothetical

20. anathematize   anathema

Word Associations

In each of the following groups, circle the word that is best defined or suggested by the given phrase.

1. behavior that is dishonest, selfish, and cowardly
   a. inconsequential   b. vulnerable   c. ignoble   d. pretentious

2. regained her citizenship by act of Congress
   a. dissension   b. restitution   c. perfidy   d. supposition

3. a tennis player who we know is too good for any of us
   a. austere   b. punctilious   c. grandiose   d. redoubtable

4. living in acute want
   a. penury   b. pillage   c. odium   d. adulation

5. provide some comfort for our deep sorrow
   a. debase   b. impugn   c. mitigate   d. equivocate

6. pander to both sides of the issue
   a. prate   b. equivocate   c. concoct   d. mitigate

7. testimony that is unemotional and unprejudiced
   a. crass   b. dispassionate   c. evanescent   d. culpable

8. "I do not believe that his motives are as unselfish as he pretends."
   a. concoct   b. pillage   c. disconcert   d. impugn

9. a lengthy speech that made few insightful points
   a. resuscitate   b. debase   c. mitigate   d. prate

10. demoted me to the second team
   a. disavow   b. relegate   c. desecrate   d. abate

11. an event planned out down to the last detail
   a. punctilious   b. squeamish   c. torpid   d. susceptible

12. revive a plan that had been abandoned
   a. resuscitate   b. prate   c. disconcert   d. disavow

13. scold the disruptive audience
   a. pillage   b. concoct   c. reprove   d. expurgate

14. someone who has just learned to play bridge
   a. novice   b. consternation   c. corpulent   d. stalwart

15. a keen perception of that nation's motives
   a. astute   b. corpulent   c. ignoble   d. nebulous

16. "I can't stand the sight of blood!"
   a. dilatory   b. evanescent   c. squeamish   d. bovine

17. a conspicuous error
   a. egregious   b. crass   c. irresolute   d. slovenly

18. "Now, let's review the main points, one by one."
   a. recapitulate   b. abate   c. reprove   d. concoct

19. deserving of blame
   a. intemperate   b. culpable   c. dispassionate   d. pretentious

20. a kind act
   a. stalwart   b. beneficent   c. dilatory   d. austere

Building with Classical Roots

mor—form, shape; **the**—to put or place

The root **mor** appears in **amorphous** (page 51), "shapeless, without definite form." The root **the** appears in **anathema** (page 98), meaning "an object of intense dislike." Some other words based on these roots are listed below.

anthropomorphic	metamorphosis	morphology	pseudomorph
epithet	parenthetical	theme	thesis

From the list of words above, choose the one that corresponds to each of the brief definitions below. Write the word in the blank space in the illustrative sentence below the definition.

1. a marked change, a transformation

The child was amazed by the ___metamorphosis___ of the caterpillar.

2. contained in parenthesis; qualifying or explanatory

She made a few ___parenthetical___ remarks before starting her speech.

3. a false, deceptive, or irregular form

Scientists are seldom fooled by a(n) ___pseudomorph___.

4. a topic of discourse or discussion; an idea, point of view

The ___theme___ of the essay was the misuse of technology.

5. the study of form and structure

Students of biological ___morphology___ analyze animal forms.

6. a term used to characterize the nature of a person or thing

"The King" is the ___epithet___ used by Elvis fans for their hero.

7. characterized by the attribution of human qualities to nonhuman phenomena

Giving pets human names is a common ___anthropomorphic___ practice.

8. a proposition that is put forth for argument

The professor offered evidence in support of her ___thesis___.

From the list of words above, choose the one that best completes each of the following sentences. Write the word in the blank space provided.

1. The gods and goddesses of ancient Greece had many ___anthropomorphic___ qualities that made them seem human as well as divine.

2. The use of a(n) ___epithet___ to briefly describe a character is a common device in epic poems such as *Beowulf.*

3. After taking a course in ____morphology____ in the linguistics department, I had a much better understanding of the formation of words.

4. In order to earn a degree, doctoral candidates are expected to defend their ____theses____ before a committee of tenured faculty.

5. The new drug therapy brought about a medical ____metamorphosis____, restoring the patient to good health in two months.

6. One ____theme____ of the most recent presidential campaign was extending economic opportunity to all segments of society.

7. The rock was a(n) ____pseudomorph____, having the crystalline composition of a mineral other than its own.

8. If the ____parenthetical____ information begins to overwhelm the main text in an essay or article, the reader is apt to get bored and confused.

---

*Circle the **boldface** word that more satisfactorily completes each of the following sentences.*

1. Poets dabble in a type of (**metamorphosis**, **anthropomorphism**) when they write of clouds weeping, oceans raging, and winds singing.

2. The lecturer first outlined the (**parenthesis**, **thesis**) he wished to propose and then presented detailed arguments in support of his idea.

3. The student asked if a chameleon was an example of a (**pseudomorph**, **morphology**), since it changes its appearance but not its form.

4. The English teacher asked the students to hold a class discussion on the (**theme**, **epithet**) of Robert Frost's poem, "Mending Wall."

5. In Shakespeare's *A Midsummer Night's Dream,* the character Bottom undergoes an embarrassing (**metamorphosis**, **anthropomorphism**) when he turns into a donkey.

6. It was hard to follow the writer's train of thought because she did not put her explanatory ideas in (**parentheses**, **theses**).

7. In their (**morphology**, **pseudomorph**) classes, the medical students learned the complete structure of the human body and all its parts.

8. Those (**epithets**, **themes**) that attempt to characterize a person according to a stereotype can be hurtful and unfair.

**Analogies**

In each of the following, circle the item that best completes the comparison.

See pages T38–T48 for explanations of answers.

1. novice is to **callow** as
a. slob is to slovenly
b. crony is to acrimonious
c. brigand is to unctuous
d. arbiter is to brusque

2. evanescent is to **transient** as
a. unwieldy is to manageable
b. austere is to opulent
c. immutable is to invariable
d. stalwart is to irresolute

3. marauder is to **pillage** as
a. insurgent is to expostulate
b. embezzler is to peculate
c. archetype is to desecrate
d. critic is to repudiate

4. sangfroid is to **consternation** as
a. umbrage is to resentment
b. avarice is to penury
c. aplomb is to clumsiness
d. ferment is to turmoil

5. supposition is to **hypothetical** as
a. equivocation is to nebulous
b. innuendo is to scathing
c. gossamer is to inscrutable
d. precept is to circuitous

6. assuage is to **mitigate** as
a. reverberate is to enjoin
b. flout is to filch
c. concoct is to contrive
d. transgress is to relegate

7. astute is to **acumen** as
a. dispassionate is to foresight
b. fractious is to wisdom
c. ignoble is to skill
d. erudite is to learning

8. punctilious is to **details** as
a. insular is to possessions
b. intrinsic is to value
c. straitlaced is to morals
d. meritorious is to awards

9. crass is to **grossness** as
a. dilatory is to speediness
b. succinct is to firmness
c. vapid is to dullness
d. tenuous is to forcefulness

10. debase is to **worse** as
a. permeate is to better
b. simulate is to worse
c. ameliorate is to better
d. transcend is to worse

**Choosing the Right Meaning**

Read each sentence carefully. Then circle the item that best completes the statement below the sentence.

See pages T38–T48 for explanations of answers.

"Americans are proud of the great waterways of our nation," the senator said, "and don't wish to see them desecrated by industrial waste and other contaminants." (2)

1. The word **desecrated** in line 2 is best defined as
a. profaned   b. exhausted   c. polluted   d. misused

"Or is it that some Force, too wise, too strong,
Even for yourselves to conquer or beguile, (2)
Sweeps earth and heaven, and men, and gods along
Like the broad volume of the insurgent Nile?" (4)
    (Matthew Arnold, "Mycerinus," 37–40)

2. The best meaning for the word **insurgent** in line 4 is
a. muddy   b. rushing   c. rebellious   d. salty

For years the feelings and experiences of Proust's youth fermented in his brain before
they distilled out in one of the world's greatest works, *A la récherche du temps perdu*.   (2)

3. The word **fermented** in line 1 most nearly means

a. lay dormant   b. cluttered   c. jostled about   (d. brewed)

The views and values typically inculcated by the gang mindset usually precipitate
themselves in various concrete behavior patterns, some of which are decidedly   (2)
antisocial.

4. The best meaning for the word **precipitate** in line 1 is

(a. embody)   b. hurry   c. provoke   d. rain

Two-Word Completions

*Circle the pair of words that best complete the meaning
of each of the following sentences.*

See pages T38–T48 for explanations of answers.

1. To the rather _____ and squeamish Victorians, some of
Shakespeare's language was so objectionable that they would only read his plays in
_____ versions, such as those produced by Thomas Bowdler.

a. jaded . . . ameliorated

(b. straitlaced . . . expurgated)

c. erudite . . . disabused

d. crass . . . expedited

2. Since all forms of idolatry were _____ to the Old Testament
prophets, they _____ relentlessly against such abhorrent
practices and castigated the people who persisted in adhering to them.

a. heinous . . . expurgated

b. salutary . . . expostulated

(c. anathema . . . inveighed)

d. axiomatic . . . remonstrated

3. Since no salary or _____ of any kind was attached to the job,
election to the Roman consulship eventually became the special _____
of a small group of wealthy nobles, who could afford the privilege of serving their
country for a year without pay.

a. aura . . . sinecure

b. contraband . . . epitome

c. amnesty . . . proclivity

(d. compensation . . . prerogative)

4. Like a summer thundershower, whose violence quickly _____
and is forgotten, his fits of temper were intense but _____.

a. intercedes . . . tenuous

(b. abates . . . transient)

c. resuscitates . . . brusque

d. dissipates . . . immutable

5. Attila the Hun soon came to be called "the _____ of God" because
the terror and devastation he wrought were looked upon as divine retribution for the
_____ of a wayward and recalcitrant Roman people.

(a. Scourge . . . transgressions)

b. Aura . . . infractions

c. Fetter . . . infringements

d. Hiatus . . . exhortations

Enriching Your Vocabulary

Read the passage below. Then complete the exercise at the bottom of the page.

Animal Words

With much of the energy of their living counterparts, animal words and expressions scamper, flock, and swim across our language. Sometimes, we juxtapose animal words

"Hungry as a bear"

against human behaviors in order to liken ourselves to animal appearances or behaviors. In other cases, it is the contrast between animal and human behavior that makes these words or phrases relevant. And still other times, these words and phrases have taken on meanings far removed from their origins.

Picture a cow lumbering slowly in an open field. She lies down and starts to graze, seemingly without a care in the world. Scientists classify the cow as a bovine. We therefore use *bovine* (Unit 8) to describe someone who is as placid and stolid as a cow. Nicknames or terms of endearment often derive from the playful characteristics of animals. We might call a young child a "pussycat," "bunny rabbit," or "lamb," or

a very mischievous child a "monkey." Someone who is very busy can be called a "busy bee" or an "eager beaver."

These expressions are part of our political vocabulary as well. "Hawks" and "doves" have opposing attitudes towards war, but "bulls" and "bears" describe the downward or upward progression of the stock market. An unknown candidate is a "dark horse," and an official soon to leave office is a "lame duck."

In Column A below are 10 more animal phrases. With or without a dictionary, match each phrase with its scientific animal term in Column B.

Column A

h	**1.** sly as a fox
e	**2.** proud as a lion
f	**3.** horsing around
d	**4.** catty behavior
i	**5.** lovesick puppy
j	**6.** bullheaded
g	**7.** pigheaded
a	**8.** hungry as a bear
c	**9.** snake-eyes
b	**10.** never cry wolf

Column B

a. ursine

b. lupine

c. ophidian

d. feline

e. leonine

f. equine

g. porcine

h. vulpine

i. canine

j. taurine

Definitions

Note carefully the spelling, pronunciation, part(s) of speech, and definition(s) of each of the following words. Then write the word in the blank space(s) in the illustrative sentence(s) following. Finally, study the lists of synonyms and antonyms given at the end of each entry.

1. accrue
(ə krü′)

(*v.*) to grow or accumulate over time; to happen as a natural result

We allowed the interest to _____**accrue**_____ on the account until it turned into a small fortune.

SYNONYMS: collect, accumulate, proceed from
ANTONYMS: dwindle, decrease, diminish, lessen

2. annotation
(an ə tā′ shən)

(*n.*) a critical or explanatory note or comment, especially for a literary work

Laurence Stern's novel *Tristram Shandy* has almost as many _____**annotations**_____ as lines of text.

3. bedlam
(bed′ ləm)

(*n.*) a state or scene of uproar and confusion

Is this the same band that caused mob scenes and virtual _____**bedlam**_____ on their first tour?

SYNONYMS: commotion, pandemonium, chaos, anarchy
ANTONYMS: peace and quiet, order, tranquility

4. covert
(kō′ vert)

(*adj.*) hidden, disguised, purposefully kept secret; sheltered, secluded; (*n.*) a sheltered place, a hiding place

Napoleon was an expert at making _____**covert**_____ preparations to attack unsuspecting opponents.

The bear made a lunge from her _____**covert**_____ before we realized she was nearby.

SYNONYMS: (*adj.*) undercover, clandestine, sub-rosa
ANTONYMS: (*adj.*) open, overt, undisguised

5. debonair
(deb ə nâr′)

(*adj.*) pleasant, courteous, lighthearted; smooth and polished in manner and appearance

Quite a few _____**debonair**_____ young men asked my cousin to dance.

SYNONYMS: carefree, jaunty, gracious, suave, urbane
ANTONYMS: distraught, agitated, boorish, churlish

6. dun
(dən)

(*v.*) to demand insistently, especially in payment of a debt; (*n.*) a creditor; (*adj.*) dark, dull, drab, dingy

Many of Charles Dickens' characters are _____**dunned**_____ by creditors because of their large debts.

SYNONYMS: (*v.*) hound, pester, harass, nag

7. efficacious
(ef ə kā′ shəs)

(*adj.*) effective, producing results

Not the most charming of senators, he nevertheless wielded the most _____**efficacious**_____ knowledge of statecraft.

SYNONYMS: effectual, efficient, potent, powerful
ANTONYMS: ineffective, worthless, useless

8. equanimity
(ek wə nim′ ə tē)

(*n.*) calmness, composure, refusal to panic

Injustice always sent him into a rage, but he could endure misfortune with _____**equanimity**_____ .

SYNONYMS: tranquility, imperturbability
ANTONYMS: excitability, flappability, agitation

9. fortuitous
(fôr tü′ ə təs)

(*adj.*) accidental, occurring by a happy chance

Due to a _____**fortuitous**_____ drop in oil prices, the shipping company showed healthy profits for the year.

SYNONYMS: unintentional, unplanned, random, lucky
ANTONYMS: intentional, deliberate, premeditated

10. gist
(jist)

(*n.*) the essential part, main point, or essence

Would the talented fellow who keeps the back row in stitches please repeat the _____**gist**_____ of what I said?

SYNONYMS: substance, core, nucleus

11. gratuitous
(grə tü′ ə təs)

(*adj.*) freely given; not called for by circumstances, unwarranted

Though she had hoped to leave the lecture early, several members of the audience asked _____**gratuitous**_____ questions, delaying her by an hour.

SYNONYMS: voluntary, unjustified, uncalled-for
ANTONYMS: justified, warranted

12. imperious
(im pir′ ē əs)

(*adj.*) overbearing, arrogant; seeking to dominate; pressing, compelling

The Wizard of Oz's _____**imperious**_____ manner failed him when he revealed himself as a fussy little man behind a curtain.

SYNONYMS: domineering, magisterial, urgent, imperative
ANTONYMS: fawning, obsequious, humble, unassuming

13. invective
(in vek′ tiv)

(*n.*) a strong denunciation or condemnation; abusive language; (*adj.*) abusive, vituperative

It was his usual hail of _____**invectives**_____ , a sort of furious, harmless shower that left the air a bit clearer.

As _____**invective**_____ speeches go, this one displayed originality, vigor, and, here and there, some wit.

SYNONYMS: (*n.*) vituperation, abuse, diatribe, philippic
ANTONYMS: (*n.*) tribute, panegyric, encomium

14. motley
(mät′ lē)

(*adj.*) showing great variety; composed of different elements or many colors; (*n.*) a jester's costume; a jester

Tall and short, thick and thin, old and young, we share the family name but are a _____ **motley** _____ bunch indeed.

To "put on _____ **motley** _____" is to say what only a king's jester would dare to say.

SYNONYMS: (*adj.*) variegated, heterogeneous, diverse; (*n.*) fool
ANTONYMS: (*adj.*) uniform, homogenous, monochromatic

15. munificent
(myü nif′ ə sənt)

(*adj.*) extremely generous, lavish

Nothing the volunteers said could save the program until our anonymous friend donated a _____ **munificent** _____ sum.

SYNONYMS: bounteous, liberal
ANTONYMS: stingy, miserly, tightfisted, parsimonious

16. procrastinate
(prə kras′ tə nāt)

(*v.*) to delay, put off until later

We all want to _____ **procrastinate** _____ when a task is no fun, but some people make delaying a way of life.

SYNONYMS: stall, temporize, dillydally

17. provocative
(prə väk′ ə tiv)

(*adj.*) tending to produce a strong feeling or response; arousing desire or appetite; irritating, annoying

The ideas discussed in the film were so _____ **provocative** _____ that I thought about them long after I left the theater.

SYNONYMS: stimulating, arousing, vexing, galling
ANTONYMS: dull, insipid, bland, unstimulating

18. recondite
(rek′ ən dīt)

(*adj.*) exceeding ordinary knowledge and understanding

The theories of relativity can seem _____ **recondite** _____, even for people who are well versed in the sciences.

SYNONYMS: esoteric, arcane, profound, abstruse
ANTONYMS: simple, uncomplicated

19. reprobate
(rep′ rə bāt)

(*n.*) a depraved, vicious, or unprincipled person, scoundrel; (*adj.*) wicked, corrupt, or unprincipled; (*v.*) to disapprove of, condemn

_____ **Reprobates** _____ are usually more charming, funny, or thrilling in fiction than they are in life.

SYNONYMS: (*n.*) scoundrel, blackguard; (*adj.*) immoral, corrupt
ANTONYMS: (*n.*) saint; (*adj.*) upright, virtuous, moral

20. sedentary
(sed′ ən ter ē)

(*adj.*) characterized by or calling for continued sitting; remaining in one place

She exchanged her _____ **sedentary** _____ job for a position as a swimming instructor.

SYNONYMS: seated, stationary, static
ANTONYMS: active, peripatetic, migratory

Completing the Sentence

From the words for this unit, choose the one that best completes each of the following sentences. Write the word in the space provided.

1. It will be helpful if you can state the _____ **gist** _____ of his arguments in a few sentences.

2. It is up to the courts to decide how far police authorities may go in making use of _____ **covert** _____ means of surveillance to catch criminals.

3. In view of the fact that I have been driving for many years without having a single accident, his advice on how to handle a car seemed entirely _____ **gratuitous** _____.

4. My opponent's last speech was filled with such wild charges, acrimonious language, and bitter _____ **invectives** _____ that I walked out of the room without even trying to reply.

5. His elegant appearance was matched by the _____ **debonair** _____ ease and polish of his manners.

6. Our meeting seemed at the time to be entirely _____ **fortuitous** _____, but I learned later that it was the result of a careful plan.

7. We have seen her accept victory with grace; now can she face defeat with _____ **equanimity** _____?

8. Think of the great advantages that will _____ **accrue** _____ for all of us if we can carry out a truly effective program to conserve and maintain our natural resources.

9. Anyone who _____ **procrastinates** _____ when the opportunity to make a very profitable deal presents itself is not going to be notably successful in the business world.

10. The kinds of books I enjoy reading range from light and airy comedies to _____ **recondite** _____ studies of social and philosophical problems.

11. As the British writer W. S. Maugham once observed, human nature is a(n) _____ **motley** _____ collection of strengths and weaknesses, foibles and follies.

12. Daily exercise is recommended particularly for people whose occupations are, for the most part, _____ **sedentary** _____.

13. Although their language was deliberately _____ **provocative** _____, I did not allow it to cause me to lose my self-control.

14. The _____ **munificent** _____ gift of the Mellon family made it possible to set up the National Gallery of Art in Washington, D.C.

15. No sooner had the incorrigible old _____ **reprobate** _____ gotten out of jail than he returned to the wicked ways that had landed him there in the first place.

16. _____ **Bedlam** _____ broke out in the meeting hall as the speaker tried vainly to be heard over the angry shouting of the audience.

17. If you resent being _____ **dunned** _____ by tradespeople, why not try paying your bills on time?

18. She is a leader who can command loyalty and instant obedience without resorting to abusive language, threats, or a(n) _____imperious_____ manner.

19. This research program is entirely devoted to developing a drug that will be _____efficacious_____ in the treatment of arthritis.

20. Next day, the instructor returned my theme with a number of comments, queries, and other _____annotations_____ penciled in the margin.

Synonyms

*Choose the word from this unit that is **the same** or **most nearly the same** in meaning as the **boldface** word or expression in the given phrase. Write the word on the line provided.*

1. pestering her for overdue payments — dunning

2. added **notes** to the text — annotations

3. the **pandemonium** of a battlefield — bedlam

4. the **core** of her complaint — gist

5. a **diverse** group of volunteers — motley

6. a film with **uncalled-for** scenes of violence — gratuitous

7. an angry **diatribe** — invective

8. another excuse to **stall** — procrastinate

9. an explanation too **esoteric** to follow — recondite

10. a **random** encounter that changed his life — fortuitous

11. a brief and **clandestine** meeting — covert

12. a **suave** greeting from our host — debonair

13. facing the challenge with **imperturbability** — equanimity

14. stimulating words that perked things up — provocative

15. a **scoundrel** in her business methods — reprobate

Antonyms

*Choose the word from this unit that is **most nearly opposite** in meaning to the **boldface** word or expression in the given phrase. Write the word on the line provided.*

16. as the level of snow **diminished** — accrued

17. a **humble** plea for order — imperious

18. tightfisted when it came to gift-giving — munificent

19. preferred being **active** after dinner — sedentary

20. worthless as a cold remedy — efficacious

Choosing the Right Word

Circle the **boldface** word that more satisfactorily completes each of the following sentences.

1. Instead of relying on facts and logic, she used all kinds of rhetorical tricks and slashing (**invective,** equanimity) to attack her opponent.

2. I am convinced that some substantial advantages will surely (**accrue,** procrastinate) to me if I complete my college education.

3. It is generally agreed that we urgently need more (**efficacious,** reprobate) methods of handling criminals, both for their own benefit and for that of the public.

4. What good will it do you to (**dun,** procrastinate) me so mercilessly when you know that I am flat broke?

5. This new book is a(n) (imperious, **provocative**) examination of our school system that may upset some of your most cherished ideas about higher education.

6. To bear evils with (invective, **equanimity**) doesn't mean that you should make no effort to correct them.

7. Scientists believe that everything in nature occurs in accordance with invariable laws and that nothing is truly (imperious, **fortuitous**).

8. The scholars who compiled the notes and (**annotations,** provocations) for my portable edition of Chaucer did a superb job of clarifying obscure or puzzling words and passages.

9. The proverb "Make haste slowly" endorses prudence—not (invective, **procrastination**).

10. The crass and (**reprobate,** fortuitous) conduct of those responsible for the scandal deserved public censure.

11. During the war, soldiers assigned to desk jobs were sometimes sarcastically called the "chairbound infantry" or the "(**sedentary,** recondite) commandos."

12. Things were already hectic in our tiny apartment, but when my sister arrived with two very excited dogs, the place was thrown into absolute (**bedlam,** annotation).

13. Instead of that highly involved and (**recondite,** debonair) discussion of the nation's energy needs, why don't you simply tell us what we can do to help solve the problem?

14. My sad story is that after working for three hours in the hot sun cleaning up the yard, I received the (imperious, **munificent**) sum of $1.75.

15. He tried to make it appear that he was speaking in a friendly spirit, but I detected the (recondite, **covert**) malice beneath his "harmless" remarks.

16. Only a genius could have converted such a (**motley,** gratuitous) group of individuals, drawn from all walks of life, into a disciplined and efficient organization.

17. His tone of voice was so (munificent, **imperious**) that I wasn't sure if he was asking me for a loan or demanding payment of tribute.

18. We appreciated the services he furnished (**gratuitously,** debonairly), but we soon came to see that it would have been cheaper to pay for a really professional job.

19. The difficult stage part called for an actress to gradually change from a morose introvert to a(n) (**debonair,** efficacious) charmer during the course of the play.

20. Although they claimed that their summary gave us the (bedlam, **gist**) of the resolution, the fact is that it omitted important details.

Vocabulary in Context

*Read the following passage, in which some of the words you have studied in this unit appear in **boldface** type. Then complete each statement given below the passage by circling the letter of the item that is **the same** or **almost the same** in meaning as the highlighted word.*

Mahalia's Music

(Line)

Together, Mahalia Jackson and gospel music moved through the twentieth century like one irresistible force. Both were formed in African-American churches and influenced by hymns and spirituals. Both rocked to the rhymes of old slave work-songs, and to the preacher's rhythmical call and the congregation's
(5) response. Jackson, born in 1911, was the daughter of a longshoreman who doubled as a barber and preacher, and she grew up in segregated New Orleans in the musical **bedlam** of waterfront streets. There, jazz and blues from phonographs and radios resounded through open windows, and marching bands played
(10) on their way back from burials. On weekends she sang hymns and spirituals at her Baptist church. But from the church down the street she heard a different music. "They had a beat," she remembered, "a powerful beat, a
(15) rhythm we held on to from slavery days, and their music was so strong . . . it used to bring the tears to my eyes." From this same **motley** fabric of music, gospel songs were being pieced together and joyously sung. They
(20) **accrued** in Jackson's memory, and, at the age of sixteen, she took them to Chicago.

Jackson at the Newport Jazz Festival, 1957

While working odd jobs, she began to make a name for herself by singing in African-American churches. Soon, her singing career took off, and she began touring the
(25) country. Always, she refused others' urging that she train her huge contralto voice to sing blues or to sing opera—to sing anything that was more commercial than the gospel she adored. She turned it all down with **equanimity**. Before she died in 1972, she had taken her **munificent** talent to Carnegie Hall, to large recording companies (with whom she could be **imperious** about money), and on tours of Europe and
(30) Asia. She almost always sang gospel, which she called "the songs of hope."

---

1. The meaning of **bedlam** (line 7) is
  a. echoes
  (c.) commotion
  b. lessons
  d. restfulness

2. Motley (line 17) most nearly means
  a. uniform
  c. expensive
  (b.) variegated
  d. inexpensive

3. Accrued (line 20) is best defined as
  a. slipped through
  c. played
  (b.) collected
  d. repeated

4. The meaning of **equanimity** (line 27) is
  (a.) tranquility
  c. regret
  b. pleasure
  d. thoughtlessness

5. Munificent (line 28) most nearly means
  (a.) bounteous
  c. overwhelming
  b. expensive
  d. well-trained

6. Imperious (line 29) most nearly means
  a. cagey
  (c.) domineering
  b. happy
  d. timid

Definitions

Note carefully the spelling, pronunciation, part(s) of speech, and definition(s) of each of the following words. Then write the word in the blank space(s) in the illustrative sentence(s) following. Finally, study the lists of synonyms and antonyms given at the end of each entry.

1. abstemious
(ab stē' mē əs)

(*adj.*) moderate, sparing (as in eating and drinking); characterized by abstinence and self-discipline

She came from a long line of quiet, thrifty, and _____**abstemious**_____ farming folk.

SYNONYMS: temperate, sober, moderate
ANTONYMS: indulgent, immoderate, intemperate

2. censurable
(sen' shər ə bəl)

(*adj.*) deserving of blame or correction

Because he was unaware of what he had done, we decided that his behavior was not _____**censurable**_____.

SYNONYMS: blameworthy, discreditable, reprehensible
ANTONYMS: commendable, laudable, meritorious

3. contingent
(kən tin' jənt)

(*adj.*) likely but not certain to happen, possible; dependent on uncertain events or conditions; happening by chance; (*n.*) a representative group forming part of a larger body

_____**Contingent**_____ on our parents' approval, we plan to take a trip through Alaska next summer.

The meeting was delayed due to the late arrival of the California _____**contingent**_____.

SYNONYMS: (*adj.*) conditional, dependent; (*n.*) a detachment
ANTONYMS: (*adj.*) independent of, unconnected with, certain

4. corroborate
(kə räb' ə rāt)

(*v.*) to confirm, make more certain, bolster, substantiate, verify

He could tell the court where I was and for how long, but he still needed a witness to _____**corroborate**_____ his statements.

ANTONYMS: (*adj.*) refute, contradict, undermine, discredit

5. denizen
(den' ə zən)

(*n.*) an inhabitant, resident; one who frequents a place

A lover of marine life, she knew all the names of the scaly _____**denizens**_____ of our lake.

SYNONYMS: resident, dweller, habitué
ANTONYMS: alien, outsider, stranger, foreigner

6. discursive
(dis kər' siv)

(*adj.*) passing aimlessly from one place or subject to another, rambling, roving, nomadic

Within the _____**discursive**_____ account of his life, there was a fairly complete history of the whole village.

SYNONYMS: digressive, diffuse, wandering, episodic
ANTONYMS: short and to the point, succinct

7. disseminate
(di sem′ ə nāt)

(*v.*) to scatter or spread widely

I decided that it was a bad idea to use my position in order to _____ disseminate _____ my personal views.

SYNONYMS: disperse, publicize, broadcast, circulate
ANTONYMS: bring together, concentrate, muster, conceal, hide

8. dowdy
(daủ′ dē)

(*adj.*) poorly dressed, shabby; lacking smartness and good taste

The actor wore _____ dowdy _____ clothing and sunglasses so that no one would recognize him.

SYNONYMS: frumpy, tacky, frowsy, drab
ANTONYMS: chic, stylish, elegant, fashionable

9. florid
(flär′ id)

(*adj.*) highly colored, reddish; excessively ornate, showy

The _____ florid _____ style of architecture in the old part of town was a welcome change from the grim, newer blocks we had seen.

SYNONYMS: flushed, ruddy, flowery, frilly, flamboyant
ANTONYMS: pale, ashen, pallid, sallow, austere, stark

10. foist
(foist)

(*v.*) to impose by fraud; to pass off as worthy or genuine; to bring about by stealth, dishonesty, or coercion

During the 19th century the unscrupulous Jay Gould _____ foisted _____ thousands of worthless railroad shares on an unsuspecting public.

SYNONYMS: pass off, palm off, fob off

11. gauche
(gōsh)

(*adj.*) awkward, lacking in social graces, tactless, clumsy

Though he was sincere when he thanked his guest for having stayed an extra week, his comment was considered _____ gauche _____.

SYNONYMS: inept, uncouth, maladroit
ANTONYMS: adroit, tactful, diplomatic, politic

12. heresy
(her′ ə sē)

(*n.*) an opinion different from accepted belief; the denial of an idea that is generally held sacred

Saving money to accumulate interest seems to be a form of _____ heresy _____ in these days of instant credit.

SYNONYMS: unorthodox belief, heterodoxy
ANTONYM: orthodoxy

13. inculcate
(in′ kəl kāt)

(*v.*) to impress on the mind by repetition, teach persistently and earnestly

It is important to _____ inculcate _____ a healthy respect for authority into army recruits.

SYNONYMS: instill, implant, infuse, ingrain, imbue
ANTONYMS: efface, extirpate, root out

14. palpable
(pal′ pə bəl)

(*adj.*) capable of being touched or felt; easily seen, heard, or recognized

The excitement in the room was almost _____**palpable**_____ .

SYNONYMS: tangible, plain, obvious, manifest
ANTONYMS: intangible, insubstantial, incorporeal

15. perceptive
(pər sep′ tiv)

(*adj.*) having sympathetic insight or understanding, capable of keen appreciation

His _____**perceptive**_____ eye went at once through the roomful of noisy children to the child who was most ill at ease.

SYNONYMS: insightful, discerning, observant
ANTONYMS: dense, thick, obtuse, dim-witted

16. pernicious
(per nish′ əs)

(*adj.*) extremely harmful; deadly, fatal

Night air was once thought to have a _____**pernicious**_____ effect on infants who were in poor health.

SYNONYMS: injurious, deleterious, baleful, noxious
ANTONYMS: harmless, innocuous, salutary, salubrious

17. salient
(sāl′ yənt)

(*adj.*) leaping, jumping, or springing forth; prominent, standing out, conspicuous; (*n.*) a projection or bulge, a land form that projects upward or outward

I think the most _____**salient**_____ feature of the new plan is its similarity to the old plan.

Our forces occupied a _____**salient**_____ that was extremely vulnerable to attack.

SYNONYMS: (*adj.*) striking, notable, protrusive, obvious
ANTONYMS: (*adj.*) inconspicuous, recessive

18. satiate
(*v.*, sā′ shē āt;
adj., sā′ shē it)

(*v.*) to satisfy completely; to fill to excess; (*adj.*) full, satisfied

Nothing will _____**satiate**_____ my hunger.

The _____**satiate**_____ brown bear had a good sleep after raiding the honey-laden beehives.

SYNONYMS: (*v.*) gratify, cloy, surfeit, gorge
ANTONYMS: (*v.*) starve, deprive entirely of

19. sear
(sir)

(*v.*) to make or become dry and withered; to char or scorch the surface of; to harden or make unfeeling; to parch, dessicate, singe

We wanted to serve grilled vegetables, but I _____**seared**_____ them, and they tasted like leather.

20. specious
(spē′ shəs)

(*adj.*) deceptive, apparently good or valid but lacking real merit

Though her resume looked very impressive, her claims of vast experience in the field were _____**specious**_____ .

SYNONYMS: deceptively plausible, sophistic, casuistic
ANTONYMS: valid, sound, solid, genuine

Completing the Sentence

From the words for this unit, choose the one that best completes each of the following sentences. Write the word in the space provided.

1. Is there any need for me to describe at length the _____**pernicious**_____ effects of smoking?

2. Though this may not be the smartest-looking blouse I own, I thought to myself, it certainly doesn't make me look _____**dowdy**_____!

3. A(n) _____**salient**_____ characteristic of every great athlete is the ability to perform at maximum efficiency when under extreme pressure.

4. The old fellow did indeed look like a typical _____**denizen**_____ of the racetrack, as described in Damon Runyon's famous stories.

5. No honest mechanic will try to _____**foist**_____ inferior replacement parts on his customers.

6. If I had the time, I could point out many flaws in the _____**specious**_____ arguments you find so impressive.

7. When I referred to her favorite singer as an "untalented, overpaid, and conceited lout," she looked at me in shock, as though I had been guilty of _____**heresy**_____.

8. Unless you can produce witnesses to _____**corroborate**_____ your claim that you stopped at the red light, the mere assertion will have little or no effect on the jury.

9. Psychologists tell us that the years of early childhood are the best time to _____**inculcate**_____ basic concepts of right and wrong.

10. The stubborn refusal to give me a chance to compete for the scholarship on the same basis as everyone else is a(n) _____**palpable**_____ injustice to the whole idea of fair play.

11. Among all those pale and sallow people, her highly _____**florid**_____ complexion stood out like a beacon.

12. I don't like to criticize your behavior, but I feel obliged to tell you that your discourtesy to that confused tourist was highly _____**censurable**_____.

13. After the long summer vacation, I was _____**satiated**_____ with loafing and eager to return to school!

14. The purpose of this program is to _____**disseminate**_____ throughout the community information about job-training opportunities for young people.

15. It is hard to believe that people coming from such a refined social milieu could be so _____**gauche**_____ and boorish in their behavior.

16. His talk on world affairs was so disorganized and _____**discursive**_____ that it left us more confused than ever.

17. Eudora Welty is considered one of the most _____**perceptive**_____ and insightful American writers of her time.

18. Her good health in old age is due in large part to the _____ abstemious _____ habits of her younger years.

19. Since we wished our group to have some say in the town council's final decision, we sent a small _____ contingent _____ of our most articulate and convincing speakers to the hearings.

20. If you wish to seal in the juices and bring out the flavor of your pot roast, _____ sear _____ it briefly in a hot pan before you put it in the oven.

Synonyms

*Choose the word from this unit that is **the same** or **most nearly the same** in meaning as the **boldface** word or expression in the given phrase. Write the word on the line provided.*

1. a long and **digressive** novel   discursive

2. **tacky** window decorations   dowdy

3. an impulsive and **awkward** embrace   gauche

4. to **singe** the marshmallows over a campfire   sear

5. **substantiate** an old rumor   corroborate

6. a **flowery** introduction   florid

7. a **tangible** change in the mood of the crowd   palpable

8. few but **discerning** remarks   perceptive

9. **gratify** the appetite for gossip   satiate

10. an **habitué** of the public library   denizen

11. **broadcast** the child's baby pictures   disseminate

12. **implant** a strong dislike   inculcate

13. ignored the **injurious** rumors   pernicious

14. **palm off** fake diamonds   foist

15. a **temperate** use of such words   abstemious

Antonyms

*Choose the word from this unit that is **most nearly opposite** in meaning to the **boldface** word or expression in the given phrase. Write the word on the line provided.*

16. judged the actions as **commendable**   censurable

17. a steadfast commitment to **orthodoxy**   heresy

18. an **inconspicuous** feature   salient

19. payment **independent of** need   contingent on

20. **genuine** grounds for complaint   specious

Choosing the Right Word

*Circle the **boldface** word that more satisfactorily completes each of the following sentences.*

1. In a series of (**searing,** contingent) attacks now known as the *Philippics,* Cicero launched his entire battery of political invective against the hapless Mark Anthony.

2. The most tragic aspect of a forest fire is its destructive effects on the innumerable plant and animal (**denizens,** heresies) of that environment.

3. Some English queens were strikingly elegant and imposing figures; others were somewhat (specious, **dowdy**) and unprepossessing.

4. Modern nutritionists emphasize that there is a(n) (palpable, **abstemious**) difference between "eating to live" and "living to eat."

5. Let's not allow them to (**foist,** satiate) on us ideas and programs that have been proved failures in other countries!

6. The study of history teaches us that many ideas regarded as (**heresies,** disseminations) by one generation are accepted as sound and orthodox by the next.

7. No doubt his efforts to advance his own interests were (**censurable,** florid), but let's try to keep a sense of proportion and not condemn him too much.

8. Before we start out to (**inculcate,** foist) certain principles in our young people, let's be very sure that these principles are truly desirable for them and their society.

9. Her (perceptive, **florid**) writing style, abounding in adjectives and fancy metaphors, is far from suitable for factual newspaper stories.

10. Although the Declaration of Independence was framed only to justify a revolution in the British colonies in North America, its ideas and ideals have been (**disseminated,** seared) throughout the world.

11. We are most likely to fall victim to (discursive, **specious**) reasoning when we have an emotional desire to believe what we are being told.

12. All the available evidence (**corroborates,** foists) my theory that the theft was planned by someone familiar with the layout of the house.

13. Children are often remarkably (discursive, **perceptive**) in understanding how adults feel about them.

14. Out of all the endless flow of dull verbiage in that long lecture, we could recognize only two or three (gauche, **salient**) points.

15. As the Scottish poet Robert Burns aptly suggests, even the best laid plans are often entirely (palpable, **contingent**) on events over which we have no earthly control.

16. Although the essays are highly (**discursive,** dowdy), covering a wide range of topics, they are written with such clarity and grace that they are easy to follow.

17. She was so (palpable, **abstemious**) that she extended her self-control even to her beloved books, and read them no more than an hour each day.

18. Though I rather like the better TV game shows, I find that after a certain point, I'm (**satiated,** inculcated) and ready for more substantial fare.

19. He thought he was being witty and charming, but I regard his conduct at the party as altogether (abstemious, **gauche**).

20. The more we studied the drug problem, the more we became aware of its (florid, **pernicious**) influence on the American people today.

*Read the following passage, in which some of the words you have studied in this unit appear in **boldface** type. Then complete each statement given below the passage by circling the letter of the item that is **the same** or **almost the same** in meaning as the highlighted word.*

War at Home

(Line)

We often hear that the United States was the only great nation never to be invaded during the Second World War (1939–1945). All the same, the war transformed American life on the Home Front. Once rationing limited the amount of meat, sugar, coffee, butter, and canned goods they could buy each month, families often ate **abstemious** meals. Blue and red ration coupons, **disseminated** to households, had (5) to be counted into grocers' hands along with the money for a given product. If there were no coupons, the families did not receive goods until the next month. In addition, ships transporting foreign goods like coffee and sugar were often turned over to the

military. The tin in tin cans was made into weapons. Even shoes were rationed, as (10) leather was needed for military gear.

On the roads gas, too, was rationed. No new cars were made, and the family car became **dowdy**. Ordinary motorists could buy between three and five gallons a week, (15) **contingent** on supplies. Commuters could buy slightly more, and only farmers, the police, the clergy, and some politicians could buy as much gasoline as they wanted. Trains were crammed full of commuters, (20) while aging cars rested at home.

It is also somewhat **specious** to say that the U.S. was never bombed or invaded. In 1942 Nazi Germany landed four agents on

School boy using ration coupons, 1943

Long Island and four more on the Florida coast. Trained and equipped to blow up (25) factories, these **gauche** invaders were picked up in no time, secretly tried, and punished. Wartime secrecy kept their story quiet, just as it silenced the story of the Japanese plane that failed to set fire to West Coast forests and the fleet of balloon-borne time bombs with which the Japanese started some random fires. And so, though no battles were fought on American soil during WWII, rationing and the threat of (30) invasion forever changed the American perspective of the world beyond its shores.

---

1. The meaning of **abstemious** (line 5) is
  a. amazing   c. temperate
  b. huge   d. bizarre

2. Disseminated (line 5) most nearly means
  a. sold   c. circulated
  b. advertised   d. e-mailed

3. Dowdy (line 14) is best defined as
  a. valuable   c. crowded
  b. shabby   d. beloved

4. The meaning of **contingent** (line 16) is
  a. conditional   c. regardless of
  b. cheating   d. imposing

5. Specious (line 22) most nearly means
  a. deceptive   c. bizarre
  b. ridiculous   d. fussy

6. Gauche (line 26) is best defined as
  a. sneaky   c. frightened
  b. dangerous   d. maladroit

Definitions

Note carefully the spelling, pronunciation, part(s) of speech, and definition(s) of each of the following words. Then write the word in the blank space(s) in the illustrative sentence(s) following. Finally, study the lists of synonyms and antonyms given at the end of each entry.

1. absolve
(ab zälv')

(*v.*) to clear from blame, responsibility, or guilt

They assumed that their alibi would _____**absolve**_____ them of suspicion.

SYNONYMS: acquit, exonerate, vindicate, excuse, pardon
ANTONYMS: condemn, convict, incriminate, inculpate

2. caricature
(kar' i kə chür)

(*n.*) a representation (especially a drawing) in which the subject's characteristic features are deliberately exaggerated; (*v.*) to present someone or something in a deliberately distorted way

What began as a hasty newspaper _____**caricature**_____ soon turned up on coffee mugs, T-shirts, and sweatshirts.

The satiric television program _____**caricatured**_____ the movie star and made him seem more clumsy than he really was.

SYNONYMS: (*n.*) cartoon, burlesque, parody, lampoon

3. clangor
(klang' ər)

(*n.*) a loud ringing sound; (*v.*) to make a loud ringing noise

For more than a century, American grade schools summoned children to school with the _____**clangor**_____ of a bell.

SYNONYMS: (*n.*) din, clamor, uproar
ANTONYMS: (*n.*) silence, stillness, peace and quiet

4. contiguous
(kən tig' yü əs)

(*adj.*) side by side, touching; near; adjacent in time

Trouble arose over who should control the weeds and bushes that rioted in the lot _____**contiguous**_____ to ours.

SYNONYMS: adjoining, abutting, next door to
ANTONYMS: detached, apart, distant, remote

5. cupidity
(kyü pid' ə tē)

(*n.*) an eager desire for something; greed

You say that these catalogue prices show the quality of the goods, but I say they show the seller's _____**cupidity**_____.

SYNONYMS: avarice, rapacity, craving, lust
ANTONYMS: generosity, contentment, satiation, gratification

6. deleterious
(del ə tir' ē əs)

(*adj.*) harmful, injurious

Wishing can give zest and purpose to anyone's life, but wishful thinking can have a _____**deleterious**_____ effect.

SYNONYMS: detrimental, destructive, pernicious, damaging
ANTONYMS: helpful, beneficial, harmless, innocuous

7. enhance
(en hans')

(v.) to raise to a higher degree; to increase the value or desirability of

She sanded and varnished the old table in order to _____ enhance _____ its appearance and value.

SYNONYMS: improve, magnify, heighten, elevate
ANTONYMS: diminish, reduce, lessen, degrade

8. enthrall
(en thrôl')

(v.) to captivate, charm, hold spellbound; to enslave; to imprison

All the critics were _____ enthralled _____ by the performance and wrote rave reviews.

SYNONYMS: fascinate, enchant, attract, bewitch
ANTONYMS: bore to tears, repel, put someone off

9. extenuate
(ek sten' yü āt)

(v.) to lessen the seriousness or magnitude of an offense by making partial excuses

Because hunger caused the novel's young hero to steal the bread, the jurors believed that the crime had been committed under _____ extenuating _____ circumstances.

SYNONYMS: moderate, mitigate, diminish, downplay
ANTONYMS: intensify, aggravate, worsen, exacerbate

10. implicit
(im plis' it)

(adj.) implied or understood though unexpressed; without doubts or reservations, unquestioning; potentially contained in

Though she never said so, it was _____ implicit _____ that she did not like to have long conversations before her morning coffee.

SYNONYMS: inferred, tacit, unspoken, unconditional
ANTONYMS: explicit, expressed, stated, revealed

11. incisive
(in sī' siv)

(adj.) sharp, keen, penetrating (with a suggestion of decisiveness and effectiveness)

I am truly thankful for your _____ incisive _____ remarks about my report.

SYNONYMS: acute, cutting, perceptive, trenchant

12. ostentatious
(äs ten tā' shəs)

(adj.) marked by conspicuous or pretentious display, showy

The inside of the restaurant was so _____ ostentatious _____ that the meager meal, when it came, seemed only a hasty afterthought.

SYNONYMS: flashy, overdone, affected, flamboyant
ANTONYMS: modest, plain, simple, demure, retiring

13. paragon
(par' ə gän)

(n.) a model of excellence or perfection

I may not be a _____ paragon _____ of scholarship, but I do try my best.

SYNONYMS: exemplar, ideal, paradigm, model, good example

14. paraphrase
(par′ ə frāz)

(*v.*) to restate in other words; (*n.*) a statement that presents a given idea in new language

You can _____**paraphrase**_____ "The Gettysburg Address," but in doing so you will diminish its force.

SYNONYMS: (*v.*) reword, rephrase; (*n.*) a rendition, version
ANTONYMS: (*v.*) repeat verbatim, duplicate, quote

15. politic
(päl′ ə tik)

(*adj.*) prudent, shrewdly conceived and developed; artful, expedient

In your angry state I think it would be _____**politic**_____ to say nothing, at least until you have calmed down.

SYNONYMS: tactful, diplomatic, judicious, circumspect
ANTONYMS: unwise, injudicious, imprudent, rash

16. prosaic
(prō zā′ ik)

(*adj.*) dull, lacking in distinction and originality; matter-of-fact, straightforward; characteristic of prose, not poetic

I remember his singing voice as being on key and clear but also _____**prosaic**_____.

SYNONYMS: commonplace, humdrum, literal, pedestrian
ANTONYMS: remarkable, distinctive, poetic, inspired

17. redundant
(ri dən′ dənt)

(*adj.*) extra, excess, more than is needed; wordy, repetitive; profuse, lush

Some _____**redundant**_____ expressions, such as "hollow tubing," are considered an acceptable part of the English language.

SYNONYMS: unnecessary, superfluous, verbose, prolix
ANTONYMS: succinct, terse, laconic, scarce, inadequate

18. sanctimonious
(saŋk tə mō′ nē əs)

(*adj.*) making a show of virtue or righteousness; hypocritically moralistic or pious, self-righteous, canting, holier-than-thou

Cautionary tales that take on a _____**sanctimonious**_____ tone often achieve the opposite of the desired result.

ANTONYMS: heartfelt, sincere, humble

19. scintillating
(sin′ tə lāt iŋ)

(*adj., part.*) sparkling, twinkling, exceptionally brilliant (applied to mental or personal qualities)

She was known for her _____**scintillating**_____ conversation.

SYNONYMS: stimulating, lively, glittering, flashing
ANTONYMS: dull, boring, insipid, flat, tame, vapid

20. winsome
(win′ səm)

(*adj.*) charming, attractive, pleasing (often suggesting a childlike charm and innocence)

When my little brother wanted something badly, he became as _____**winsome**_____ as a puppy.

SYNONYMS: winning, engaging, delightful, prepossessing
ANTONYMS: unattractive, unappealing, repulsive

Completing the Sentence

From the words for this unit, choose the one that best completes each of the following sentences. Write the word in the space provided.

1. Her new hairstyle greatly _____ **enhances** _____ her appearance.

2. The jury may have found him not guilty, but the "court of public opinion" will never _____ **absolve** _____ him of responsibility for the crime.

3. Detective stories seem to _____ **enthrall** _____ her to such a degree that she reads virtually nothing else.

4. Until he rose to speak, the meeting had been dull, but he immediately enlivened it with his _____ **scintillating** _____ wit.

5. We resented his _____ **sanctimonious** _____ self-assurance that he was morally superior to everyone else.

6. She did her work so quietly that it took us time to realize that she was a veritable _____ **paragon** _____ of efficiency and diligence.

7. His highly technical discussion will have to be _____ **paraphrased** _____ if it is to be understood by most readers.

8. How can anyone be so foolish as to develop a smoking habit when it has been proven that cigarettes are _____ **deleterious** _____ to health?

9. Since we had been told the new TV series was original and witty, we were disappointed by the obvious and _____ **prosaic** _____ situation comedy that unfolded on our screen.

10. The fact that he had hungry children at home does not justify what he did, but it does _____ **extenuate** _____ his crime.

11. With that one _____ **incisive** _____ comment, she brought an end to all the aimless talk and directed our attention to the real problem facing us.

12. "Evening dress is far too _____ **ostentatious** _____ for such an informal occasion," I thought to myself as I tried to decide what to wear that night.

13. In most contracts there are _____ **implicit** _____ duties and obligations that must be fulfilled even though they aren't expressed in so many words.

14. There are some situations in life when it is _____ **politic** _____ to remain quiet and wait for a better opportunity to assert yourself.

15. To characterize the literary style of Edgar Allan Poe as "unique and one of a kind" is certainly _____ **redundant** _____.

16. The _____ **clangor** _____ of the fire bells as they echoed through the night filled our hearts with terror.

17. His long nose and prominent teeth give the candidate the kind of face that cartoonists love to _____ **caricature** _____.

18. Marie's engaging personality and charming manner make her quite ____winsome____.

19. Since the gym is ____contiguous____ to the library, it is easy for me to shift from academic to athletic activities.

20. His normal desire for financial security was eventually distorted into a boundless ____cupidity____.

Synonyms

*Choose the word from this unit that is **the same** or **most nearly the same** in meaning as the **boldface** word or expression in the given phrase. Write the word on the line provided.*

1. a **din** of cowbells from the bleachers — clangor

2. to **improve** the sound of the chorus — enhance

3. an **exemplar** of team spirit — paragon

4. a **trenchant** report — incisive

5. a **lively** play of wit — scintillating

6. the **commonplace** routines of housework — prosaic

7. a **parody** of his behavior — caricature

8. a book with the power to **enchant** — enthrall

9. a **hypocritical** accusation — sanctimonious

10. an **engaging** smile — winsome

11. a **flashy** new car — ostentatious

12. a **detrimental** effect on the harvest — deleterious

13. an **unspoken** but lifelong loyalty — implicit

14. a **judicious** decision — politic

15. bought lots that were **adjoining** — contiguous

Antonyms

*Choose the word from this unit that is **most nearly opposite** in meaning to the **boldface** word or expression in the given phrase. Write the word on the line provided.*

16. never exhibited **generosity** — cupidity

17. evidence to **incriminate** — absolve

18. charges **aggravated** by circumstances — extenuated

19. issuing **succinct** instructions — redundant

20. to **quote** her memorable words — paraphrase

Choosing the Right Word

Circle the **boldface** word that more satisfactorily completes each of the following sentences.

1. What we do now to remedy the evils in our society will determine whether or not we are to be (**absolved,** paraphrased) of blame for the injustices of the past.

2. Is it logical to conclude that because this substance has had a (**prosaic,** **deleterious**) effect on some test animals, it is not at all safe for human consumption?

3. When he demanded that I immediately "return back" the money I owed him, I found him not merely unpleasant but (**redundant,** winsome).

4. I will try to tell the story in a balanced way, without either exaggerating or (**extenuating,** scintillating) his responsibility for those sad events.

5. It is hardly (**politic,** clangorous) for someone who hopes to win a popularity contest to go about making such brutally frank remarks.

6. Words about "tolerance" are empty and (**sanctimonious,** contiguous) when they come from one who has shown no concern about civil liberties.

7. As long as we are (**enthralled,** extenuated) by the idea that it is possible to get something for nothing, we will not be able to come up with a sound economic program.

8. "In seeking to discredit me," I replied, "my opponent has deliberately (**caricatured,** paraphrased) my ideas, making them seem simplistic and unrealistic."

9. She delivered her lines with such artistry and verve that she made the rather commonplace dialogue seem (**scintillating,** deleterious).

10. In the Lincoln-Douglas debates, Lincoln asked a few (**incisive,** prosaic) questions that showed up the fatal weaknesses in his opponent's position.

11. The aspiring salesperson stood in front of the mirror for hours, practicing a (**winsome,** redundant) smile.

12. A fresh coat of paint and some attention to the lawn would greatly (enhance, **absolve**) the appearance of our bungalow.

13. He was the type of officer who expected (ostentatious, **implicit**) obedience from the troops he commanded. When he gave an order, he assumed it would be carried out.

14. She tried to convince me that the proposed advertisement would be "dynamic" and a "real eye-catcher," but I found it utterly (politic, **prosaic**).

15. I realized I was being kept awake not by the (paragon, **clangor**) of the city traffic but by a gnawing fear that I had done the wrong thing.

16. The Gettysburg Address is so concise, so lucid, and so beautiful, that it would be folly to attempt to (**paraphrase,** enthrall) it.

17. My parents set up my older brother as such a (caricature, **paragon**) that I despaired of ever being able to follow in his footsteps.

18. Isn't it rather (**ostentatious,** redundant) to wear a Phi Beta Kappa key on a chain around your neck?

19. We wanted to find a house that was near that of my parents, but not (**contiguous,** prosaic) to it.

20. The rumors of "easy money" and "lush profits" to be made in the stock market aroused the (clangor, **cupidity**) of many small investors.

Read the following passage, in which some of the words you have studied in this unit appear in **boldface** type. Then complete each statement given below the passage by circling the letter of the item that is **the same** or **almost the same** in meaning as the highlighted word.

Truffles

(Line)

The truffle, considered by gourmets to be a **paragon** among foods, grows underground but cannot be planted, is hunted by dogs and fed to royalty, costs a small fortune, and looks like a battered golf ball. No less famous for its mystery than for its flavor, the truffle has **enthralled**
(5)   cooks and growers of food since 1800 B.C. Because it reproduces by spores that cannot be seen by the naked eye, people once thought that truffles only grew in soil struck by
(10)   lightning. Today experts tell a less **ostentatious** story; they say that white truffles can be found near small oak trees in chalky soil in northern Italy and black ones in the South of
(15)   France in similar patches of oaks.

Man and pet harvesting truffles in France

Like a mushroom, the truffle is a fungus—but one that grows under the ground, sometimes inches deep. Unlike a carrot or radish, it
(20)   sends up no **winsome** little plume of green leaves to announce its location. Only its scent gives the truffle away, and that scent is much too faint for a human to perceive. Pigs have long been said to lead hunters to the treasure —but pigs will in fact eat the truffles they find. Trained dogs are content to track them, then leave them for the hunter
(25)   to collect.

Though many parts of the world boast of local truffles, cooks find most too mundane to eat, let alone hunt. By contrast, the French black truffle has been called "the black diamond." American chefs cook it in sauces made with eggs, cream, and cheese, and sometimes add it to pastries. The white they cut in little
(30)   pieces and sprinkle on finished dishes to **enhance** them. One experienced diner, when asked how he preferred his truffles, gave an **incisive** reply: "In great quantity."

1. The meaning of **paragon** (line 1) is
   a. most fattening   c. prettiest
   b. most nutritious   d. ideal

2. Enthralled (line 4) most nearly means
   a. repulsed   c. defeated
   b. bewitched   d. distressed

3. Ostentatious (line 11) is best defined as
   a. hackneyed   c. frightening
   b. flamboyant   d. foolish

4. The meaning of **winsome** (line 20) is
   a. waving   c. victorious
   b. tangled   d. delightful

5. Enhance (line 30) most nearly means
   a. cover   c. disguise
   b. improve   d. cool

6. Incisive (line 31) is best defined as
   a. unpleasant   c. trenchant
   b. puzzling   d. greedy

REVIEW UNITS 10–12

Visit us at www.sadlier-oxford.com
for interactive puzzles and games.

Vocabulary for Comprehension

*Read the following passage, in which some of the words you have studied in Units 10–12 appear in **boldface** type. Then answer questions 1–11 on page 139 on the basis of what is <u>stated</u> or <u>implied</u> in the passage and in the introductory statement.*

Early maps of the Americas were based on the memories of explorers and therefore full of errors, as this passage shows.

(Line)

Modern maps record **palpable** scientific measurements, but in the Middle Ages maps drew upon the excited and imprecise recollections of

(5) hired explorers. Employed to aggrandize a nation's wealth by finding new colonies and better trade routes to the riches of India, these explorers were driven more by their

(10) clients' **cupidity** than by a thirst for scientific knowledge. Thus, they came to some **gratuitous** assumptions and made some big mistakes.

Most commonly, explorers

(15) misjudged the size and shape of North and South America while searching the seas for Cathay. So intent was Columbus on reaching the East that he thought that Cuba, when

(20) he saw it, was actually Japan and that the coast of Central America was the shore of southern Asia. In 1525 Giovanni da Verrazano, sailing south of New England, "discovered"

(25) and named the "Sea of Verrazano," which cartographers dutifully included on their maps for the next hundred years. This grand waterway led, said Verrazano, to India and

(30) China; more likely it was the wet doorstep to North Carolina.

Eventually, rough sizes and shapes for North and South America—

caricatures, really—were determined.

(35) But the ocean beyond them continued to be overlooked by European eyes fastened on Asia; for years the Pacific was mapped as a narrow strait between North America and Japan.

(40) Harder to explain is why California changed from being part of the mainland on some maps to an island on others.

Juan Ponce de León, discovering

(45) Florida in 1513, reported that it, too, was an island (this was clearly not **corroborated** by the facts). But he didn't call it "land of flowers" (*flores* in Spanish), as some current **denizens**

(50) of the state might suppose. He found it on Easter, which the Spaniards called Pascua Florida for the flowers displayed in their churches. Ponce was honoring Easter.

(55) Very old place names can also be confusing. North and South Carolina, once a single British colony, pay tribute to no one named Caroline. Instead, they honor King Charles I of

(60) England, who set up the colony and whose name in Latin was Carolus.

1. Palpable (line 1) most nearly means
- a. tangible
- b. questionable
- c. controversial
- d. esoteric
- e. accurate

2. Which of the following best states the main idea of the first paragraph (lines 1–13)?
- a. The greed of the early explorers led them to take some frightening risks.
- b. Modern science has mastered the art of map-making.
- c. Early explorers soon succeeded in finding trade routes to India.
- d. Early maps reflected explorers' inaccurate impressions and erroneous assumptions.
- e. The early explorers' most important goal was to found new colonies.

3. The meaning of **cupidity** (line 10) is
- a. thrift
- b. affection
- c. repentance
- d. avarice
- e. stupidity

4. Gratuitous (line 12) is best defined as
- a. peculiar
- b. surprising
- c. predictable
- d. unwarranted
- e. innovative

5. In paragraph 2 (lines 14–31), the author cites the examples of Columbus and Verrazano in order to
- a. show how these explorers failed to reach China, India, and Japan
- b. compare and contrast the achievements of these explorers
- c. emphasize that Verrazano was influenced by the mistakes of Columbus
- d. single out these two explorers as the most inspiring leaders of their time
- e. show how explorers commonly misjudged the size and shape of North and South America

6. In lines 28–31, the sharp contrast the writer draws results in which of the following?
- a. anticlimax
- b. symbolism
- c. foreshadowing
- d. satire
- e. restatement

7. According to paragraph 3 (lines 32–43), early maps of California
- a. exaggerated its size
- b. misspelled its name
- c. showed it sometimes as part of the mainland and sometimes as an island
- d. placed it in the center of North America
- e. attributed its discover to Juan Ponce de León

8. Corroborated (line 47) most nearly means
- a. contradicted
- b. refuted
- c. substantiated
- d. reported
- e. described

9. You can infer from paragraph 4 (lines 44–54) that which of the following played a role in the naming of Florida?
- a. geographic location
- b. the wishes of the King of Spain
- c. religious customs
- d. the appearance of the region's inhabitants
- e. trade

10. Denizens (line 49) is best defined as
- a. critics
- b. tourists
- c. employees
- d. legislators
- e. inhabitants

11. Which of the following best describes the writer's tone in the passage?
- a. skeptical
- b. pessimistic
- c. nostalgic
- d. admiring
- e. factual

In the sentence "Employed to aggrandize a nation's wealth by finding new colonies and better trade routes to the riches of India, these explorers were driven more by their clients' cupidity than by a thirst for scientific knowledge" (lines 5–11 on page 138), the modifying phrase "Employed . . . riches of India" describes "explorers." However, if the author had placed the modifying phrase at the end of the sentence, it would have illogically described "scientific knowledge." A modifying phrase or clause that is placed too far away from the word it sensibly modifies is called a **misplaced modifier**.

Because a misplaced modifier is incorrectly placed, it does not describe the word for which it is logically intended. Instead, it modifies another word—sometimes with comical results. To correct a misplaced modifier, move it as close as possible to the word it is meant to modify, or reword the sentence.

On the lines provided, rewrite each of the following sentences, correcting misplaced modifiers. Write "correct" if the sentence is correct.

Answers may vary; sample answers given.

1. Many explorers were employed to increase a nation's wealth of North and South America.
Many explorers of North and South America were employed to increase a nation's wealth

2. Usually greedy and often reckless, the ships carried explorers to the New World.
The ships carried explorers, who were usually greedy and often reckless, to the New World.

3. Named the "Sea of Verrazano," mapmakers recorded a body of water off the coast of North Carolina.
Mapmakers recorded a body of water named the "Sea of Verrazano" off the coast of North Carolina.

4. Sailing off the coast of Central America, Columbus believed he had glimpsed the shore of southern Asia.
correct

5. As a child in Florida, my father told me tales about Ponce de León.
When I was a child in Florida, my father told me tales of Ponce de León.

6. Florida was named in honor of the flowers displayed in Spanish churches discovered on Easter.
Discovered on Easter, Florida was named in honor of the flowers displayed in Spanish churches.

7. The names of North and South Carolina honor King Charles I of England, once a single British colony.
The names of North and South Carolina, once a single British colony, honor King Charles I of England.

Two-Word Completions

Circle the pair of words that best complete the meaning of each of the following passages.

See pages T38–T48 for explanations of answers.

1. Office workers usually lead relatively _____ lives between nine and five. For that reason, many a "desk jockey" finds a weekly trip to the gym a(n) _____ way to keep fit.

a. covert . . . gratuitous
b. ostentatious . . . provocative
c. sedentary . . . efficacious
d. prosaic . . . pernicious

2. "The flamboyant plumage of the male of the species has always struck me as overly _____," the ornithologist observed. "In contrast, the female looks so drab and _____ in her somber browns and grays."

a. debonair . . . censurable
b. specious . . . gauche
c. prosaic . . . scintillating
d. ostentatious . . . dowdy

3. In a series of _____ attacks, chock-full of the most withering political _____, the famous orator Demosthenes fulminated against King Philip of Macedon's nefarious efforts to curtail Greek rights and liberties.

a. scintillating . . . heresies
b. gratuitous . . . clangor
c. searing . . . invective
d. motley . . . annotations

4. Most of the adults seemed to find Kal's Kiddie Karnival a bit of a bore, but their children were _____. Though the grown-ups had clearly had enough halfway through the performance, the youngsters' appetites for the kind of fare that Kal served up were by no means _____ when the show was over.

a. enhanced . . . accentuated
b. enthralled . . . satiated
c. seared . . . absolved
d. exuded . . . extenuated

5. Florida Fats and the other _____ of McDuffy's Billiard Emporium seem to come from every walk of life. One is unlikely to find such a(n) _____ crew under any other roof in town.

a. denizens . . . motley
b. caricatures . . . abstemious
c. paragons . . . fortuitous
d. reprobate . . . contiguous

6. "We must take immediate steps to counteract this highly dangerous development," the new President told his advisors, "for the longer we _____, the more _____ its effects will be."

a. procrastinate . . . pernicious
b. quail . . . prosaic
c. disseminate . . . deleterious
d. accrue . . . inimical

Choosing the Right Meaning

Read each sentence carefully. Then circle the item that best completes the statement below the sentence.

See pages T38–T48 for explanations of answers.

Though the enemy line held on the flanks, it fell back in the center, producing a large salient, of which our commander was quick to take advantage. (2)

1. In line 2 the word **salient** may best be defined as
(a. bulge)　　b. gap　　c. bottleneck　　d. spread

"Alas! 'tis true I have gone here and there,
And made myself a motley to the view, (2)
Gor'd mine own thoughts, sold cheap what is most dear
Made old offenses of affections new." (4)
　　(Shakespeare, Sonnet 110, 1–4)

2. The best meaning for the word **motley** in line 2 is
a. mixture of odd elements　　c. brightly colored uniform
(b. jester)　　d. gaudy fabric

When Hamlet sourly observes,
　　"Thrift, thrift, Horatio. The funeral baked meats (2)
　　did coldly furnish forth the marriage tables,"
he is essentially registering his disapproval of the fact that the funeral (4)
of his father and the remarriage of his mother were so contiguous.

3. The best definition for the word **contiguous** in line 5 is
a. close in size　　b. related in blood　　(c. near in time)　　d. adjacent in space

During the "Neolithic Revolution," as it is called, human beings exchanged the highly discursive lifestyle of the hunter-gatherer for the more sedentary (2) one of the farmer.

4. In line 2 the word **discursive** is used to mean
a. primitive　　b. digressive　　c. episodic　　(d. nomadic)

Antonyms

*In each of the following groups, circle the word or expression that is most nearly the **opposite** of the word in **boldface** type.*

1. censurable
(a. laudable)
b. conscientious
c. puzzling
d. habitual

2. specious
a. special
b. strange
(c. valid)
d. deceptive

3. extenuating
a. poor
(b. aggravating)
c. unexpected
d. mitigating

4. munificent
a. generous
(b. stingy)
c. thoughtful
d. sensible

5. satiated
a. horrified
b. bored
c. angered
(d. unsatisfied)

6. florid
(a. unadorned)
b. truthful
c. effective
d. dull

7. palpable
a. careless
(b. unnoticeable)
c. obvious
d. significant

8. pernicious
a. contagious
b. painful
c. destructive
(d. harmless)

9. heresy
a. orthodoxy
b. fear
c. bravery
d. belief

11. dowdy
a. drab
b. ruddy
c. chic
d. conspicuous

13. silence
a. dun
b. clangor
c. salient
d. bedlam

15. foreigner
a. salient
b. denizen
c. gist
d. covert

10. scintillating
a. humorous
b. dull
c. taped
d. impromptu

12. fortuitous
a. unexpected
b. chance
c. prearranged
d. longed for

14. politic
a. wise
b. imprudent
c. prosaic
d. digressive

16. inconspicuous
a. munificent
b. imperious
c. prosaic
d. salient

Word Families

A. *On the line provided, write the word you have learned in Units 10–12 that is related to each of the following nouns.*
EXAMPLE: provocation—**provocative**

1. dowdiness — dowdy
2. inculcation, inculcator — inculcate
3. gaucheness, gaucherie — gauche
4. abstemiousness — abstemious
5. fortuity, fortuitousness — fortuitous
6. efficacy, efficaciousness — efficacious
7. imperiousness — imperious
8. munificence — munificent
9. gratuity, gratuitousness — gratuitous
10. corroboration — corroborate
11. dissemination — disseminate
12. satiation — satiate
13. inculcation — inculcate
14. censure — censurable
15. discourse — discursive

B. *On the line provided, write the word you have learned in Units 10–12 that is related to each of the following verbs.*
EXAMPLE: clang—**clangor**

16. scintillate — scintillating
17. annotate — annotation
18. perceive — perceptive
19. imply — implicit
20. provoke — provocative

In each of the following groups, circle the word that is best defined or suggested by the given phrase.

1. confirm a report
a. satiate　　　　b. foist　　　　c. accrue　　　　(d. corroborate)

2. the ringing of the fire alarm
a. invective　　(b. clangor)　　c. dun　　　　d. bedlam

3. a tendency to delay
a. foist　　　　b. satiate　　　　c. enthrall　　(d. procrastinate)

4. a courteous and gracious host
(a. debonair)　　b. gauche　　　　c. munificent　　d. discursive

5. a harmful effect
(a. deleterious)　　b. motley　　　　c. palpable　　d. winsome

6. an abstruse report
a. florid　　　　b. covert　　　　(c. recondite)　　d. abstemious

7. a prudent decision
(a. politic)　　b. gauche　　　　c. debonair　　d. fortuitous

8. broadcast the news
(a. disseminate)　　b. inculcate　　c. foist　　　　d. satiate

9. passing rhinestones off as diamonds
a. accrue　　　(b. foist)　　　c. extenuate　　d. sear

10. instill a desire for success
a. procrastinate　　(b. inculcate)　　c. disseminate　　d. enthrall

11. a representative group
a. salient　　　　b. denizen　　　　c. reprobate　　(d. contingent)

12. a wordy expression
a. motley　　　(b. redundant)　　c. incisive　　d. efficacious

13. effective remedies
a. specious　　　b. deleterious　　(c. efficacious)　　d. pernicious

14. the gist of the story
a. paragon　　　(b. paraphrase)　　c. heresy　　d. invective

15. gaudy display of opulence
a. winsome　　　b. provocative　　c. scintillating　　(d. ostentatious)

16. an unstated agreement
a. gratuitous　　(b. implicit)　　c. covert　　d. redundant

17. a meager meal
a. satiate　　　(b. abstemious)　　c. winsome　　d. fortuitous

18. collect over time
a. absolve　　　b. procrastinate　　c. dun　　　　(d. accrue)

19. unwarranted violence on television
a. censurable　　(b. gratuitous)　　c. provocative　　d. dowdy

20. harmful rumors that caused much pain
a. scintillating　　(b. pernicious)　　c. invective　　d. reprobate

equa, equi, ega, iqui—equal

This root appears in **equanimity** (page 118), literally "equal-mindedness." The word now means "composure, evenness of mind or temper." Other words based on the same root are listed below.

egalitarian	equate	equilibrium	iniquitous
equable	equidistant	inequity	unequivocal

From the list of words above, choose the one that corresponds to each of the brief definitions below. Write the word in the blank space in the illustrative sentence below the definition.

1. uniform, marked by lack of noticeable or extreme variation; steady

Los Angeles is famous for its _____**equable**_____ climate.

2. to regard or treat as equivalent; to make equal, equalize

It's a mistake to _____**equate**_____ politeness with kindness.

3. clear, plain, absolute, certain

There was no mistaking his _____**unequivocal**_____ refusal to compromise.

4. wicked, very unjust, vicious

The former dictator was tried for _____**iniquitous**_____ deeds.

5. asserting or promoting social, political, or economic equality; advocating the removal of inequalities among people

Most utopian societies are envisioned as _____**egalitarian**_____.

6. balance (*"equal balance"*)

It's not easy to maintain one's _____**equilibrium**_____ in a difficult situation.

7. an act or situation of injustice and unfairness

A society based on _____**inequity**_____ is ripe for revolution.

8. equally separated from a given point or location

The two suburbs are _____**equidistant**_____ from St. Louis.

From the list of words above, choose the one that best completes each of the following sentences. Write the word in the space provided.

1. The _____**egalitarian**_____ principles of Lafayette led him to fight for the rights of a people thousands of miles from his homeland.

2. The company agreed to set up a committee that would correct any _____**inequities**_____ in their hiring practices.

3. All points on the circumference of a circle are _____ equidistant _____ from its center.

4. A wise leader does not _____ equate _____ disagreement with disloyalty.

5. Will yoga exercises help me maintain my emotional _____ equilibrium _____ during periods of stress?

6. The evidence in favor of her innocence is so _____ unequivocal _____ that I am sure she will be acquitted.

7. Anyone who is going to be your companion on a long and exhausting backpacking trip should have not only the right physical attributes but a(n) _____ equable _____ disposition as well.

8. In any just society, the persecution of racial, ethnic, or religious minorities must be condemned as _____ iniquitous _____ .

Circle the **boldface** word that more satisfactorily completes each of the following sentences.

1. Fair-minded judges do not (**equate,** equivocate) justice with retribution.

2. The Senator's objection to the proposed increase in the federal minimum wage was (**equidistant,** **unequivocal**).

3. The union attacked the blatant (**inequity,** equilibrium) of raising management's salaries while freezing worker's wages.

4. The (**equable,** **egalitarian**) values of Abraham Lincoln had their origin in his own experience of rising from obscurity to the Presidency.

5. The international human rights organization condemned the (**equable,** **iniquitous**) practice of imprisoning and torturing political dissidents.

6. The delicate (**equilibrium,** inequity) in the region was disturbed when the discovery of oil promised to make one country very rich.

7. The fountain in the middle of the garden is (**unequivocal,** **equidistant**) from each of the trellised entrances.

8. Because the father's will called for a(n) (**equable,** iniquitous) distribution of his wealth among all his children, there was no squabbling after his death.

Analogies

In each of the following, circle the item that best completes the comparison.

See pages T38–T48 for explanations of answers.

1. fortuitous is to **adventitious** as
a. egregious is to inconsequential
b. callow is to unctuous
c. cadaverous is to florid
d. recondite is to arcane

2. salutary is to **deleterious** as
a. vitriolic is to acrimonious
b. abstemious is to intemperate
c. pernicious is to seditious
d. insular is to provincial

3. precept is to **inculcate** as
a. caveat is to enjoin
b. aspersion is to enliven
c. exhortation is to urge
d. allegation is to corroborate

4. succinct is to **discursive** as
a. prosaic is to hackneyed
b. scurrilous is to nebulous
c. bombastic is to pretentious
d. incisive is to vapid

5. skinflint is to **munificent** as
a. ignoramus is to erudite
b. workaholic is to sedulous
c. showoff is to ostentatious
d. spy is to covert

6. ferment is to **agitation** as
a. clangor is to serenity
b. drivel is to effervescence
c. bedlam is to noise
d. lassitude is to petulance

7. beneficent is to **inimical** as
a. meritorious is to censurable
b. inscrutable is to irrevocable
c. intrinsic is to implicit
d. vulnerable is to susceptible

8. bovine is to **disposition** as
a. soporific is to background
b. corpulent is to personality
c. sedentary is to lifestyle
d. sepulchral is to attitude

9. affable is to **debonair** as
a. fractious is to equitable
b. anomalous is to amorphous
c. sleazy is to dark
d. transient is to evanescent

10. sagacity is to **astute** as
a. wisdom is to provocative
b. prejudice is to dispassionate
c. discernment is to perceptive
d. intelligence is to efficacious

11. dilatory is to **procrastination** as
a. querulous is to commiseration
b. straitlaced is to dissipation
c. noncommittal is to equivocation
d. crass is to peculation

12. avarice is to **cupidity** as
a. sangfroid is to equanimity
b. innuendo is to supposition
c. annotation is to coalition
d. heresy is to penury

13. satiate is to **jaded** as
a. absolve is to culpable
b. disabuse is to fatigued
c. dun is to grateful
d. whet is to stimulated

14. mitigate is to **extenuate** as
a. foist is to expiate
b. infer is to erudite
c. relegate is to infringe
d. remonstrate is to expostulate

15. enthrall is to **disconcert** as
a. avouch is to repudiate
b. scourge is to flout
c. resound is to reverberate
d. fetter is to shackle

16. aplomb is to **gauche** as
a. ennui is to bored
b. elegance is to lackluster
c. megalomania is to grandiose
d. aura is to awkward

17. tyrant is to **imperious** as
a. diplomat is to brusque
b. lackey is to subservient
c. spendthrift is to austere
d. hero is to ignoble

18. sear is to **fire** as
a. scald is to steam
b. scintillate is to water
c. wheedle is to air
d. filch is to dirt

19. scholar is to **erudite** as
- (a. greenhorn is to callow)
- b. curmudgeon is to unctuous
- c. orator is to bombastic
- d. parent is to straitlaced

20. infer is to **surmise** as
- a. blazon is to conceal
- b. assuage is to intensify
- (c. filch is to swipe)
- d. fetter is to liberate

Choosing the Right Meaning

Read each sentence carefully. Then circle the item that best completes the statement below the sentence.

See pages T38–T48 for explanations of answers.

"Our feathered friend the thrush chirrups his beauteous song
Above the crocus beds, whose fragrant denizens   (2)
Lie nestled snugly in the umbrage of the pine."
(A.E. Glug, "Alexandrines in a Country Churchyard," 5–7)

1. In line 3, the word **umbrage** most nearly means
a. branches   b. resentment   c. power   (d. shade)

"Come, thick night,
And pall thee in the dunnest smoke of hell   (2)
That my keen knife see not the wound it makes,
Nor heaven peep through the blanket of the dark   (4)
To cry, '"Hold, hold!'"
(Shakespeare, *Macbeth*, I, V, 49–53)

2. The word **dunnest** in line 2 most nearly means
a. smelliest   (b. blackest)   c. dullest   d. thickest

Far from fulfilling the bright promise of this early years, the hero drivels away his life
by the teaspoonful in meaningless social pastimes.   (2)

3. The best meaning for the word **drivels** in line 1 is
a. slavers   b. hastens   (c. fritters)   d. baby talks

A true child of the Marshalsea Prison, Tip Dorrit soon finds himself employment
in one or another of the sleazier forms of human enterprise.   (2)

4. The word **sleazier** in line 2 may best be defined as
- a. socially lower
- (b. ethically meaner)
- c. physically thinner
- d. financially cheaper

The oil spill had been so devastating that centuries, rather than years, would be
needed to effect the restitution of the environments and ecologies affected, one (2)
eminent conservationist wrote.

5. The best meaning for the word **restitution** in line 2 is
(a. restoration)   b. compensation   c. reimbursement   d. indemnification

"In order to protect the confidentiality of my sources," the reporter replied, "I often abate all mention of their names in the articles I write." (2)

6. The word **abate** in line 2 may best be defined as

a. deduct   b. nullify   (c. omit)   d. decrease

Vocabulary for Comprehension *Circle the pair of words that best complete the meaning of each of the following sentences.*

See pages T38–T48 for explanations of answers.

1. Modern scientists smile in bemusement at the faulty methodology and _____ reasoning behind the medieval alchemists' vain endeavors to _____ base metals such as iron or copper into gold and silver.

(a. specious . . . transmute)
b. irrevocable . . . aggrandize
c. anomalous . . . debase
d. hypothetical . . . relegate

2. "The large cache of _____ drugs we found in the suspect's possession clearly _____ the charges of smuggling that we have brought against him," the chief of detectives observed with an air of satisfaction.

(a. contraband . . . corroborates)
b. covert . . . dissipates
c. surreptitious . . . mitigates
d. occult . . . abets

3. "The girl may not be Einstein," I remarked, "but her comments on life are often quite _____ and show that she possesses a(n) _____ store of common sense."

a. soporific . . . ignoble
b. equitable . . . enigmatic
c. vapid . . . contiguous
(d. astute . . . redoubtable)

4. In earlier times, people who professed views that conflicted with the official teachings of their religion were often forced to _____ their ideas publicly or face charges of _____.

a. disavow . . . decadence
b. abominate . . . cupidity
(c. repudiate . . . heresy)
d. disseminate . . . perfidy

5. The lead paragraph of any newspaper article provides a kind of _____ of events in that it gives the reader only the most _____ features of a story in language that is as clear and concise as possible.

a. gist . . . lurid
b. collation . . . inconsequential
c. caricature . . . provocative
(d. epitome . . . salient)

6. It must take a lifetime to acquire the vast _____ needed to compile the kind of scholarly notes and comments that one meets with at the foot of every page of an _____ edition of Shakespeare.

a. megalomania . . . ameliorated
(b. erudition . . . annotated)
c. avarice . . . expurgated
d. acculturation . . . enhanced

Read the passage below. Then complete the exercise at the bottom of the page.

Words from Place Names

Certain words and phrases in the English language are derived from place names. For example the word *ascot*, a tie-like scarf, comes from the town of Ascot, England, where the item originated. Often as time passes, these words lose their association with their original place names, and are adapted into the English language as words in their own right. Studying the meaning and manner in which these words and phrases slowly became incorporated into common English usage often reveals historical and cultural information about the society from which they came.

In addition to nouns associated with particular places, such as *Boston cream pie*, *Philadelphia cheese steak*, and *Texas chili*, there are words such as *bedlam* that also tell a story. *Bedlam* (Unit 10), meaning "noisy uproar, chaos, or confusion," is a corruption of Bethlehem, from the St. Mary of Bethlehem Insane Asylum in north London, the oldest mental institution in the world. Though it began by admitting the poor and destitute, it

The Dalmatian gets its name from Dalmatia, Croatia.

soon took in "lunatics," as they were called, in the 1300s. By the 1700s the patients were seriously mistreated, and staff members sold admission tickets to the wealthy so that they could see the mentally ill up close.

In Column A below are 10 more place name words. With or without a dictionary, match the words to the professions or descriptions associated with them in Column B.

Column A

_e_	**1.** academy
_c_	**2.** cologne
_a_	**3.** limerick
_d_	**4.** varnish
_g_	**5.** sybaritic
_h_	**6.** limousine
_b_	**7.** blarney
_i_	**8.** hackneyed
_f_	**9.** mecca
_j_	**10.** sardonic

Column B

a. poet

b. liar; exaggerator

c. perfume

d. carpenter

e. professor; student

f. pilgrim

g. hedonist, epicure

h. driver

i. cliché

j. poisonous plant; mocking, cynical

Definitions

Note carefully the spelling, pronunciation, part(s) of speech, and definition(s) of each of the following words. Then write the word in the blank space(s) in the illustrative sentence(s) following. Finally, study the lists of synonyms and antonyms given at the end of each entry.

1. abet
(ə bet′)

(*v.*) to encourage, assist, aid, support (especially in something wrong or unworthy)

To allow a man in his condition behind the wheel of a car is to _____**abet**_____ a potential crime.

ANTONYMS: hamper, hinder, impede, frustrate

2. aver
(ə vər′)

(*v.*) to affirm, declare confidently

I will _____**aver**_____ your fitness to do the work to any prospective employer who inquires.

SYNONYMS: assert, asseverate, avouch
ANTONYMS: deny, disavow, repudiate, disclaim

3. blatant
(blāt′ ənt)

(*adj.*) noisy in a coarse, offensive way; obvious or conspicuous, especially in an unfavorable sense

Your comments showed a _____**blatant**_____ disregard for my feelings.

SYNONYMS: flagrant, glaring, egregious, disagreeably loud
ANTONYMS: inconsequential, trifling, piddling, petty

4. broach
(brōch)

(*v.*) to bring up or begin to talk about (a subject); to announce, introduce; to break the surface of the water; to turn sideways to the wind and waves; to pierce (a keg or cask) in order to draw off liquid; (*n.*) a spit for roasting; a tool for tapping casks

Though he did not like scrambled eggs, he opted not to _____**broach**_____ the subject for fear of insulting his hosts.

5. buttress
(bə′ trəs)

(*v.*) to support, prop up, strengthen; (*n.*) a supporting structure

He has read so widely and in such depth that he can produce facts to _____**buttress**_____ any argument he advances.

I had to add _____**buttresses**_____ on either side of my rickety shed to keep it from collapsing.

SYNONYMS: (*v.*) bolster, reinforce, brace, shore up
ANTONYMS: (*v.*) undermine, weaken, impair

6. carousal
(kə raú′ zəl)

(*n.*) noisy revelry or merrymaking (often with a suggestion of heavy drinking)

Vikings are notorious for having enjoyed a _____**carousal**_____ after each of their battles.

SYNONYMS: drinking bout, drunken revel, binge

7. collate
(kō' lāt)

(*v.*) to compare critically in order to note differences, similarities, etc.; to arrange in order for some specific purpose

We decided to _____ collate _____ the recipes according to how complicated they are.

SYNONYMS: sort out, cross-check, rearrange

8. connoisseur
(kän ə sər')

(*n.*) an expert; one who is well qualified to pass critical judgments, especially in one of the fine arts

She was a _____ connoisseur _____ of both music and film.

SYNONYMS: authority, savant, pundit
ANTONYMS: ignoramus, philistine, yahoo

9. disconsolate
(dis kän' sə lət)

(*adj.*) deeply unhappy or dejected; without hope, beyond consolation

Shakespeare's Macbeth hardly seems _____ disconsolate _____ when his wife dies, and bluntly says he has no time to grieve.

SYNONYMS: grief-stricken, inconsolable, comfortless
ANTONYMS: cheerful, blithe, buoyant, jaunty

10. encumber
(in kəm' bər)

(*v.*) to weigh down or burden (with difficulties, cares, debt, etc.); to fill up, block up, hinder

I feared that joining another club would _____ encumber _____ me with too many obligations.

SYNONYMS: overload, saddle, hamper, clog
ANTONYMS: unburden, unload, relieve

11. foment
(fō ment')

(*v.*) to promote trouble or rebellion; to apply warm liquids to, warm

Toward the end of the film, the peasant leader attempts to _____ foment _____ a storming of the scientist's castle.

SYNONYMS: instigate, incite, stir up
ANTONYMS: quell, quash, squelch, suppress

12. grisly
(griz' lē)

(*adj.*) frightful, horrible, ghastly

Katherine Anne Porter's "Pale Horse, Pale Rider" reveals the _____ grisly _____ effects of the influenza virus during the epidemic that followed World War I.

SYNONYMS: gruesome, gory, hideous
ANTONYMS: pleasant, delightful, attractive

13. herculean
(hər kyü lē' ən)

(*adj.*) (*capital H*) relating to Hercules; (*lowercase h*) characterized by great strength; very hard to do in the sense of requiring unusual strength

We carried the desk into the house successfully but saw that getting it up the stairs would require a _____ herculean _____ effort.

SYNONYMS: mighty, powerful, arduous, onerous, colossal
ANTONYMS: puny, Lilliputian, bantam

14. impassive
(im pas′ iv)

(*adj.*) showing no feeling or emotion; inanimate; motionless

Since nervous laughter is the sign of an inexperienced actor, I tried to adopt an _____ impassive _____ expression on stage.

SYNONYMS: emotionless, stoical, unemotional, insensible
ANTONYMS: emotional, passionate, excitable

15. inauspicious
(in ô spish′ əs)

(*adj.*) unfavorable, unlucky, suggesting bad luck for the future

Our road trip got off to an _____ inauspicious _____ start when we ran out of gas within five miles of home.

SYNONYMS: unpropitious, unpromising, untimely
ANTONYMS: propitious, favorable

16. incontrovertible
(in kän trə vər′ tə bəl)

(*adj.*) unquestionable, beyond dispute

The document was remarkable for its tact yet also _____ incontrovertible _____ in its facts.

SYNONYMS: incontestable, indisputable, indubitable
ANTONYMS: debatable, dubious, open to question

17. nonplussed
(nän pləst′)

(*adj., part.*) puzzled, not knowing what to do, at a loss

Prepared as she thought she was for all contingencies, she found herself _____ nonplussed _____ by the surprising turn of events.

SYNONYMS: perplexed, baffled, stumped, flabbergasted
ANTONYMS: poised, confident, assured

18. opportune
(äp ər tün′)

(*adj.*) suitable or convenient for a particular purpose; occurring at an appropriate time

If you intend to give that dog a bath, you had better pick an _____ opportune _____ moment, and then pounce!

SYNONYMS: timely, appropriate, felicitous
ANTONYMS: untimely, inconvenient, inappropriate

19. prolific
(pro lif′ ik)

(*adj.*) abundantly productive; abundant, profuse

Haydn was a more _____ prolific _____ composer than Mozart, in part because he lived much longer.

SYNONYMS: fruitful, fecund, proliferous
ANTONYMS: barren, unproductive, sterile, sparse

20. rejoinder
(ri join′ dər)

(*n.*) a reply to a reply, especially from the defendant in a legal suit

When he explained where he had been and what he had done, her _____ rejoinder _____ was sharp and critical.

SYNONYMS: answer, reply, response, riposte, retort

Completing the Sentence

From the words for this unit, choose the one that best completes each of the following sentences. Write the word in the space provided.

1. I don't think you can really accuse the producers of _____**blatant**_____ favoritism simply because they chose a friend for the title role.

2. I will not in any way _____**abet**_____ their plans to play a cruel and humiliating trick on an unoffending person.

3. "When I first _____**broached**_____ this topic two years ago," I observed, "my ideas were met by a very indifferent reception."

4. Aren't you exaggerating when you suggest that the job of stock clerk calls for someone with _____**herculean**_____ strength?

5. If the pages aren't _____**collated**_____ properly, they'll be out of proper sequence when our class magazine is bound.

6. The mangled bodies of the victims told their own _____**grisly**_____ story of what had happened.

7. When I saw the worried expression on the face of my employer, I realized that it wasn't a(n) _____**opportune**_____ time to ask for a raise.

8. One need not be a(n) _____**connoisseur**_____ of modern dance to recognize that Martha is exceptionally talented in that field.

9. The New Year's Eve party started off quietly enough, but it soon became a full-fledged _____**carousal**_____.

10. The testimony of three different witnesses, all confirming the same basic facts, made the guilt of the accused _____**incontrovertible**_____.

11. He is such a(n) _____**prolific**_____ writer that his books occupy almost an entire shelf in the school library.

12. The big game had a truly _____**inauspicious**_____ start for us when our star quarterback fumbled and lost the ball on the first play.

13. She is so _____**encumbered**_____ with family obligations that she rarely has a free moment for herself.

14. Although we have had our disagreements, I will _____**aver**_____ now that she was always been scrupulously honest in her dealings with me.

15. Although she remained outwardly _____**impassive**_____ during the trial, I could sense the emotional turmoil beneath the surface.

16. I know you are really disappointed at not getting that job, but don't allow yourself to feel so _____**disconsolate**_____ that you won't have the energy to look for another.

17. The towering walls of many medieval cathedrals are prevented from falling down by huge "flying _____**buttresses**_____" on the outsides of the buildings.

18. I was utterly _____ nonplussed _____ when I realized that football practice and the rehearsal for the class show were at the same time.

19. It would be impossible to _____ foment _____ racial discord in a school where students of different backgrounds understand and respect one another.

20. Now that you mention it, I don't think that "Sez you" was a particularly effective _____ rejoinder _____ to her trenchant and insightful criticisms of your proposal.

Synonyms

Choose the word from this unit that is **the same** or **most nearly the same** in meaning as the **boldface** word or expression in the given phrase. Write the word on the line provided.

1. introduce a complete change of plan — broach

2. was **grief-stricken** after the tragedy — disconsolate

3. gave a conciliatory **reply** — rejoinder

4. support her sleazy scheme — abet

5. an **unpromising** beginning — inauspicious

6. baffled by the answer — nonplussed

7. woken by the **drunken revel** — carousal

8. overloaded with cares and troubles — encumbered

9. a **colossal** challenge — herculean

10. a **timely** moment to act — opportune

11. shore up their declining popularity — buttress

12. sort out in order of relevance — collate

13. gruesome evidence of the wreck — grisly

14. stir up fury in the crowd — foment

15. indisputable proof of innocence — incontrovertible

Antonyms

Choose the word from this unit that is **most nearly opposite** in meaning to the **boldface** word or expression in the given phrase. Write the word on the line provided.

16. going through an **unproductive** period — prolific

17. an **inconsequential** error — blatant

18. a disturbingly **excitable** nature — impassive

19. a **philistine's** appreciation of food — connoisseur's

20. disavow an earlier statement — aver

Circle the **boldface** word that more satisfactorily completes each of the following sentences.

1. Dr. Slavin's original diagnosis, although questioned by several colleagues, was strongly (**buttressed,** fomented) by the results of the laboratory tests.

2. I like a good time as much as anyone, but I don't think that the celebration of our nation's birthday should become a rowdy (**carousal,** rejoinder).

3. Well-meaning but misguided friends (**abetted,** averred) his plans to run away to Hollywood and "become a movie star."

4. You will never be able to complete this hike if you (**encumber,** collate) yourself with so much "essential equipment."

5. What could be more (**disconsolate,** herculean) than the long drive home on a rainy night after we had lost the championship game by one point!

6. His parents are such sensitive people that I'm not at all sure how I should (**broach,** foment) the news of his untimely death to them.

7. In spite of her long and (grisly, **prolific**) career, her reputation today rests entirely on one great play.

8. Cleaning up the old beach house seemed an almost impossible task, but she attacked it with (**herculean,** disconsolate) energy.

9. Psychologists tell us that people who seem to be unusually (**impassive,** blatant) are often the ones most likely to lose control of their emotions in times of stress.

10. I wasn't so much surprised at not getting the job as I was (**nonplussed,** encumbered) by his strange explanation that I was "overqualified."

11. The speaker's inept replies to questions from the floor were met with a barrage of indignant (carousals, **rejoinders**).

12. When they offered to help him, he proudly (**averred,** abetted) that he could handle the situation entirely on his own.

13. If you are going to wait for an occasion that seems (**opportune,** grisly) in *every* respect, then in all probability you will have to wait forever.

14. I don't know anything about quiches and soufflés, but I'm a true (buttress, **connoisseur**) when it comes to pizza.

15. I know that he is wealthy and comes from a "prominent" family, but does that excuse his (**blatant,** impassive) disregard of good manners?

16. I truly felt that reality could never be as horrible as the (prolific, **grisly**) phantoms that were disturbing my dreams.

17. The opening of our show took place most (**inauspiciously,** opportunely) in the midst of a transit strike and a record-breaking snowstorm.

18. Isn't it ridiculous to say that the disorder was (**fomented,** nonplussed) by "outsiders" when we all know that it resulted from bad conditions inside the institution?

19. With tireless patience, the wily detective (encumbered, **collated**) bits and pieces of evidence until he gained an insight into how the crime had been committed.

20. What we need is not opinions or "educated guesses" but (impassive, **incontrovertible**) proof that can stand up under the closest examination.

Vocabulary in Context

*Read the following passage, in which some of the words you have studied in this unit appear in **boldface** type. Then complete each statement given below the passage by circling the letter of the item that is **the same** or **almost the same** in meaning as the highlighted word.*

Risky Business

(Line)

John Peter Zenger entered history when he was locked in a New York jail by the British Colonial Government in 1734. Twenty-four years earlier, the British Crown had paid his fare as an immigrant German boy seeking a home in America. Eager for colonists the Crown had not known what it was getting in Zenger.

(5) Young Zenger apprenticed for a New York printer named Bradford in a shop that published the city's first newspaper, the *New-York Gazette*. After eight years Zenger became Bradford's partner but, seeking independence, Zenger quit the shop one year later in order

(10) to open a store of his own.

Competing with his former master and partner, a man of many connections, proved a **herculean** task. Zenger published stories in

(15) Dutch for the Dutch community and hoped to **buttress** his publishing endeavor with a Dutch arithmetic book. But the choice proved **inauspicious**; the shop was not

(20) **prolific**. Only when he began printing leaflets from a party that opposed the policies of a new

18th century print room workers

colonial governor did Zenger find an **opportune** alliance; he started representing an opposition party with a newspaper of his own. The new governor remained

(25) a target, and Zenger was soon jailed for printing what was characterized as dangerous libel. The Crown did its **blatant** worst, trying him a second time when the first jury failed to convict him. Just in time, a Philadelphian named Hamilton, brought by Zenger's friends, took over the case. He made the novel argument that no true statement can be libelous—and that what Zenger had published was true.

(30) In minutes, the jury aquitted the defendant. Zenger's name has ever since been an emblem for freedom of the press in the United States.

1. The meaning of **herculean** (line 13) is
a. peculiar
c. arduous
b. memorable
d. unpopular

2. Buttress (line 16) most nearly means
a. to explain
c. to advertise
b. to bolster
d. to outsell

3. Inauspicious (line 19) is best defined as
a. unfavorable
c. unwieldy
b. unusual
d. little known

4. The meaning of **prolific** (line 20) is
a. healthy
c. popular
b. productive
d. pleasant

5. Opportune (line 23) most nearly means
a. secret
c. desperate
b. exciting
d. timely

6. Blatant (line 26) is best defined as
a. flagrant
c. usual
b. timid
d. silly

Definitions

Note carefully the spelling, pronunciation, part(s) of speech, and definition(s) of each of the following words. Then write the word in the blank space(s) in the illustrative sentence(s) following. Finally, study the lists of synonyms and antonyms given at the end of each entry.

1. amenable
(ə mē′ nə bəl)

(*adj.*) willing to follow advice or authority, tractable, submissive; responsive; liable to be held responsible

They will be _____**amenable**_____ to your instructions as long as what you say makes sense.

SYNONYMS: agreeable, compliant, docile
ANTONYMS: unresponsive, resistant, recalcitrant

2. berate
(bi rāt′)

(*v.*) to scold sharply

He removed the dog from obedience school when he discovered that they had _____**berated**_____ it too harshly.

SYNONYMS: chide, rebuke, reprove, reprimand
ANTONYMS: praise, compliment, pat on the back

3. carnage
(kär′ nəj)

(*n.*) large-scale slaughter or loss of life

Until television broadcast film footage of it, the _____**carnage**_____ of war was rarely made real to far-off civilian populations.

SYNONYMS: butchery, bloodbath, massacre

4. credulous
(krej′ ə ləs)

(*adj.*) too ready to believe, easily deceived

Though he was no dolt, his _____**credulous**_____ nature and desire to believe the best of people made him easy to deceive.

SYNONYM: gullible
ANTONYMS: dubious, skeptical

5. criterion
(*pl.,* **criteria**)
(krī tir′ ē ən)

(*n.*) a rule, test; a standard for judgment or evaluation

She was disturbed to discover that the _____**criterion**_____ for the award was based on style, not substance.

SYNONYMS: yardstick, touchstone, gauge, canon

6. deplete
(di plēt′)

(*v.*) to use up as a result of spending or consumption; to diminish greatly

Dwelling on all that could go wrong with your project will _____**deplete**_____ your energy and courage.

SYNONYMS: exhaust, empty, drain, bankrupt
ANTONYMS: replenish, refill, restock, resupply

7. expatiate
(ek spā′ shē āt)

(*v.*) to expand on, write or talk at length or in detail; to move about freely

We would like you to _____ expatiate _____ on the interesting matters you only touched upon earlier today.

SYNONYMS: elaborate, enlarge, descant, wander, roam
ANTONYMS: sketch roughly, summarize, condense, adumbrate

8. extraneous
(ek strā′ nē əs)

(*adj.*) coming from the outside, foreign; present but not essential, irrelevant

One handy way to dodge a difficult question is to earnestly begin talking about something _____ extraneous _____ to it.

SYNONYMS: incidental, extrinsic
ANTONYMS: intrinsic, relevant, pertinent, germane

9. inception
(in sep′ shən)

(*n.*) the beginning, start, earliest stage of some process, institution, etc.

He has worked here quietly and steadily since the firm's _____ inception _____, and knows how to do everybody's job.

SYNONYMS: commencement, inauguration, outset
ANTONYMS: completion, conclusion, termination

10. infirmity
(in fərm′ ə tē)

(*n.*) a weakness or ailment (physical, mental, moral, etc.)

Was his "deafness" an _____ infirmity _____ of old age, or a lack of interest in the conversation?

SYNONYMS: affliction, malady, defect

11. jejune
(ji jün′)

(*adj.*) lacking in nutritive value; lacking in interest or substance; immature, juvenile

My favorite teacher turned history from a _____ jejune _____ study of the distant past into a relevant topic of discussion.

SYNONYMS: vapid, insipid, puerile, childish
ANTONYMS: stimulating, mature

12. obdurate
(äb′ dyü rət)

(*adj.*) stubborn, unyielding

Vincent van Gogh was _____ obdurate _____ in painting whatever he wished, despite the fact that no one would buy his pictures.

SYNONYMS: obstinate, adamant
ANTONYMS: yielding, tractable, flexible

13. potpourri
(pō pü rē′)

(*n.*) A collection of diverse or miscellaneous items; a general mixture; petals mixed with spices for scent

The furniture was a _____ potpourri _____ of hand-me-downs from my father's parents and my stepmother's uncle and aunt.

SYNONYMS: hodgepodge, mélange, farrago, medley
ANTONYMS: homogenous or uniform group

14. precocious
(pri kō' shəs)

(*adj.*) showing unusually early development (especially in talents and mental capacity)

She showed a _____ **precocious** _____ talent for science.

SYNONYMS: forward, gifted, advanced
ANTONYMS: backward, retarded, slow

15. sadistic
(sə dis' tik)

(*adj.*) delighting in cruelty, excessively cruel

The Geneva Convention of 1949 outlawed torture and _____ **sadistic** _____ treatment of prisoners of war.

SYNONYMS: brutal, vicious, inhuman, fiendish
ANTONYMS: masochistic, clement, humane, merciful

16. sententious
(sen ten' shəs)

(*adj.*) self-righteous, characterized by moralizing; given to use of maxims or adages; saying much in few words, pithy

The _____ **sententious** _____ advice, though wise, was too general to help their particular situation.

SYNONYMS: aphoristic, epigrammatic, moralistic
ANTONYMS: discursive, diffuse, episodic

17. supplicate
(səp' lə kāt)

(*v.*) to beg earnestly and humbly

He chose to _____ **supplicate** _____ for mercy not on his own account, but so that his wife would not suffer.

SYNONYMS: plead, petition, implore, entreat

18. surfeit
(sər' fət)

(*n.*) an excess or overindulgence, as in eating or drinking, causing disgust; (*v.*) to feed or supply with anything to excess

A _____ **surfeit** _____ of food, drink, and clowning puts Shakespeare's Falstaff in disgrace with the King.

SYNONYMS: (*n.*) excess, glut; (*v.*) cloy, satiate
ANTONYMS: (*n.*) dearth, paucity, lack

19. tortuous
(tôr' chü əs)

(*adj.*) winding, twisted, crooked; highly involved, complex; devious

The cameras had to be portable in order to follow the athletes up the narrow and _____ **tortuous** _____ path to the summit.

SYNONYMS: circuitous, serpentine, labyrinthine
ANTONYMS: direct, straight, straightforward

20. turgid
(tər' jid)

(*adj.*) swollen, bloated, filled to excess; overdecorated or excessive in language

The heavy rains turned the fields swampy and the river _____ **turgid** _____ .

SYNONYMS: inflated, pompous, bombastic, overblown
ANTONYMS: muted, understated, unadorned, austere

**Completing
the Sentence**

*From the words for this unit, choose the one that best
completes each of the following sentences. Write the
word in the space provided.*

1. Any child who can read at the age of four must be considered remarkably
   precocious .

2. Her instructions told me exactly what I wanted to know, without a single
   extraneous detail.

3. In spite of all our efforts to appeal to whatever human sympathies the kidnappers
   might have, they remained **obdurate** .

4. At the very **inception** of his administration, the new President
   announced a list of the objectives he hoped to accomplish.

5. When my stubborn younger brother proved so **amenable** to my
   request, I began to suspect that he had some special reason for wanting to please me.

6. Although I ask no special consideration for myself, I am not too proud to
   supplicate on behalf of my children.

7. The simple and austere prose of the Gettysburg Address stands in stark contrast
   to the **turgid** and overblown rhetoric of a great many other
   19th-century orations.

8. Wouldn't you agree that TV has been **surfeited** lately with sitcoms
   and soap operas?

9. The more **credulous** you are, the easier it will be for swindlers and con
   artists to hoodwink you.

10. "How do you expect your mind to grow when you feed it solely on the
    jejune pap that comes out of the boob tube?" I asked him pointedly.

11. The stream followed a(n) **tortuous** course as it twisted through the
    broken countryside.

12. Usefulness is not the only **criterion** for including words in this book,
    but it is the primary one.

13. Our reading program this term is a delightful **potpourri** of stories,
    essays, poetry, and drama from many different periods.

14. My last date turned out to be such an expensive affair that my funds were sadly
    depleted for the rest of the month.

15. When I asked him why he wasn't going to the prom, he answered in his usual
    sententious style, "No dough, no dance!"

16. It's painful to have to listen to him **expatiate** on his own virtues when
    I'm dying to give some fascinating details about my own life and accomplishments.

17. One of the many benefits that I derived from my summer job in the new hospital was
    learning to be patient with people suffering from various types of **infirmities** .

18. You deserve to be severely _____ berated _____ for your misbehavior during such a solemn ceremony.

19. It is difficult to imagine the _____ carnage _____ that would result from an all-out war fought with nuclear weapons.

20. Although he announces piously how much it hurts him to punish people, I think he takes a(n) _____ sadistic _____ pleasure in it.

Synonyms

Choose the word from this unit that is **the same** or **most nearly the same** in meaning as the **boldface** word or expression in the given phrase. Write the word on the line provided.

1. exhaust his supply of good stories — deplete

2. adamant in refusing to join in — obdurate

3. entreat the captain on behalf of her son — supplicate

4. a **serpentine**, complicated plot — tortuous

5. always full of **moralistic** advice — sententious

6. an **affliction** of aging dancers — infirmity

7. a **mélange** of spices — potpourri

8. was present at the **outset** — inception

9. not **agreeable** to that idea — amenable

10. too **gullible** to perceive trickery — credulous

11. to **elaborate** on her years in Chicago — expatiate

12. a **vicious** love of teasing — sadistic

13. a **gauge** by which to judge — criterion

14. a **massacre** of the English language — carnage

15. quicker to **rebuke** than to praise — berate

Antonyms

Choose the word from this unit that is **most nearly opposite** in meaning to the **boldface** word or expression in the given phrase. Write the word on the line provided.

16. a **relevant** comment — extraneous

17. a **stimulating** discussion — jejune

18. a **backward** capability — precocious

19. thought the decor **muted** — turgid

20. a **dearth** of good things to eat — surfeit

Choosing the Right Word

*Circle the **boldface** word that more satisfactorily completes each of the following sentences.*

1. You cannot dismiss everything he says as (**obdurate, jejune**) simply because he is young and lacks experience of the world.

2. "The Lord hath heard my (**expatiation, supplication**); the Lord will receive my prayer."—PSALMS

3. In his efforts to impress moral principles on the children, he made use of (**sententious, tortuous**) formulas, such as "To be good, do good."

4. Instead of constantly (**berating, depleting**) the children, why don't you try to explain quietly and clearly how you expect them to behave?

5. The sales manager said she would apply only one (**criterion, carnage**) to my plan for an advertising campaign: "Will it sell more mouthwash?"

6. Given the kinds of tools the ancient Egyptians had to work with, the raising of the pyramids was an extraordinarily (**precocious, jejune**) feat of engineering.

7. I think the class show will be much more effective if it has a constant theme running through it, instead of being just a (**potpourri, surfeit**) of songs, dances, and sketches.

8. Many students feel that our dean is a strict disciplinarian, but I have always found her (**amenable, turgid**) to reasonable requests.

9. Although he is not given to physical maltreatment, I think there is a truly (**sadistic, precocious**) element in his willingness to humiliate people by belittling them in public.

10. I have had my (**surfeit, carnage**) of excuses and evasions; now I want action.

11. My rules for effective writing are: "Emphasize what is essential, play down what is secondary, eliminate what is (**extraneous, turgid**)."

12. She tried to justify the lies she had told us, but I was unable to follow her (**tortuous, amenable**) explanation.

13. Vic is so (**sententious, credulous**) that he actually believed me when I said that I had invented an automatic composition-writing machine.

14. Although he (**expatiates, supplicates**) fluently on the need for a new community action program, I have yet to see him do anything to bring it about.

15. His (**turgid, extraneous**) conversation, with its exaggerated adjectives and far-fetched figures of speech, made me realize once and for all the virtues of simplicity in language.

16. The (**infirmity, carnage**) caused on our streets and highways each year by careless driving has become a major national scandal.

17. The prolonged drought has so (**depleted, berated**) the supplies in our reservoir that we may have to consider rationing water.

18. Few things are more tragic than to see a great mind fall victim to a serious (**inception, infirmity**).

19. What disturbs the coach is not that Tom called the wrong play but he refuses (**obdurately, precociously**) to admit that he made a mistake.

20. At the very (**inception, criterion**) of my career, I set the goals and adopted the basic strategies that were to guide me through many years of outstanding success.

Vocabulary in Context

*Read the following passage, in which some of the words you have studied in this unit appear in **boldface** type. Then complete each statement given below the passage by circling the letter of the item that is **the same** or **almost the same** in meaning as the highlighted word.*

Marking Time

(Line)

In mid-nineteenth-century America, riding the shiny new railroads across the United States was a nightmare of time-travel and a **tortuous** search among differing schedules and clocks in each town and city. Those who wanted to reform this confusing system had to combat the outrage of many Americans who believed that human beings did not have sovereignty over time. (5)

In the 1840s rail lines had rapidly multiplied and vastly extended their reach. And yet, every city and town marked 12 o'clock noon by when the sun stood straight overhead,

regardless of the fact that the sun was not overhead and it was still a little before noon in the next town to the west. Add to (10) this nationwide **potpourri** of local times the fact that each railroad pegged its own timetable to the clocks in the city where its headquarters stood. Imagine boarding the New York Central line in (15) Stamford, Connecticut: you would read Stamford time on the watch in your pocket, New York City time on the station clock and the conductor's watch, and a different time in each town the train (20) passed through. Try changing trains in yet

Modern Amtrak Superliner Train

another city and you'd better find out what time it is there. For unwitting travelers who found themselves stranded in far-off cities, this might seem a **sadistic** ordeal indeed!

Soon the idea was advanced of giving up local times altogether—of dividing the country by four longitudinal zones, the hour to be the same within each. But (25) thousands of **obdurate** citizens viewed their local time with strong civic pride. Many others gave it the same reverence they felt for the sun and the stars.

Furious letter-writers **berated** the railroads for trying to usurp power from Nature itself. It took years to persuade city governments to adopt the change. Its **inception** came on November 18, 1883, at noon. Thirty-five years later, the new daylight saving (30) time set off the same storm once more.

---

1. The meaning of **tortuous** (line 2) is
　a. torturing　　c. comical
　b. labyrinthine　　d. boring

2. Potpourri (line 11) is best defined as
　a. hodgepodge　　c. history
　b. system　　d. disaster

3. Sadistic (line 23) most nearly means
　a. satisfying　　c. careless
　b. brutal　　d. unnecessary

4. The meaning of **obdurate** (line 26) is
　a. disorderly　　c. obstinate
　b. organized　　d. educated

5. Berated (line 28) most nearly means
　a. congratulated　　c. sued
　b. fired upon　　d. rebuked

6. Inception (line 29) is best defined as
　a. commencement　　c. high point
　b. success　　d. defeat

164 ■ *Unit 14*

Definitions

Note carefully the spelling, pronunciation, part(s) of speech, and definition(s) of each of the following words. Then write the word in the blank space(s) in the illustrative sentence(s) following. Finally, study the lists of synonyms and antonyms given at the end of each entry.

1. adamant
(ad' ə mənt)

(*adj.*) firm in purpose or opinion, unyielding, obdurate, implacable, inflexible; (*n.*) an extremely hard substance

The government was _____**adamant**_____ in its refusal to negotiate with terrorists.

By what they called _____**adamant**_____, writers centuries ago sometimes meant diamonds and sometimes magnetized iron.
ANTONYMS: (*adj.*) yielding, flexible, pliable

2. brouhaha
(brü' hä hä)

(*n.*) a confused hodgepodge of sounds, hubbub; an uproar or commotion that goes far beyond what is justified

After the _____**brouhaha**_____ had finally subsided, we asked the group to give us a written list of all their complaints.
SYNONYMS: furor, hullabaloo, tumult, pandemonium

3. bulwark
(bəl' wərk)

(*n.*) a strong defense or protection, a solid wall-like structure for defense; (*v.*) to provide such defense or protection

The only remaining evidence of a once thriving civilization is this _____**bulwark**_____ against the encroachments of the sea.

His staff had to _____**bulwark**_____ him against fans who wanted to get near him.
SYNONYMS: (*n.*) stronghold, citadel, bastion, rampart
ANTONYMS: (*n.*) breach, weak point in the defense

4. choleric
(käl' ər ik)

(*adj.*) easily made angry, bad-tempered

His _____**choleric**_____ temperament and erratic behavior made him an ineffective ruler.
SYNONYMS: irascible, testy, splenetic, bilious
ANTONYMS: affable, genial, even-tempered

5. cloy
(kloi)

(*v.*) to spoil or destroy an appetite by too much indulgence, especially in sweet or rich things; to glut, satiate, surfeit

A steady diet of TV began to _____**cloy**_____, and I was glad to begin a book.
ANTONYMS: stimulate, whet

6. curtail
(kər tāl')

(*v.*) to cut short, bring to a halt or end sooner than expected; to reduce

It is time yet again to _____**curtail**_____ the flow of unsolicited nonsense that somehow reaches me as e-mail.
SYNONYMS: limit, abbreviate, abridge, contract
ANTONYMS: protract, extend

7. deference
(def′ ər əns)

(n.) courteous yielding to the wishes and ideas of another person; great respect marked by submission, as to a superior

Some moderate _____deference_____ is due the boss, but too much can seem to conceal other motives.

SYNONYMS: respect, consideration, courtesy
ANTONYMS: contempt, disrespect, scorn, disdain

8. definitive
(də fin′ ə tiv)

(adj.) conclusive, final, representing the limit of what can be done

She is working on what she hopes will be the __definitive__ biography of Emily Dickinson.

SYNONYMS: exhaustive, authoritative
ANTONYMS: tentative, inconclusive

9. demeanor
(di mē′ nər)

(n.) the way a person behaves, overall impression made by comportment, manner, etc.; facial appearance, mien

Charles Dickens' Mr. Pickwick has such a cheerful and sympathetic _____demeanor_____ that few can resist him.

SYNONYMS: conduct, behavior, bearing, carriage

10. enigmatic
(en ig mat′ ik)

(adj.) puzzling, perplexing, inexplicable, not easily understood

He was staring me straight in the eye, neither pleased nor displeased, his expression _____enigmatic_____ .

SYNONYMS: baffling, mysterious, inexplicable
ANTONYMS: intelligible, understandable, fathomable

11. impromptu
(im prämp′ tü)

(adj., adv.) without preparation, offhand, suddenly or hastily done; (n.) an extemporaneous composition or remark; a minimal piece suggestive of improvisation

His _____impromptu_____ speech allowed him to express not only what he was thinking but what he was feeling.

At first, an _____impromptu_____ by Schubert may not stun you, but hours later you'll find that you haven't forgotten it.

SYNONYMS: (adj.) spontaneous, improvised, unrehearsed
ANTONYMS: (adj.) rehearsed, planned, prepared, premeditated

12. mawkish
(mô′ kish)

(adj.) excessively and objectionably sentimental; having a mildly sickening flavor

In It's a Wonderful Life, Jimmy Stewart was praised for making his character poignant without being __mawkish__ .

SYNONYMS: sentimentalized, maudlin, mushy, nauseating
ANTONYMS: unsentimental, callous, insensitive

13. mollify
(mäl′ ə fī)

(v.) to soften, make gentle, pacify; to calm, allay (as an emotion), assuage, appease, placate; to reduce in intensity

The Senator hoped to _____mollify_____ her angry public, but nothing she said was likely to get her reelected.

ANTONYMS: enrage, anger, aggravate, exacerbate

14. onus
(ō′ nəs)

(*n.*) something that is heavy or burdensome (especially an unwelcome responsibility); a stigma; blame

If the _____**onus**_____ for a defective product is placed on the consumer, some complicated legal and ethical questions are sure to arise.

SYNONYMS: burden, obligation, duty, stigma

15. presentiment
(pre zen′ tə ment)

(*n.*) a vague sense of approaching misfortune

It was a strange irony that in denying their _____**presentiments**_____, they made their worst fears come true.

SYNONYMS: foreboding, premonition, hunch

16. profligate
(präf′ lə gət)

(*adj.*) given over to dissipation and self-indulgence, immoral; recklessly extravagant; (*n.*) a person given to self-indulgent and wild spending

This was the _____**profligate**_____ son in the family, the one who could charm, the one of whom nothing was expected.

She was a _____**profligate**_____, and no matter how much money she earned, she always spent more than she had.

SYNONYMS: (*adj.*) prodigal, improvident; (*n.*) spendthrift
ANTONYMS: (*adj.*) penny-pinching, frugal, economical

17. remit
(ri mit′)

(*v.*) to send or hand in (as money); to cancel (as a penalty or punishment), forgive, pardon; to lessen, diminish; to put off, postpone, defer

They would _____**remit**_____ a certain sum each year to a local charity.

SYNONYMS: pay, absolve, subside, abate

18. requisite
(rek′ wə zit)

(*adj.*) needed, necessary, regarded as essential or indispensable

If you have the _____**requisite**_____ physical strength and an ear for music, I'll pay for your first year of dance instruction.

SYNONYMS: required, obligatory, incumbent
ANTONYMS: nonessential, superfluous, optional

19. sartorial
(sär tôr′ ē əl)

(*adj.*) of or pertaining to a tailor or his work; having to do with clothes or dress (especially men's)

Paging through historical picture books is a fascinating study in _____**sartorial**_____ standards through the years.

20. thwart
(thwôrt)

(*v.*) to oppose successfully; to prevent, frustrate

Our dog's friendliness would _____**thwart**_____ the sternest efforts of the most expensive guard-dog trainer.

SYNONYMS: foil, baffle
ANTONYMS: aid, assist, abet, further

Completing the Sentence

From the words for this unit, choose the one that best completes each of the following sentences. Write the word in the space provided.

1. I was surprised that so trivial an incident should have provided such a fearful _____**brouhaha**_____ in the popular press.

2. The circumstances surrounding the death are so _____**enigmatic**_____ that the police are not even sure that a crime was committed.

3. By talking so much about your _____**presentiment**_____ that "we're going to have an accident," you are simply making me nervous and preventing me from driving properly.

4. I see no point in your applying for that job when it is perfectly clear that you lack the _____**requisite**_____ qualifications.

5. He was so _____**profligate**_____ with his inheritance that he consumed in a few years the fortune it had taken his parents a lifetime to accumulate.

6. By getting the students to apologize for their thoughtless discourtesy, we _____**mollified**_____ the anger of the elderly elevator operator.

7. I think that the phrase "having a short fuse" aptly describes my new boss's _____**choleric**_____ and curmudgeonly disposition.

8. Somehow, whenever more money is needed for our club activities, the _____**onus**_____ of raising it always seems to fall on me.

9. We are still looking for a(n) _____**definitive**_____ answer to the question of whether or not our prisons can rehabilitate as well as punish.

10. At first, I was glad to see my old classmate again, but he embarrassed me with his _____**mawkish**_____ talk about "those wonderful, golden school days."

11. In his plaid jacket, light gray slacks, and tailored sport shirt, he was a model of _____**sartorial**_____ elegance.

12. Although we must have armed forces to protect the country, the most important _____**bulwark**_____ of national security is the devotion of the people to our democratic institutions.

13. How can you watch those silly soap operas day after day without being _____**cloyed**_____ by their gooey sentimentality?

14. Throughout the trial she maintained a(n) _____**demeanor**_____ of quiet dignity and confidence that made a favorable impression on the jury.

15. He was willing to compromise on many issues, but elimination of the "Male Only" requirements for those jobs was the one point on which he was absolutely _____**adamant**_____.

16. The candidate seems much more human and appealing when she delivers a(n) _____**impromptu**_____ speech than when she reads a prepared text.

17. In _____**deference**_____ to the wishes of the widow, the funeral services will be brief, and no eulogy will be delivered.

18. When the chairperson saw that the speakers were becoming more heated, without offering any new facts or ideas to clarify the situation, she decided to _____curtail_____ the discussion period.

19. We heard that the South High fans were planning to "kidnap" our mascot before the game, and we were determined to _____thwart_____ them.

20. Attached to every bill for the merchandise was a brief notice asking the customer to _____remit_____ payment promptly.

Synonyms

*Choose the word from this unit that is **the same** or **most nearly the same** in meaning as the **boldface** word or expression in the given phrase. Write the word on the line provided.*

1. a clearly expressed yet **mystifying** statement _____enigmatic_____

2. a weighty and mournful **bearing** _____demeanor_____

3. a heavy **burden** _____onus_____

4. **pay** the fine _____remit_____

5. visited by a **premonition** _____presentiment_____

6. **foil** a complicated plot _____thwart_____

7. a **sentimentalized** love story _____mawkish_____

8. the **furor** over the court's decision _____brouhaha_____

9. felt protected inside the **citadel** _____bulwark_____

10. to **surfeit** my taste for ice cream _____cloy_____

11. **improvident** with her energies _____profligate_____

12. not owning the **obligatory** dark suit _____requisite_____

13. **implacable** in the face of conflict _____adamant_____

14. **abridge** the length of the working day _____curtail_____

15. a store for all your **tailoring** needs _____sartorial_____

Antonyms

*Choose the word from this unit that is **most nearly opposite** in meaning to the **boldface** word or expression in the given phrase. Write the word on the line provided.*

16. draw up a **tentative** agreement _____definitive_____

17. show **disrespect** for the leader _____deference_____

18. a **prepared** statement for the press _____impromptu_____

19. an explanation that will **anger** them _____mollify_____

20. a **genial** reply to the question _____choleric_____

Circle the **boldface** word that more satisfactorily completes each of the following sentences.

1. His bitter anger was eventually (**mollified,** **thwarted**) by the effects of time and by our skillful appeals to his vanity.

2. Expressing his mystification at the Soviet Union, Churchill referred to it as a "riddle wrapped in a mystery inside a(n) (**enigma,** **presentiment**)."

3. Scholastic proficiency, emotional stability, and a genuine interest in young people are the (**requisites,** **profligates**) for a good teacher.

4. The special privileges extended to members of the senior class have not been entirely withdrawn, but they have been sharply (**thwarted,** **curtailed**) for the rest of the term.

5. I am a great admirer of Dickens, but even I must admit that the death of Little Nell in *The Old Curiosity Shop* is too (**sartorial,** **mawkish**) to be truly effective.

6. We all admired her (**demeanor,** **presentiment**), which was dignified without any suggestion of superiority or stuffiness.

7. Their efforts to win the game by a last-minute trick play were (**thwarted,** **remitted**) when our alert safety intercepted the deep pass.

8. The recent (**presentiment,** **brouhaha**) over the choice of a host for our local beauty pageant seemed to me nothing more than a "tempest in a teapot."

9. The cancer from which she was suffering went into (**remission,** **deference**).

10. Let us place the (**presentiment,** **onus**) for the defeat where it belongs—on each and every of us!

11. Her unvarying sweetness, like a diet composed entirely of desserts, does become (**cloying,** **choleric**) after a while.

12. He delivered his speech poorly, but since he was the best dressed man on the dais that afternoon, he enjoyed a (**sartorial,** **profligate**) if not an oratorical triumph.

13. His constant blustering and (**definitive,** **choleric**) behavior may be no more than an unconscious attempt to conceal his lack of self-confidence.

14. I came to realize that the demure little woman who never raised her voice had a will of pure (**adamant,** **deference**).

15. Scientific knowledge and the scientific method stand as a(n) (**bulwark,** **onus**) against the tides of irrationality, superstition, and wishful thinking.

16. Far from being (**impromptu,** **profligate**), all those jokes and wisecracks you hear on TV talk shows are usually prepared by professional writers and are carefully rehearsed.

17. There are so many aspects to Shakespeare that there will never be a truly (**definitive,** **bumptious**) study of his work.

18. I am really surprised that he now shows such exaggerated (**deference,** **adamant**) to people whose "aristocratic" pretensions he has always regarded with contempt.

19. According to psychologists, when you have an "uncanny" feeling that something is about to happen, you may unconsciously act in a way that will help the (**forbearance,** **presentiment**) to come true.

20. After years of (**profligate,** **enigmatic**) living, he experienced a religious conversion and devoted the rest of his life to serving mankind.

Vocabulary in Context

*Read the following passage, in which some of the words you have studied in this unit appear in **boldface** type. Then complete each statement given below the passage by circling the letter of the item that is **the same** or **almost the same** in meaning as the highlighted word.*

Looking at Laughter

(Line)

Stop and think about laughter and you'll begin to see why psychologists want to study it. This seemingly automatic action, a sudden exhaling of single syllables ("ha-ha-ha" or "huh-huh-huh") expresses no concrete meaning and yet it peppers our everyday conversations. One psychologist found ordinary laughter so **enigmatic** that he spent
(5) years investigating how, when, and why we do it. What he found was surprising.

It goes without saying that laugher's **demeanor** often expresses some degree of cheer or amusement. But the study found that what sets off the laugh is most often neither funny nor intended to be.The
requisite condition for a laugh is simply the
(10) presence of another person. When people
are alone and lacking such substitutes for
company as television, radio, or reading,
they almost never laugh. (Similarly, you
cannot tickle yourself.) Very often when two
(15) or more people *are* together, a remark as
simple as "I've got to go now" can trigger an
impromptu laugh. And the one who laughs,
the study found, is far more often the
speaker than the person who is spoken to.

Laughing at danger on a rollercoaster

(20)   All this suggests two things about
comedy programs on television. First, the
laughter of a studio audience is greatly
helped by the fact that its members sit
sociably together in the studio. Second, the recorded laughter—the "laugh
(25) track"—that is broadcast for programs without a studio audience really does
stimulate people watching at home to laugh.

The study also confirmed that laughter can be a sign of **deference** or an
attempt by the laugher to **mollify** someone with greater power or higher social
standing—a charming defense we all use. Though the psychological intricacies of
(30) laughter have not been fully determined, it is clear that laughter is a healthy
expression of joy as well as a tool used to form human connections.

---

1. The meaning of **enigmatic** (line 4) is
  a. distracting   c. mystifying
  b. ridiculous   d. obvious

2. Demeanor (line 6) most nearly means
  a. embarrassment   c. state of mind
  b. behavior   d. background

3. Requisite (line 9) is best defined as
  a. obligatory   c. surprising
  b. pleasantest   d. funny

4. The meaning of **impromptu** (line 17) is
  a. extreme   c. prepared
  b. spontaneous   d. inappropriate

5. Deference (line 27) most nearly means
  a. stalling   c. respect
  b. high spirits   d. distraction

6. Mollify (line 28) is best defined as
  a. amuse   c. disturb
  b. distract   d. placate

REVIEW UNITS 13–15

Visit us at **www.sadlier-oxford.com** for interactive puzzles and games.

Vocabulary for Comprehension

Read the following passage, in which some of the words you have studied in Units 13–15 appear in **boldface** *type. Then answer questions 1–11 on page 173 on the basis of what is* <u>stated</u> *or* <u>implied</u> *in the passage and in the introductory statement.*

American political campaigns have a long and colorful history, as this passage shows.

(Line)

Before the birth of the modern media, staging a campaign to elect an American President was a scattered, street-level affair. Professional
(5) pollsters, convention planners, and spin doctors did not yet exist, and the task of drawing attention to a candidate's name and platform was relegated to party members and
(10) neighborhood volunteers.

The very idea of campaigning would have **nonplussed** the first Presidential candidate. George Washington, running without an opponent, was
(15) unanimously elected president. He served two terms in office purely out of a sense of duty. Having led an amateur army to defeat the British Empire, this tall, **impassive**, and dignified hero
(20) seemed, by any **criterion**, a national leader beyond compare.

But when the right to vote was extended, political parties formed. These parties needed to publicize
(25) their ideas in order to stir up party sentiment and attract new members. Colorful banners were unfurled in public places, blazoning a candidate's virtues and ideology. Citizens were
(30) encouraged to announce their party loyalty by wearing it where one could see it—on cheap badges hung from around the neck or else from printed

ribbons hung from a pin. (Campaign
(35) buttons with pins on the back, still produced today, did not appear until 1896.) All such attention-getters (they included printed bandanas) bore the candidate's name or nickname—and a
(40) slogan if there was room. Slogans were hugely popular. Campaigners for William Henry Harrison rolled enormous metal spheres, painted with slogans, through city streets.

(45) From Andrew Jackson's second campaign onward, rowdy picnics, barbecues, and loud parades were used to attract the voters, much as they are used in primary-election
(50) campaigns today. Even Abraham Lincoln had his carnival-like supporters who contributed to the general **brouhaha**; the Wide-Awakes, as they called themselves (awake to
(55) **thwart** the enemy, slavery), marched in closely drilled formations, sporting shiny hats and capes.

In addition, countless speeches were made and handbills printed.
(60) But first and last the message was simply: "Look here, look here!"

1. The primary purpose of the first paragraph (lines 1–10) is to
  a. highlight the distortions introduced by spin doctors
  b. show how primitive old-style campaigns were
  c. compare and contrast campaigns before and after the birth of the modern media
  d. draw attention to the writer's expertise
  e. refute the notion that campaigns are overly scripted and therefore predictable

2. According to the passage, who handled old-style political campaigns?
  a. convention planners
  b. the candidates themselves
  c. professional pollsters
  d. party members and neighborhood volunteers
  e. sloganeers

3. The meaning of **nonplussed** (line 12) is
  a. perplexed
  b. outraged
  c. amused
  d. excited
  e. bored

4. Impassive (line 19) most nearly means
  a. proud
  b. stoical
  c. conceited
  d. hard-working
  e. charismatic

5. Criterion (line 20) is best defined as
  a. yardstick
  b. vote
  c. opinion
  d. name
  e. alias

6. The writer discusses Washington in paragraph 2 (lines 11–21) primarily to
  a. emphasize Washington's military genius
  b. compare Washington with Lincoln
  c. credit Washington with designing the first organized political campaign
  d. give the reader a sense of Washington's personality

  e. emphasize that the election of Washington bore little resemblance to modern-day election campaigns

7. It can be inferred from paragraph 3 (lines 22–44) that which of the following was a watershed in the transformation of political campaigns?
  a. the formation of political parties
  b. the increasing ingenuity with which slogans were coined
  c. the westward expansion of the Untied States
  d. the presidential campaign of William Henry Harrison
  e. the invention of campaign buttons

8. According to the passage, how did the "Wide-Awakes" get their name?
  a. They campaigned for the candidate day and night.
  b. Their name emphasized their intelligence.
  c. They were "wide awake" against slavery.
  d. They carefully examined the records of opposing candidates.
  e. They marched wearing shiny hats and capes.

9. Brouhaha (line 53) most nearly means
  a. cheerfulness
  b. anger
  c. fear
  d. hullabaloo
  e. confusion

10. Thwart (line 55) is best defined as
  a. capture
  b. debate
  c. foil
  d. reform
  e. analyze

11. The author's attitude is best described as
  a. sarcastic
  b. quizzical
  c. charitable
  d. animated
  e. indifferent

Grammar in Context

Parallel structure is the use of the same grammatical form for equal ideas or elements in a sentence. For example, in the sentence "Professional pollsters, convention planners, and spin doctors did not yet exist' (lines 4–6 on page 172), the three elements in the compound subject are parallel. However, if the author had written "Professional pollsters, the planners of conventions, and people called spin doctors did not yet exist," the sentence would contain **faulty parallelism**. In order to ensure clear meaning and smooth rhythm in your sentences, you should avoid faulty parallelism.

To create parallel structure, pair a noun with a noun, a prepositional phrase with a prepositional phrase, an infinitive with an infinitive, a noun clause with a noun clause, and so on. For example, the following sentence contains faulty parallelism: "Her goals were to focus on early Presidential candidates and analyzing their campaigns." To correct the sentence, use an infinitive with an infinitive: "Her goal was to focus on early Presidential candidates and to analyze their campaigns." Sometimes you need to repeat an article, a preposition, or a pronoun before each of the parallel elements in order to make your meaning clear. Here is an example: "Chapter Two contained anecdotes about the President and Vice President." To correct the faulty parallelism, repeat the article: "Chapter Two contained anecdotes about the President and the Vice President."

On the lines provided, rewrite each of the following sentences to correct faulty parallelism. Write "correct" if the sentence is correct.

Answers may vary; sample answers given.

1. Before the birth of the modern media, political campaigns were notable for their brevity and because they were casual.

<u>Before the birth of the modern media, political campaigns were notable for</u>
<u>their brevity and their casualness.</u>

2. Party members drew attention to a candidate's name and what his platform was.
<u>Party members drew attention to a candidate's name and platform.</u>

3. For political parties, attracting new members was as important as to stir up party sentiment.
<u>For political parties, attracting new members was as important as stirring</u>
<u>up party sentiment.</u>

4. Slogans and cheap badges advertised party loyalty and that members were enthusiastic.
<u>Slogans and cheap badges advertised party loyalty and members' enthusiasm.</u>

5. Slogans often revealed less about the candidate than the party members who coined them.
<u>Slogans often revealed less about the candidate than about the party</u>
<u>members who coined them.</u>

6. Andrew Jackson's second campaign was marked by rowdy picnics, large barbecues, and boisterous parades.
<u>correct</u>

Two-Word Completions

Circle the pair of words that best complete the meaning of each of the following passages.

See pages T38–T48 for explanations of answers.

1. Mozart was a(n) _____ youngster who wrote his first opera at the age of eleven. Though he was never as _____ a composer of theater music as some of his contemporaries, his output of stage works was by no means negligible.

a. precocious . . . prolific
b. sententious . . . incontrovertible
c. credulous . . . profligate
d. enigmatic . . . blatant

2. Friends hoped that the tearful _____ of the mother would soften the king's heart toward the young reprobates, but the dour old man _____ refused to yield to her entreaties.

a. presentiments . . . obdurately
b. demeanor . . . mawkishly
c. supplications . . . adamantly
d. deference . . . floridly

3. Though one of his parents reacted to the unexpected news of his death with a(n) _____ display of emotion, the other received it with all the _____ and restraint of a true stoic.

a. enigmatic . . . credulity
b. mawkish . . . choler
c. sadistic . . . deference
d. blatant . . . impassivity

4. During the battle, the _____ had been horrendous. Where the fighting had been the fiercest, the bodies were piled three deep. It took days to complete the _____ task of burying the dead.

a. surfeit . . . turgid
b. brouhaha . . . herculean
c. carnage . . . grisly
d. onus . . . mawkish

5. Once our fossil-fuel reserves are exhausted, they are gone forever. For that reason, we should try to _____ our use of these precious resources so that they are not _____ too quickly.

a. abet . . . nonplussed
b. curtail . . . depleted
c. remit . . . expatiated
d. mollify . . . buttressed

6. No matter how much protective consumer legislation we pass in order to _____ would-be swindlers and con artists, there probably will always be _____ people around for them to prey on.

a. buttress . . . adamant
b. thwart . . . credulous
c. abet . . . jejune
d. curtail . . . precocious

Choosing the Right Meaning

Read each sentence carefully. Then circle the item that best completes the statement below the sentence.

See pages T38–T48 for explanations of answers.

"They hove the wheel up just in time to save her from broaching to.   (1)
(Richard Henry Dana, *Two Years Before the Mast,* Ch. 32)

1. The best meaning for the phrase **broaching to** in line 1 is
(a. turning sideways to the wind)   c. breaking the surface of the water
b. tapping a cask of rum   d. striking a hidden reef

"We can load up a piece of amber . . . with the greatest possible excess of negative charge, and still it remains absolutely impassive in the presence of a magnet."   (2)
(K.K. Darrow)

2. The word **impassive** in line 2 most nearly means
a. stoical   b. insensible   c. unemotional   **(d. motionless)**

Try as I might, I simply could not swallow the mawkish-tasting medicine without gagging.   (2)

3. The term **mawkish-tasting** in line 1 most nearly means
a. insipid   **(c. nauseating)**
b. excessively sentimental   d. mushy

As I was dusting the sideboard, I accidentally knocked against the potpourri and spilled it all over the new rug.   (2)

4. The word **potpourri** in line 1 may best be defined as
a. meat-and-potato stew   c. album of family photos
(b. jar of mixed petals and spices)   d. collection of sheet music

Antonyms

*In each of the following groups, circle the word or expression that is most nearly the **opposite** of the word in **boldface** type.*

1. grisly
a spectacular
b. horrible
(c. pleasant)
d. natural

2. mollify
(a. arouse)
b. quiet
c. amuse
d. disperse

3. infirmities
(a. strengths)
b. intentions
c. vices
d. misconceptions

4. impromptu
(a. prepared)
b. amusing
c. spontaneous
d. praiseworthy

5. averred
a. proved
(b. denied)
c. predicted
d. proclaimed

6. berate
a. expel
(b. praise)
c. lecture
d. join

7. definitive
a. critical
b. logical
(c. unreliable)
d. new

8. deference
a. fear
(b. disrespect)
c. impulse
d. reverence

9. thwart
a. facilitate
b. criticize
c. evaluate
d. consider

11. tortuous
a. tricky
b. straightforward
c. circuitous
d. bizarre

13. turgid
a. austere
b. cloying
c. thick
d. ornate

15. foment
a. excite
b. forage
c. suppress
d. disguise

10. encumbered
a. unburdened
b. sensitized
c. cautioned
d. tortured

12. curtail
a. enjoy
b. plan
c. lengthen
d. pay for

14. sadistic
a. excessive
b. humane
c. supine
d. understated

16. jejune
a. serious
b. stimulating
c. irrelevant
d. essential

Word Families

A. *On the line provided, write the word you have learned in Units 13–15 that is related to each of the following nouns.*
EXAMPLE: remission—**remit**

1. opportuneness, opportunist, opportunism — opportune
2. supplication, supplicant, suppliant, suppliance — supplicate
3. turgidity, turgidness — turgid
4. precocity, precociousness — precocious
5. expatiation — expatiate
6. mawkishness — mawkish
7. obdurateness, obduracy — obdurate
8. credulity, credulousness — credulous
9. sadism, sadist — sadistic
10. collation, collator — collate
11. depletion — deplete
12. impassiveness, impassivity — impassive
13. encumbrance, encumbrancer — encumber
14. choler — choleric

B. *On the line provided, write the word you have learned in Units 13–15 that is related to each of the following verbs.*
EXAMPLE: controvert—**incontrovertible**

15. proliferate — prolific
16. console — disconsolate
17. carouse — carousal
18. defer — deference
19. require — requisite
20. demean — demeanor

In each of the following groups, circle the word that is best defined or suggested by the given phrase.

1. assuage her guilt
   a. buttress   b. foment   (c. mollify)   d. aver

2. at the beginning of the journey
   (a. inception)   b. presentiment   c. brouhaha   d. rejoinder

3. an unpromising set of circumstances
   a. amenable   (b. inauspicious)   c. enigmatic   d. herculean

4. perplexed by their reaction
   a. thwarted   (b. nonplussed)   c. fomented   d. mollified

5. not too proud to beg
   a. berate   (b. supplicate)   c. remit   d. buttress

6. support the cause
   a. deplete   b. foment   c. mollify   (d. bulwark)

7. an advanced student
   a. sartorial   b. sadistic   c. profligate   (d. precocious)

8. testimony unrelated to the case
   a. mawkish   (b. extraneous)   c. requisite   d. sententious

9. too much information to process
   a. rejoinder   b. onus   (c. surfeit)   d. bulwark

10. a noted expert
   a. onus   (b. connoisseur)   c. supplicant   d. impromptu

11. an announcement that incited a furor
   (a. brouhaha)   b. carnage   c. potpourri   d. lassitude

12. the grief-stricken victim
   a. nonplussed   b. obdurate   c. credulous   (d. disconsolate)

13. a self-indulgent lifestyle
   a. definitive   b. blatant   (c. profligate)   d. extraneous

14. remain unyielding
   a. jejune   (b. obdurate)   c. tortuous   d. sadistic

15. pay a penalty
   a. supplicate   b. thwart   (c. remit)   d. mollify

16. a heavy burden
   a. rejoinder   b. demeanor   (c. onus)   d. buttress

17. a foreboding dream
   a. surfeit   (b. presentiment)   c. onus   d. carnage

18. a quick retort
   (a. rejoinder)   b. surfeit   c. presentiment   d. inception

19. an aphoristic speech
   (a. sententious)   b. turgid   c. tortuous   d. obdurate

20. a bastion of civilization
   a. requisite   (b. bulwark)   c. onus   d. inception

Building with Classical Roots

quer, ques, quis—to seek, ask

This root appears in **requisite** (page 167), which means "essential, necessary." Other words based on the same root are listed below.

disquisition	inquisition	perquisite	query
inquest	inquisitive	prerequisite	requisition

From the list of words above, choose the one that corresponds to each of the brief definitions below. Write the word in the blank space in the illustrative sentence below the definition.

1. to ask, ask about, inquire into; to express doubts about; a question or inquiry

If you have a question about that newspaper article, _____**query**_____ the editor.

2. eager for knowledge; given to inquiry or research, curious; nosy, prying

A good detective needs a(n) _____**inquisitive**_____ mind.

3. a demand or application made in an authoritative way; to demand or call for with authority

The department made a(n) _____**requisition**_____ for ten additional trucks.

4. an extra payment; anything received for work besides regular compensation (*"that which is sought"*)

She enjoyed the _____**perquisites**_____ of her office.

5. a legal inquiry before a jury (*"asking into"*)

The family of the victim attended the coroner's _____**inquest**_____.

6. that which is necessary beforehand; a qualification (as for enrolling in a course)

Beginning Spanish is a(n) _____**prerequisite**_____ for advanced Spanish.

7. a long and formal speech or writing about a subject

The scientist prepared a scholarly _____**disquisition**_____ on her findings.

8. a severe investigation; an official inquiry conducted with little regard for human rights

The zealous reporter turned a simple interview into a(n) _____**inquisition**_____.

From the list of words above, choose the one that best completes each of the following sentences. Write the word in the blank space provided.

1. The pay for this job is not very good, but the _____**perquisites**_____, such as free housing and use of a car, make it attractive.

2. Can you understand why she is being so _____**inquisitive**_____ about matters that are really none of her concern?

3. Her long ___disquisition___ on the need for personal values and standards was so abstract that I found little in it that I could relate to.

4. A law degree is the minimum ___prerequisite___ for this job.

5. Because of the suspicious circumstances surrounding her sudden death, the body was exhumed and a(n) ___inquest___ held.

6. We objected strenuously to his questioning, which we felt had turned into a(n) ___inquisition___ into our behavior.

7. The public library is prepared to answer ___queries___ on a wide variety of subjects.

8. We can issue no supplies without a properly executed ___requisition___.

---

*Circle the **boldface** word that more satisfactorily completes each of the following sentences.*

1. American citizenship is among the few (**perquisites**, **(prerequisites)**) for running for the Presidency of the United States.

2. The school administration plans to (**(query,)** **inquire**) all parents about the inoculation histories of their children.

3. The secret police conducted illegal (**disquistions,** **(inquisitions)**) of those whom they suspected of having antigovernment views.

4. The parents had a difficult time keeping anything, especially presents, hidden from their (**(inquisitive,)** **requisite**) three-year-old.

5. The teacher submitted a(n) (**(requisition,)** **inquest**) to the principal for more painting and drawing supplies for her preschool classes.

6. The company officers offered stock options as (**prerequisites,** **(perquisites)**) to those executives whom they were particularly eager to recruit.

7. The (**(inquest,)** **disquisition**) into the sudden death of the young schoolteacher resulted in a finding of death from natural causes.

8. The anthropologist delivered a detailed (**requisition,** **(disquisition)**) on the culture of the Mayans, which he has studied for many years.

Analogies

In each of the following, circle the item that best completes the comparison.

See pages T38–T48 for explanations of answers.

1. thwart is to **expedite** as
a. contrive is to concoct
b. expostulate is to remonstrate
c. aver is to repudiate
d. surmise is to infer

2. impromptu is to **improvise** as
a. bizarre is to precipitate
b. resilient is to sear
c. anomalous is to enhance
d. synthetic is to fabricate

3. hoodwink is to **credulous** as
a. persuade is to adamant
b. touch is to callous
c. incense is to choleric
d. manage is to fractious

4. adage is to **sententious** as
a. caveat is to hypothetical
b. cliché is to hackneyed
c. precept is to recondite
d. axiom is to nebulous

5. connoisseur is to **erudite** as
a. novice is to callow
b. interloper is to querulous
c. paragon is to heinous
d. demagogue is to surreptitious

6. beaver is to **sedulous** as
a. sheep is to obdurate
b. cow is to imperious
c. horse is to politic
d. pig is to slovenly

7. abstemious is to **forbear** as
a. intemperate is to peculate
b. crass is to expatiate
c. pretentious is to enjoin
d. profligate is to dissipate

8. cloy is to **jaded** as
a. surfeit is to satiated
b. encumber is to absolved
c. prate is to enthralled
d. foist is to dunned

9. contretemps is to **disconcerted** as
a. hiatus is to scourged
b. dissension is to disabused
c. dilemma is to nonplussed
d. irony is to reproved

10. buttress is to **strength** as
a. reverberate is to echo
b. ameliorate is to improvement
c. expiate is to sin
d. debase is to quality

11. irrevocable is to **retract** as
a. intrinsic is to resusitate
b. incontrovertible is to impugn
c. inadvertent is to deliberate
d. irresolute is to waver

12. enigmatic is to **inscrutable** as
a. definitive is to redoubtable
b. dilatory is to punctilious
c. pernicious is to deleterious
d. subservient is to pretentious

13. reprove is to **reprimand** as
a. prate is to captious
b. abate is to continue
c. restrain is to fetter
d. satiate is to quell

14. prodigy is to **precocious** as
a. denizen is to sanctimonious
b. interloper is to unctuous
c. reprobate is to astute
d. insurgent is to seditious

15. jejune is to **substance** as
a. brusque is to brevity
b. vapid is to zest
c. provocative is to interest
d. efficacious is to effect

16. berate is to **castigate** as
a. remit is to abate
b. wheedle is to deplete
c. equivocate is to wheedle
d. broach is to elicit

17. mollify is to **assuage** as
a. blazon is to flout
b. collate is to wheedle
c. extenuate is to mitigate
d. permeate is to invoke

18. torpid is to **lassitude** as
a. affable is to dissension
b. noncommittal is to umbrage
c. querulous is to approbation
d. jaded is to ennui

19. cadaverous is to **corpse** as
a. vitriolic is to cemetery
b. (sepulchral is to grave)
c. soporific is to funeral
d. adventitious is to coffin

20. mawkish is to **sentiment** as
a. sleazy is to sincerity
b. grisly is to appeal
c. tortuous is to direction
d. (lurid is to sensation)

Choosing the Right Meaning

Read each sentence carefully. Then circle the item that best completes the statement below the sentence.

See pages T38–T48 for explanations of answers.

"Anon comes Pyramus, sweet youth and tall
    And finds his trusty Thisbe's mantle slain;   (2)
Whereat with blade—with bloody, blameful blade—
    He bravely broached his boiling bloody breast."   (4)
        (Shakespeare, *A Midsummer Night's Dream,* V, 1, 143–146)

1. The word **broached** in line 4 most nearly means

a. brought up
b. turned sideways
c. (pierced)
d. touched upon

"The bars survive the captive they enthrall."   (1)
        (George Gordon, Lord Byron, *Childe Harold's Pilgrimage*)

2. The word **enthrall** in line 1 may best be defined as

a. hold responsible
b. (hold captive)
c. hold hostage
d. hold spellbound

At that memorable feast, we found ourselves surrounded by enough food to assuage the hunger of even the most ravenous guest.   (2)

3. In line 2, the word **assuage** most nearly means

a. whet acutely
b. relieve moderately
c. (satisfy thoroughly)
d. ease slightly

The constant rocking of the great ship made me quite squeamish for the first few days of the voyage, but I soon got used to the motion and had no further trouble with my stomach.   (2)

4. The word **squeamish** in line 1 most nearly means

a. fastidious   b. (nauseous)   c. priggish   d. delicate

For several weeks after their birth, the callow young birds are completely helpless and must be fed, warmed, and protected constantly by their parents.   (2)

5. The best meaning for the word **callow** in line 1 is

a. (featherless)   b. numerous   c. unsophisticated   d. small

Circle the pair of words that best complete the meaning
of each of the following sentences.

See pages T38–T48 for explanations of answers.

1. In the eyes of the law, the accomplices who aid and _____ the
   commission of a crime are just as _____ as the actual perpetrator,
   even though they may not have been present when the deed was committed.
   a. expedite . . . nominal
   b. disavow . . . autonomous
   c. abet . . . culpable
   d. corroborate . . . scurrilous

2. An evening's fare at an old-fashioned vaudeville house consisted of a(n)
   _____ of circus and nightclub acts performed by a(n)
   _____ assortment of singers, dancers, comedians, and other
   entertainers.
   a. aura . . . ostentatious
   b. gauntlet . . . prolific
   c. onus . . . inadvertent
   d. potpourri . . . motley

3. _____ of crack troops drawn from the various branches of the
   armed forces were sent in to quell the riots and other disorders that a few malcontent
   firebrands had managed to _____ in the wake of the premier's
   assassination.
   a. Potpourris . . . exhort
   b. Contingents . . . foment
   c. Coalitions . . . simulate
   d. Infractions . . . transmute

4. Some of my friends are the epitome of _____ splendor; others
   always look as if they've slept in their clothes. Personally, I am neither as dapper as
   the first group nor as _____ as the second.
   a. provincial . . . mawkish
   b. herculean . . . sleazy
   c. sedulous . . . vapid
   d. sartorial . . . slovenly

5. The _____ fears and suspicions that had haunted his troubled
   dreams like so many shapeless ghosts _____ and vanished in the
   strong light of day.
   a. squeamish . . . curtailed
   b. nebulous . . . dissipated
   c. amorphous . . . relegated
   d. intemperate . . . absolved

6. Unfortunately for the accused, there was no possible _____ to the
   _____ evidence of guilt that the prosecution's airtight case laid
   before the jury.
   a. rejoinder . . . incontrovertible
   b. precept . . . specious
   c. repudiation . . . inconsequential
   d. caveat . . . bizarre

Read the passage below. Then complete the exercise at the bottom of the page.

Words from Greek Mythology

Greek mythology, like a soap opera, is full of thwarted love, betrayal, ignoble acts, and Promethean feats of glory. Though many know that Zeus was the ruler of the gods, few

The Trojan Horse comes to Hollywood

remember that the gods overthrew their parents, the titans, in order to control Olympia. Zeus, Poseidon, and Hades drew lots to determine who would rule which provinces, and it was in this manner that Zeus, with his thunderbolt, became supreme ruler of the heavens and earth, Poseidon, with his pronged triton, controlled the seas, and Hades dwelled in the underworld of the dead.

The Olympian gods had many children, such as: Aphrodite, the goddess of beauty; Athena, the warlike goddess of Olympia; Apollo, the god of music and truth; the Muses; the Fates; and half-mortal children such as Hercules, Helen of Troy, and Perseus. There are many interesting myths that stem from these characters, such as the story of Hercules, mortal son of Zeus. At birth, Hercules strangled a serpent that had been sent to kill him, and became known as the strongest man in the world. The word

herculean (Unit 13), meaning "strength," comes from the superhuman strength exhibited by Hercules in performing his tasks.

In Column A below are 7 more words derived from Greek myths. With or without a dictionary, match each word with its definition in Column B.

Column A

__f__	**1.** Adonis
__g__	**2.** atlas
__d__	**3.** labyrinth
__c__	**4.** mentor
__b__	**5.** Odyssey
__a__	**6.** paean
__e__	**7.** stentorian

Column B

a. song of joyful praise; ancient Greek hymn of thanksgiving to the gods, especially Apollo

b. the second book of Homer's epic recounting the adventures of King Odysseus; long journey

c. wise and trusted advisor; Odysseus' trusted friend

d. maze in which the Minotaur, who was half man, half bull, was confined

e. extremely loud; a loud-voiced Greek messenger

f. handsome young man; a man loved by Aphrodite for his beauty

g. book of maps; a titan condemned to support the heavens on his shoulders

Selecting Word Meanings

*In each of the following groups, circle the word or expression that is **most nearly the same** in meaning as the word in **boldface** type in the given phrase.*

1. **foment** disagreements
   - **a. cause**
   - b. repress
   - c. take part in
   - d. solve

2. struggle for **autonomy**
   - a. recognition
   - b. honor
   - **c. independence**
   - d. self-respect

3. **enthrall** the audience
   - **a. charm**
   - b. horrify
   - c. expel
   - d. compensate

4. view with **approbation**
   - a. fear
   - b. distaste
   - c. indifference
   - **d. approval**

5. **scintillating** company
   - a. discordant
   - **b. witty**
   - c. international
   - d. dull

6. an awkward **hiatus**
   - **a. pause**
   - b. disagreement
   - c. revival
   - d. situation

7. a **gauche** remark
   - **a. graceless**
   - b. clever
   - c. humorous
   - d. bitter

8. filled with **lassitude**
   - a. eagerness
   - b. food
   - **c. weariness**
   - d. sadness

9. a **motley** gathering
   - a. uniform
   - b. dull
   - **c. diverse**
   - d. enthusiastic

10. **permeate** the area
    - **a. saturate**
    - b. scour
    - c. destroy
    - d. cleanse

11. **recapitulate** the lesson
    - a. begin
    - b. end
    - **c. summarize**
    - d. learn

12. an **implicit** agreement
    - a. overt
    - b. untrustworthy
    - **c. unstated**
    - d. unhealthy

13. an act of **perfidy**
    - a. cowardice
    - b. valor
    - c. faith
    - **d. treachery**

14. a **sanctimonious** attitude
    - a. intense
    - b. spontaneous
    - c. genuine
    - **d. hypocritical**

15. a **grandiose** scheme
    - a. profitable
    - **b. extravagant**
    - c. prudent
    - d. wicked

16. an **amorphous** mass of old papers
    - a. tidy
    - b. surprising
    - **c. shapeless**
    - d. compact

17. a **bovine** temperament
    - a. angry
    - b. fearful
    - **c. placid**
    - d. nervous

18. **aura** of respectability
    - a. result
    - b. cause
    - c. fear
    - **d. atmosphere**

19. **disconcert** the players
    - a. criticize
    - b. replace
    - c. praise
    - **d. upset**

20. wise precepts
    a. rulers   b. followers   c. actions   (d. principles)

21. the adulation of the crowd
    (a. admiration)   b. disorder   c. indifference   d. scorn

22. in the sepulchral gloom
    (a. gravelike)   b. sudden   c. nocturnal   d. surrounding

23. blazoned on the pages of history
    a. discovered   (b. displayed)   c. ignored   d. explained

24. bizarre findings
    a. expected   (b. weird)   c. disconcerting   d. lucky

25. transmute the economic system
    (a. change)   b. improve   c. disorganize   d. revive

Antonyms

*In each of the following groups, circle the **two** words that are **most nearly opposite** in meaning.*

26. a. collate   (b. extricate)   (c. embroil)   d. rearrange

27. (a. hackneyed)   b. provincial   (c. novel)   d. insular

28. a. vitriolic   (b. deliberate)   (c. inadvertent)   d. harsh

29. (a. dissension)   b. gossamer   c. simple   (d. agreement)

30. a. fractious   (b. dilatory)   c. expensive   (d. prompt)

31. a. infirmity   (b. sadistic)   c. decisive   (d. humane)

32. (a. implicit)   (b. expressed)   c. beneficent   d. constructive

33. (a. politic)   (b. imprudent)   c. abundant   d. resilient

34. a. unctuous   (b. torpid)   (c. energetic)   d. intellectual

35. a. impassive   (b. imperious)   c. remarkable   (d. subservient)

36. a. remit   (b. mollify)   c. profligate   (d. irritate)

37. a. produce   (b. aver)   (c. disavow)   d. paraphrase

38. (a. abate)   b. intercede   c. exorcise   (d. resume)

39. a. vicarious   (b. surreptitious)   (c. overt)   d. substitute

40. a. legendary   (b. even-tempered)   c. slovenly   (d. petulant)

41. a. adventitious   (b. lenient)   c. childish   (d. stringent)

42. a. paragon   (b. contiguous)   c. champion   (d. remote)

43. (a. intelligible)   b. contingent   c. egregious   (d. inscrutable)

44. (a. salutary)   b. vapid   (c. pernicious)   d. talkative

45. (a. pallid)   (b. florid)   c. discursive   d. unkempt

Words Pairs

In the space before each pair of words, write:
S—if the words are synonyms or near-synonyms;
O—if the words are antonyms or near-antonyms;
N—if the words are unrelated in meaning.

__O__ **46.** corpulent—cadaverous

__S__ **47.** cajole—wheedle

__S__ **48.** susceptible—vulnerable

__N__ **49.** herculean—punctilious

__O__ **50.** censurable—meritorious

__N__ **51.** querulous—sartorial

__O__ **52.** tenuous—palpable

__S__ **53.** remonstrate—expostulate

__S__ **54.** propensity—proclivity

__N__ **55.** turgid—ignoble

__O__ **56.** thwart—expedite

__S__ **57.** circuitous—tortuous

__N__ **58.** nominal—provincial

__N__ **59.** recondite—heinous

__O__ **60.** opportune—inauspicious

Words That Describe the Presentation of Ideas

Some words that describe the way arguments are developed and ideas are presented, in speech or writing, are listed below. Write the appropriate word on the line next to each of the following descriptive sentences.

nebulous	innuendo	extraneous	dispassionate
specious	rejoinder	hypothetical	caveat
incontrovertible	criteria	recondite	astute
erudite	redundant	provocative	precocious

61. He has unnecessarily repeated the same ideas over and over again, in slightly different language. __redundant__

62. Rather than using something that had really happened, the speaker proved his point with an invented story. __hypothetical__

63. In writing this article, the author has drawn on a vast store of learning, covering many different sciences and other specialties. __erudite__

64. You have confused the issue by bringing in facts and ideas which have no bearing on the matter under discussion. __extraneous__

65. The argument is so strongly backed by sound reasoning and verifiable data that it is really beyond dispute. __incontrovertible__

66. The speaker raised a number of interesting questions that aroused the audience and led to a lively discussion. __provocative__

67. Your line of reasoning is fallacious, and your conclusions don't stand up under careful analysis. __specious__

68. The article was written for specialists in the field, and made little sense to the rest of us. __recondite__

69. The ideas that emerge from the article are so vague and wispy that it is impossible to say if they are right or wrong. _____nebulous_____

70. She used several standards for judgment in trying to decide whether the politician's speech had merit. _____criteria_____

Using Verbs

Verbs are the "action words" that, more than any other part of speech, make language forceful and vivid. In the space before each verb in Column A, write the letter of the item in Column B that best identifies it.

	Column A	**Column B**
i	**71.** remonstrate	a. to encroach on the rights of another
b	**72.** dissipate	b. to live self-indulgently
d	**73.** wheedle	c. to spread far and wide
f	**74.** mitigate	d. to coax or flatter for a desired end
h	**75.** corroborate	e. to go beyond, surpass
a	**76.** infringe	f. to make less severe or painful
e	**77.** transcend	g. to reject, disown
g	**78.** repudiate	h. to confirm the truth of
j	**79.** scourge	i. to offer objections or protests
c	**80.** disseminate	j. to punish severely

Word Associations

*In each of the following, circle the word or expression that best completes the meaning of the sentence or answers the question, with particular reference to the meaning of the word in **boldface** type.*

81. A practitioner of the **occult** sciences might specialize in
a. astronomy
b. biology
c. fortune-telling
d. sociology

82. The distinguishing symptom of a person suffering from **megalomania** is
a. chronic depression
b. high blood pressure
c. delusions of grandeur
d. problem dandruff

83. Good advice to someone who is constantly being **dunned** is
a. Go home!
b. Keep your eye on the ball!
c. Don't waste fuel!
d. Pay your bills!

84. A scene of **carnage** would be most likely to occur in a
a. collection of literary essays
b. love story
c. fairy tale
d. novel about World War II

85. Taking **umbrage** would be a reasonable reaction when you are
a. complimented
b. insulted
c. rewarded
d. introduced to someone new

86. Which of the following is the best remedy for being **callow**?
a. time and experience
b. dancing lessons
c. vitamins
d. sun and surf

87. If you are suffering from **penury**, you should look for
a. new hobbies
b. gainful employment
c. medical advice
d. a better mouthwash

88. The best thing to do with an **onus** is to
a. ride it
b. feed it
c. show it off to your friends
d. try to get rid of it

89. A person regarded as **squeamish** would probably be reluctant to
a. visit an art museum
b. dissect a frog in the biology lab
c. play tennis
d. prepare for final examinations

90. You would probably be **disconsolate** if you
a. added all the words in this program to your active vocabulary
b. ran across some of these words in the works of a favorite writer
c. checked the word origins in a dictionary
d. did poorly on this final mastery test

91. Which of the following reactions would best characterize someone suffering from **ennui**?
a. a smile
b. a wink
c. a yawn
d. a grimace

92. It's hard to behave with **equanimity** when
a. nothing much is happening
b. everything seems to be going wrong
c. you're very drowsy
d. you have just finished a good meal

93. A person who is the **epitome** of wit
a. uses it maliciously
b. is actually not very witty
c. is an ideal example of wittiness
d. employs wit in a strange way

94. You would **buttress** an argument if you wanted to
a. incite it
b. support it
c. avoid it
d. repudiate it

95. A person who has suffered an **egregious** defeat has lost
a. gloriously
b. conspicuously
c. by a close score
d. as a result of unfair tactics

96. Which of the following would by definition be guilty of **peculation**?
a. a judge
b. a coward
c. an embezzler
d. a philanthropist

97. The usual reason for **expurgating** a book is to
a. get rid of objectionable material
b. make it more readable
c. translate it into a foreign language
d. reissue it in paperback

98. To describe an author as **prolific** refers to
a. nationality
b. the size of the author's bank account
c. relations with critics
d. the number of books produced

99. If you receive a **noncommittal** reply to a request, you will probably be
a. in a state of uncertainty
b. deeply depressed
c. overjoyed
d. ready to fight

100. A famous literary character known for **avarice** is
a. Ivanhoe
b. Silas Marner
c. David Copperfield
d. Hester Prynne

INDEX

The following tabulation lists all the basic words taught in the various units of this workbook, as well as those introduced in the *Vocabulary of Vocabulary, Working with Analogies, Building with Classical Roots,* and *Enriching Your Vocabulary* sections. Words taught in the units are printed in **boldface** type. The number following each entry indicates the page on which the word is first introduced. Exercises and review materials in which the word also appears are not cited.